Jinkun Liu
Xinhua Wang

Advanced Sliding Mo
Mechanical Systems

Design, Analysis and MAT

Jinkun Liu
Xinhua Wang

Advanced Sliding Mode Control for Mechanical Systems

Design, Analysis and MATLAB Simulation

With 165 figures

Authors
Jinkun Liu
Beijing University of Aeronautics
and Astronautics
Beijing 100191, P.R.China
E-mail: ljk@bucc.edu.cn

Xinhua Wang
National University of Singapore
21 Lower Kent Ridge Road
Singapore 119077
E-mail: wangxinhua04@gmail.com

ISBN 978-7-302-24827-9
Tsinghua University Press, Beijing

ISBN 978-3-642-20906-2   e-ISBN 978-3-642-20907-9
Springer Heidelberg Dordrecht London New York

Library of Congress Control Number: 2011926501

© Tsinghua University Press, Beijing and Springer-Verlag Berlin Heidelberg 2012
This work is subject to copyright. All rights are reserved, whether the whole or part of the material is concerned, specifically the rights of translation, reprinting, reuse of illustrations, recitation, broadcasting, reproduction on microfilm or in any other way, and storage in data banks. Duplication of this publication or parts thereof is permitted only under the provisions of the German Copyright Law of September 9, 1965, in its current version, and permission for use must always be obtained from Springer. Violations are liable to prosecution under the German Copyright Law.
The use of general descriptive names, registered names, trademarks, etc. in this publication does not imply, even in the absence of a specific statement, that such names are exempt from the relevant protective laws and regulations and therefore free for general use.

Printed on acid-free paper

Springer is part of Springer Science+Business Media (www.springer.com)

Preface

In the formulation of any control problem there will be typical discrepancies between the actual plant and the mathematical model developed for the controller design. This mismatch may be due to unmodelled dynamics, variation in system parameters or the approximation of complex plant behavior by a straightforward model. The engineer must ensure the practical applicability of the resulting controller to produce the required performance levels despite such plant /model mismatches. This has led to an intense interest in the development of robust control methods to solve this problem. One particular approach to robust controller design is the sliding mode control methodology.

One of the most intriguing aspects of the sliding mode is the discontinuous nature of the control action. The primary function of each of the feedback channels is to switch between two distinctively different system structures (or components) such that a new type of system motion called the sliding mode exists in a manifold. This peculiar system characteristic is claimed to result in superb system performance which includes insensitivity to parameter variations and complete rejection of disturbances.

Sliding mode control is a specific type of variable structure control. The control systems are designed to drive and then constrain the system state to lie within a neighborhood of the switching function. There are two main advantages to this approach. Firstly, the dynamic behavior of the system may be tailored by the particular choice of switching function. Secondly, the closed-loop response becomes totally insensitive to a particular class of uncertainty. The latter invariance property clearly makes the methodology appropriate for robust control. Additionally, the ability to specify performance directly makes the sliding mode control attractive from the design perspective.

The sliding mode design approach consists of two components. The first involves the design of a switching function so that the sliding motion satisfies design specifications. The second is concerned with the selection of a control law to make the switching function attractive to the system state. Note that this control law is not necessarily discontinuous.

The chattering phenomenon is generally perceived as a motion which oscillates about the sliding manifold. There are two possible mechanisms which produce such a motion. Firstly, in the absence of switching nonidealities such as delays, i.e., the switching device is switching ideally at an infinite frequency, the presence of a parasitic dynamics in series with the plant causes a small amplitude high-frequency oscillation to appear in the neighborhood of the sliding manifold. These parasitic dynamics represent the fast actuator and sensor dynamics. Secondly, the switching nonidealities alone can cause such high-frequency oscillations.

It is our goal to accomplish these objectives:
- Provide reasonable methods of the chattering phenomenon alleviating;
- Offer a catalog of implementable robust sliding mode control design solutions for engineering applications;
- Provide advanced sliding mode controller design methods and their stability analysis;
- For each sliding mode control algorithm, we offer its simulation example and Matlab program.

This book provides the reader with a thorough grounding in the sliding mode controller design. More advanced theoretical results are developed on the basis. Typical sliding mode controller design is emphasized using Matlab simulation. In this book, concrete case studies, which present the results of sliding mode controller implementations are used to illustrate the successful practical application of the theory.

The book is structured as follows. Chapter 1 introduces the concept of sliding mode control and illustrates the attendant features of robustness and performance specification using a straightforward example and graphical exposition, several typical sliding mode controllers for continuous system are introduced, and concrete stability analysis, simulation examples and Matlab programs are given. Chapter 2 introduces several normal sliding mode controllers design, including sliding mode control based on nominal model, global sliding mode control, sliding mode control based on linearization feedback technology and sliding mode control based on low pass filter. Chapter 3 introduces two kind of advanced sliding mode controllers design, including sliding mode control based on LMI technology and sliding mode control based on backstepping technology. Chapter 4 introduces discrete sliding mode controller design, including discrete sliding mode controller design analysis and a kind of discrete sliding mode controller design based on disturbance observer. Chapter 5 introduces a kind of dynamic sliding mode controller design. Chapter 6 introduces a kind of adaptive sliding mode controller design for mechanical systems. Chapter 7 introduces three kind of terminal sliding mode controllers design, including a typical terminal sliding mode controller design, a nonsingular terminal sliding mode controller design and a fast terminal sliding mode controller design. Chapter 8 introduces sliding mode control based on several observers; four kinds of observers are used, including high gain observer, extended state observer, integral-chain differentiator, disturbance observer and delayed output observer. Chapter 9 introduces four kinds of fuzzy sliding mode controllers design, including fuzzy sliding mode control based on equivalent control, sliding mode control based on fuzzy switch-gain regulation, sliding mode control based on fuzzy system approximation and adaptive fuzzy control based on fuzzy compensation for manipulator. Chapter 10 introduces two kinds of neural network sliding mode controllers design, including sliding mode controller design based on RBF neural network approximation and adaptive RBF network sliding mode control for manipulator. Chapter 11 introduces three kinds of sliding mode controllers design for robot, including sliding mode controller design based on input-output stability, sliding mode controller design based on computed torque method and adaptive sliding mode controller design for manipulator. Chapter 12 introduces two kinds of sliding mode controllers design for aircraft, which are sliding mode control for helicopter and sliding mode control for an uncertain VTOL aircraft.

Welcome to find and download the simulation programs of the book from http://ljk.buaa.edu.cn/ or email to ljk@buaa.edu.cn.

Contents

1 Introduction 1
   1.1 Parameters of Sliding Surface Design 7
   1.2 Sliding Mode Control Based on Reaching Law 8
      1.2.1 Classical Reaching Laws 8
      1.2.2 Controller Design 9
   1.3 Robust Sliding Mode Control Based on Reaching Law 14
      1.3.1 System Description 14
      1.3.2 Simulation Example 15
   1.4 Sliding Mode Robust Control Based on Upper Bound 19
      1.4.1 System Description 19
      1.4.2 Controller Design 19
      1.4.3 Simulation Example 20
   1.5 Sliding Mode Control Based on Quasi-Sliding Mode 25
      1.5.1 Quasi-Sliding Mode 25
      1.5.2 Simulation Example 26
   1.6 Sliding Mode Control Based on the Equivalent Control 31
      1.6.1 System Description 31
      1.6.2 Sliding Mode Controller Design 31
      1.6.3 Simulation Example 33
   1.7 Digital Simulation of Sliding Mode Control 36
      1.7.1 Basic Theory 36
      1.7.2 Simulation Example 37
   References 40

2 Normal Sliding Mode Control 41
   2.1 Sliding Mode Control Based on Nominal Model 41
      2.1.1 System Description 41
      2.1.2 The Structure of Control System 42
      2.1.3 Design of Nominal Model 42
      2.1.4 Sliding Mode Controller Design for Actual Plant 43
      2.1.5 Simulation 45
   2.2 Global Sliding Mode Control for an Uncertain System 50
      2.2.1 System Description 50

		2.2.2	Global Sliding Mode Design	51
		2.2.3	Sliding Mode Controller Design	51
		2.2.4	Simulation Example	52
	2.3	Sliding Mode Control Based on Linearization Feedback Control		57
		2.3.1	Linearization Feedback Control	57
		2.3.2	Simulation Example	57
		2.3.3	Sliding Mode Control Based on Linearization Feedback	61
		2.3.4	Simulation Example	62
	2.4	Input-Output Feedback Linearization Control		65
		2.4.1	System Description	65
		2.4.2	Controller Design	66
		2.4.3	Simulation Example	67
	2.5	Sliding Mode Control Based on Input-Output Feedback Linearization		70
		2.5.1	System Description	70
		2.5.2	Controller Design	70
		2.5.3	Simulation Example	72
	2.6	Sliding Mode Control Based on Low Pass Filter		75
		2.6.1	System Description	75
		2.6.2	Sliding Mode Controller Design	75
		2.6.3	Simulation Example	77
	References			80

3 Advanced Sliding Mode Control 81

	3.1	Sliding Mode Control Based on a Linear Matrix Inequality for Inverted Pendulum		81
		3.1.1	System Description	81
		3.1.2	Equivalent Sliding Mode Control	82
		3.1.3	Sliding Mode Control Based on Auxiliary Feedback	83
		3.1.4	Simulation Example	84
	3.2	Backstepping Sliding Mode Control for a Inverted Pendulum		91
		3.2.1	The Basic Theory	91
		3.2.2	System Description	91
		3.2.3	Controller Design	92
		3.2.4	Simulation Example	93
	References			96

4 Discrete Sliding Mode Control 97

	4.1	Discrete Sliding Mode Controller Design and Analysis		97
		4.1.1	System Description	97
		4.1.2	Controller Design and Analysis	98
		4.1.3	Simulation Example	100

4.2	Discrete Sliding Mode Control Based on Disturbance Observer		102
	4.2.1	System Description	102
	4.2.2	Discrete Sliding Mode Control Based on Disturbance Observer	103
	4.2.3	Convergent Analysis of Disturbance Observer	104
	4.2.4	Stability Analysis	105
	4.2.5	Simulation Example	107
Reference			110

5 Dynamic Sliding Mode Control 111
    5.1 Problem Statement 111
    5.2 Dynamic Sliding Mode Control Based on Dynamic Switching Functions 111
        5.2.1 System Description 111
        5.2.2 Design of Controller 112
        5.2.3 Simulation Example 113
    Reference 116

6 Adaptive Sliding Mode Control for Mechanical Systems 117
    6.1 Adaptive Sliding Mode Control for Mechanical Systems 117
        6.1.1 System Description 117
        6.1.2 Design of Adaptive Sliding Mode Controller 118
        6.1.3 Simulation Example 119
    6.2 Adaptive Sliding Mode Control of Inverted Pendulum 126
        6.2.1 System Description 126
        6.2.2 Control System Design 126
        6.2.3 Simulation Example 129
    References 135

7 Terminal Sliding Mode Control 137
    7.1 Terminal Sliding Mode Control 137
        7.1.1 System Description 137
        7.1.2 Design of Terminal Sliding Mode Controller 138
        7.1.3 The Solution of $p(t)$ 139
        7.1.4 Simulation Example: Terminal Sliding Mode Control for the Inverted Pendulum 141
    7.2 Nonsingular Terminal Sliding Mode Control 146
        7.2.1 System Description 146
        7.2.2 Normal Terminal Sliding Mode Control 147
        7.2.3 Nonsingular Terminal Sliding Mode Control 148
        7.2.4 Simulation Example 149
    7.3 Fast Terminal Sliding Mode Control 155

7.3.1 Design of Fast Terminal Sliding Mode Controller 155
7.3.2 Design of Global Fast Sliding Mode Controller 157
7.3.3 Design of Position Tracking Controller 158
7.3.4 Simulation Example 158
References 162

8 Sliding Mode Control Based on Observer 163
8.1 High-Gain Observer 163
   8.1.1 High-Gain Observer Description 163
   8.1.2 Stability Analysis for Second-Order System 164
   8.1.3 Simulation Example 166
8.2 Sliding Mode Control Based on High Gain Observer 168
   8.2.1 System Description 168
   8.2.2 Controller Design 169
   8.2.3 Simulation Example 170
8.3 Extended State Observer Design 174
   8.3.1 System Description 174
   8.3.2 Extended State Observer Design 175
   8.3.3 Simulation Example 178
8.4 Sliding Mode Control Based on Extended State Observer 183
   8.4.1 System Description 183
   8.4.2 Sliding Mode Controller Design 184
   8.4.3 Simulation Example 185
8.5 Universal Approximation Using High-Order Integral-Chain
   Differentiator 191
   8.5.1 System Description 191
   8.5.2 Integral-Chain Differentiator 191
   8.5.3 Simulation Example 193
8.6 Sliding Mode Control Based on Integral-Chain Differentiator 197
   8.6.1 Integral-Chain Differentiator Approximation 197
   8.6.2 Design of Sliding Mode Controller 198
   8.6.3 Simulation Example 201
8.7 Design and Analysis of Slow Time-Varying Disturbance
   Observer 206
   8.7.1 System Description 206
   8.7.2 Disturbance Observer Design 206
   8.7.3 Simulation Example 207
8.8 Sliding Mode Control Based on Disturbance Observer 210
   8.8.1 Problem Statement 210
   8.8.2 Design and Analysis of Disturbance Observer 210
   8.8.3 Sliding Mode Controller Design 211
   8.8.4 Simulation Example 212

8.9	Delayed Output Observer		217
	8.9.1	System Description	217
	8.9.2	Delayed Output Observer Design	218
	8.9.3	Delayed Output Observer Analysis	218
	8.9.4	Simulation Example	220
8.10	Design of Controller Based on Delayed Output Observer		221
	8.10.1	Design of Controller	221
	8.10.2	Simulation Example	223
References			231

9 Fuzzy Sliding Mode Control 233

9.1	Fuzzy Sliding Mode Control Based on Equivalent Control		234
	9.1.1	Design of Fuzzy Control	234
	9.1.2	Simulation Example	235
9.2	Sliding Mode Control Based on Fuzzy Switch-Gain Regulation		242
	9.2.1	System Description	242
	9.2.2	Design of Sliding Mode Controller	242
	9.2.3	Design of Fuzzy System	243
	9.2.4	Simulation Example	245
9.3	Sliding Mode Control Based on Fuzzy System Approximation		251
	9.3.1	Problem Statement	251
	9.3.2	Controller Design Based on Fuzzy System	251
	9.3.3	Simulation Example	254
9.4	Adaptive Fuzzy Control Based on Fuzzy Compensation for Manipulator		260
	9.4.1	System Description	260
	9.4.2	Control Based on Fuzzy Compensation	260
	9.4.3	Control Based on Friction Compensation	262
	9.4.4	Simulation Example	263
9.5	Adaptive Sliding Mode Control Based on Switching Fuzzy		271
	9.5.1	Plant Description	271
	9.5.2	Design of Adaptive Fuzzy Sliding Mode Controller	272
	9.5.3	Simulation Example	274
References			279

10 Neural Network Sliding Mode Control 281

10.1	Sliding Mode Control Based on RBF Neural Network Approximation		282
	10.1.1	Problem Statement	282
	10.1.2	Controller Design Based on a Radial Basis Function Neural Network	282
	10.1.3	Simulation Example	284

10.2 RBF Network Adaptive Sliding Mode Control for
Manipulator 288
    10.2.1 Problem Statement 288
    10.2.2 Sliding Mode Control with Respect to the
           Approximation of $f(x)$ 290
    10.2.3 Simulation Example 291
References 300

11 Sliding Mode Control for Robot 301
  11.1 Model of Robotic Joints 301
    11.1.1 Model Description 301
    11.1.2 Model Description Example 302
  11.2 Sliding Mode Control Based on Input-Output Stability 303
    11.2.1 System Description 303
    11.2.2 Design of Controller 304
    11.2.3 Simulation Example 306
  11.3 Sliding Mode Control Based on Computed Torque Method 312
    11.3.1 Design of Controller 312
    11.3.2 Simulation Example 313
  11.4 Adaptive Sliding Mode Control for Manipulator 318
    11.4.1 Adaptive Sliding Mode Controller 318
    11.4.2 Simulation Example 319
References 329

12 Sliding Mode Control for Aircraft 331
  12.1 Sliding Mode Control for a Helicopter 331
    12.1.1 Mathematical Model of a Helicopter 331
    12.1.2 Dynamic Inversion Uncoupling Linearization 332
    12.1.3 Sliding Mode Controller Design 333
    12.1.4 Simulation Example 334
  12.2 Sliding Mode Control for an Uncertain Vertical Take-Off and
Landing Aircraft 339
    12.2.1 System Description 339
    12.2.2 Transform of Model 341
    12.2.3 Controller Design 344
    12.2.4 Simulation Example 347
References 353

Index 355

1 Introduction

Jinkun Liu

Beijing University of Aeronautics and Astronautics

P.R.China

E-mail: ljk@buaa.edu.cn

Xinhua Wang

National University of Singapore

Singapore

E-mail: wangxinhua04@gmail.com

Abstract   This chapter introduces the concept of sliding mode control and illustrates the attendant features of robustness and performance specification using a straightforward example, several typical sliding mode controllers for continuous system are given, a concrete stability analysis, simulation examples and Matlab programs are given too.

Keywords   sliding mode control, sliding surface, Reaching Law, quasi-sliding mode, equivalent control

One of the methods used to solve control problems are the sliding mode techniques. These techniques are generating greater interest.

This book provides the reader with an introduction to classical sliding mode control design examples. Fully worked design examples, which can be used as tutorial material, are included. Industrial case studies, which present the results of sliding mode controller implementations, are used to illustrate successful practical applications of the theory.

Typically, discrepancies may occur between the actual plant and the mathematical model developed for the controller design. These mismatches may be due to various factors. The engineer's role is to ensure required performance levels despite such mismatches. A set of robust control methods have been developed to eliminate any discrepancy. One such approach to the robust control controller design is called the sliding mode control (SMC) methodology. This is a specific type of variable structure control system (VSCS).

In the early 1950s, Emelyanov and several co-researchers such as Utkins and Itkis[1] from the Soviet Union, proposed and elaborated the variable structure control

(VSC) with sliding mode control. During the past decades, VSC and SMC have generated significant interest in the control research community.

SMC has been applied into general design method being examined for wide spectrum of system types including nonlinear system, multi-input multi-output (MIMO) systems, discrete-time models, large-scale and infinite-dimension systems, and stochastic systems. The most eminent feature of SMC is it is completely insensitive to parametric uncertainty and external disturbances during sliding mode[2].

VSC utilizes a high-speed switching control law to achieve two objectives. Firstly, it drives the nonlinear plant's state trajectory onto a specified and user-chosen surface in the state space which is called the sliding or switching surface. This surface is called the switching surface because a control path has one gain if the state trajectory of the plant is "above" the surface and a different gain if the trajectory drops "below" the surface. Secondly, it maintains the plant's state trajectory on this surface for all subsequent times. During the process, the control system's structure varies from one to another and thereby earning the name variable structure control. The control is also called as the sliding mode control[3] to emphasize the importance of the sliding mode.

Under sliding mode control, the system is designed to drive and then constrain the system state to lie within a neighborhood of the switching function. Its two main advantages are (1) the dynamic behavior of the system may be tailored by the particular choice of switching function, and (2) the closed-loop response becomes totally insensitive to a particular class of uncertainty. Also, the ability to specify performance directly makes sliding mode control attractive from the design perspective.

Trajectory of a system can be stabilized by a sliding mode controller. The system states "slides" along the line $s = 0$ after the initial reaching phase. The particular $s = 0$ surface is chosen because it has desirable reduced-order dynamics when constrained to it. In this case, the $s = cx_1 + \dot{x}_1$, $c > 0$ surface corresponds to the first-order LTI system $\dot{x}_1 = -cx_1$, which has an exponentially stable origin. Now, we consider a simple example of the sliding mode controller design as under.

Consider a plant as

$$J\ddot{\theta}(t) = u(t) \tag{1.1}$$

where J is the inertia moment, $\ddot{\theta}(t)$ is the angle signal, and $u(t)$ is the control input.

Firstly, we design the sliding mode function as

$$s(t) = ce(t) + \dot{e}(t) \tag{1.2}$$

where c must satisfy the Hurwitz condition, $c > 0$.

The tracking error and its derivative value are

$$e(t) = \theta(t) - \theta_{\mathrm{d}}(t), \quad \dot{e}(t) = \dot{\theta}(t) - \dot{\theta}_{\mathrm{d}}(t)$$

where $\theta(t)$ is the practical position signal, and $\theta_d(t)$ is the ideal position signal. Therefore, we have

$$\dot{s}(t) = c\dot{e}(t) + \ddot{e}(t) = c\dot{e}(t) + \ddot{\theta}(t) - \ddot{\theta}_d(t) = c\dot{e}(t) + \frac{1}{J}u - \ddot{\theta}_d(t) \quad (1.3)$$

and

$$s\dot{s} = s\left(c\dot{e} + \frac{1}{J}u - \ddot{\theta}_d\right)$$

Secondly, to satisfy the condition $s\dot{s} < 0$, we design the sliding mode controller as

$$u(t) = J(-c\dot{e} + \ddot{\theta}_d - \eta\,\mathrm{sgn}(s)), \quad \mathrm{sgn}(s) = \begin{cases} 1, & s > 0 \\ 0, & s = 0 \\ -1, & s < 0 \end{cases} \quad (1.4)$$

Then, we get

$$s\dot{s} = -\eta\,|s| < 0$$

A simulation example is presented for explanation. Consider the plant as

$$J\ddot{\theta}(t) = u(t)$$

where $J = 10$.

The initial state is set as [0.5 1.0] after choosing the position ideal signal $\theta_d(t) = \sin t$. Using controller Eq. (1.4) wherein $c = 0.5$, $\eta = 0.5$ the results are derived as shown in Fig. 1.1 – Fig. 1.3.

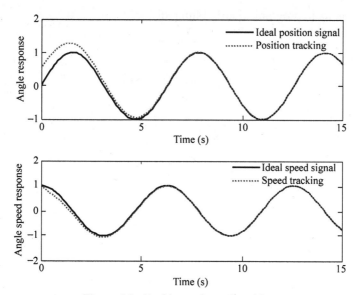

Figure 1.1 Position and speed tracking

3

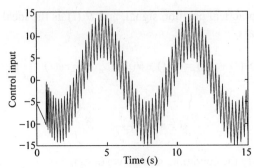

Figure 1.2 Control input

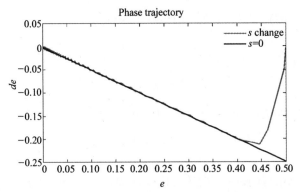

Figure 1.3 Phase trajectory

Simulation programs:

(1) Simulink main program: chap1_1sim.mdl

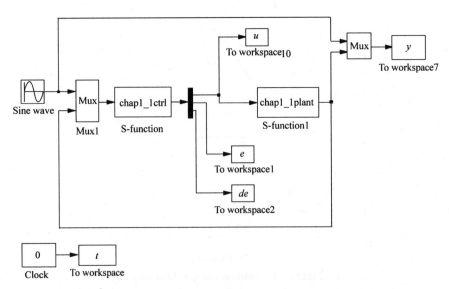

(2) Controller: chap1_1ctrl.m

```
function [sys,x0,str,ts] = spacemodel(t,x,u,flag)
switch flag,
case 0,
    [sys,x0,str,ts]=mdlInitializeSizes;
case 3,
    sys=mdlOutputs(t,x,u);
case {2,4,9}
    sys=[];
otherwise
    error(['Unhandled flag = ',num2str(flag)]);
end
function [sys,x0,str,ts]=mdlInitializeSizes
sizes = simsizes;
sizes.NumContStates  = 0;
sizes.NumDiscStates  = 0;
sizes.NumOutputs     = 3;
sizes.NumInputs      = 3;
sizes.DirFeedthrough = 1;
sizes.NumSampleTimes = 0;
sys = simsizes(sizes);
x0  = [];
str = [];
ts  = [];
function sys=mdlOutputs(t,x,u)
thd=u(1);
dthd=cos(t);
ddthd=-sin(t);

th=u(2);
dth=u(3);

c=0.5;
e=th-thd;
de=dth-dthd;
s=c*e+de;

J=10;
xite=0.50;
ut=J*(-c*de+ddthd-xite*sign(s));

sys(1)=ut;
sys(2)=e;
sys(3)=de;
```

(3) Plant: chap1_1plant.m

```
function [sys,x0,str,ts]=s_function(t,x,u,flag)
switch flag,
case 0,
    [sys,x0,str,ts]=mdlInitializeSizes;
case 1,
```

```
    sys=mdlDerivatives(t,x,u);
case 3,
    sys=mdlOutputs(t,x,u);
case {2, 4, 9 }
    sys = [];
otherwise
    error(['Unhandled flag = ',num2str(flag)]);
end
function [sys,x0,str,ts]=mdlInitializeSizes
sizes = simsizes;
sizes.NumContStates  = 2;
sizes.NumDiscStates  = 0;
sizes.NumOutputs     = 2;
sizes.NumInputs      = 1;
sizes.DirFeedthrough = 0;
sizes.NumSampleTimes = 0;
sys=simsizes(sizes);
x0=[0.5 1.0];
str=[];
ts=[];
function sys=mdlDerivatives(t,x,u)
J=10;
sys(1)=x(2);
sys(2)=1/J*u;
function sys=mdlOutputs(t,x,u)
sys(1)=x(1);
sys(2)=x(2);
```

(4) Plot program: chap1_1plot.m

```
close all;

figure(1);
subplot(211);
plot(t,y(:,1),'k',t,y(:,2),'r:','linewidth',2);
legend('Ideal position signal','Position tracking');
xlabel('time(s)');ylabel('Angle response');
subplot(212);
plot(t,cos(t),'k',t,y(:,3),'r:','linewidth',2);
legend('Ideal speed signal','Speed tracking');
xlabel('time(s)');ylabel('Angle speed response');

figure(2);
plot(t,u(:,1),'k','linewidth',0.01);
xlabel('time(s)');ylabel('Control input');

c=0.5;
figure(3);
plot(e,de,'r',e,-c'.*e,'k','linewidth',2);
xlabel('e');ylabel('de');
legend('s change','s=0');
title('phase trajectory');
```

1 Introduction

Sliding mode control is a nonlinear control method that alters the dynamics of a nonlinear system by the multiple control structures are designed so as to ensure that trajectories always move towards a switching condition. Therefore, the ultimate trajectory will not exist entirely within one control structure. The state-feedback control law is not a continuous function of time. Instead, it switches from one continuous structure to another based on the current position in the state space. Hence, sliding mode control is a variable structure control method. The multiple control structures are designed so as to ensure that trajectories always move towards a switching condition. Therefore, the ultimate trajectory will not exist entirely within one control structure. Instead, the ultimate trajectory will slide along the boundaries of the control structures. The motion of the system as it slides along these boundaries is called a sliding mode[3] and the geometrical locus consisting of the boundaries is called the sliding (hyper) surface. Figure 1.3 shows an example of the trajectory of a system under sliding mode control. The sliding surface is described by $s = 0$, and the sliding mode along the surface commences after the finite time when system trajectories have reached the surface. In the context of modern control theory, any variable structure system like a system under SMC, may be viewed as a special case of a hybrid dynamical system.

Intuitively, sliding mode control uses practically infinite gain to force the trajectories of a dynamic system to slide along the restricted sliding mode subspace. Trajectories from this reduced-order sliding mode have desirable properties (e.g., the system naturally slides along it until it comes to rest at a desired equilibrium). The main strength of sliding mode control is its robustness. Because the control can be as simple as a switching between two states, it need not be precise and will not be sensitive to parameter variations that enter into the control channel. Additionally, because the control law is not a continuous function, the sliding mode can be reached in finite time (i.e., better than asymptotic behavior).

There are two steps in the SMC design. The first step is designing a sliding surface so that the plant restricted to the sliding surface has a desired system response. This means the state variables of the plant dynamics are constrained to satisfy another set of equations which define the so-called switching surface. The second step is constructing a switched feedback gains necessary to drive the plant's state trajectory to the sliding surface. These constructions are built on the generalized Lyapunov stability theory.

1.1 Parameters of Sliding Surface Design

For linear system

$$\dot{x} = Ax + bu, \ x \in \mathbf{R}^n, \ u \in \mathbf{R} \tag{1.5}$$

where x is system state, A is an $n \times n$ matrix, b is an $n \times 1$ vector, and u is control input. A sliding variable can be designed as

$$s(x) = C^T x = \sum_{i=1}^{n} c_i x_i = \sum_{i=1}^{n-1} c_i x_i + x_n \quad (1.6)$$

where x is state vector, $C = [c_1 \ \cdots \ c_{n-1} \ 1]^T$.

In sliding mode control, parameters $c_1, c_2, \cdots, c_{n-1}$ should be selected so that the polynomial $p^{n-1} + c_{n-1} p^{n-2} + \cdots + c_2 p + c_1$ is a Hurwitz polynomial, where p is a Laplace operator.

For example, $n = 2$, $s(x) = c_1 x_1 + x_2$, to satisfy the condition that the polynomial $p + c_1$ is Hurwitz, the eigenvalue of $p + c_1 = 0$ should have a negative real part, i.e. $c_1 > 0$.

Consider another example, $n = 3$, $s(x) = c_1 x_1 + c_2 x_2 + x_3$, to satisfy the condition that the polynomial $p^2 + c_2 p + c_1$ is Hurwitz, the eigenvalue of $p^2 + c_2 p + c_1 = 0$ should have a negative real part. For a positive constant λ in $(p + \lambda)^2 = 0$, we can get $p^2 + 2\lambda p + \lambda^2 = 0$. Therefore, we have $c_2 = 2\lambda$, $c_1 = \lambda^2$.

1.2 Sliding Mode Control Based on Reaching Law

Sliding mode based on reaching law includes reaching phase and sliding phase. The reaching phase drive system is to maintain a stable manifold and the sliding phase drive system ensures slide to equilibrium. The idea of sliding mode can be described as Fig. 1.4.

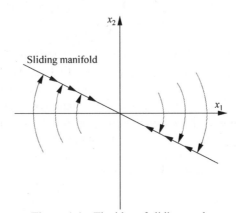

Figure 1.4 The idea of sliding mode

1.2.1 Classical Reaching Laws

(1) Constant Rate Reaching Law

$$\dot{s} = -\varepsilon \, \text{sgn}(s), \quad \varepsilon > 0 \quad (1.7)$$

where ε represents a constant rate.

This law constrains the switching variable to reach the switching manifold s at a constant rate ε. The merit of this reaching law is its simplicity. But, as will be shown later, if ε is too small, the reaching time will be too long. On the other hand, too large a ε will cause severe chattering.

(2) Exponential Reaching Law

$$\dot{s} = -\varepsilon \operatorname{sgn}(s) - ks, \quad \varepsilon > 0, \quad k > 0 \tag{1.8}$$

where $\dot{s} = -ks$ is exponential term, and its solution is $s = s(0)e^{-kt}$.

Clearly, by adding the proportional rate term $-ks$, the state is forced to approach the switching manifolds faster when s is large.

(3) Power Rate Reaching Law

$$\dot{s} = -k \, | \, s \, |^{\alpha} \operatorname{sgn}(s), \quad k > 0, \quad 1 > \alpha > 0 \tag{1.9}$$

This reaching law increases the reaching speed when the state is far away from the switching manifold. However, it reduces the rate when the state is near the manifold. The result is a fast and low chattering reaching mode.

(4) General Reaching Law

$$\dot{s} = -\varepsilon \operatorname{sgn}(s) - f(s), \quad \varepsilon > 0 \tag{1.10}$$

where $f(0) = 0$ and $sf(s) > 0$ when $s \neq 0$.

It is evident that the above four reaching laws can satisfy the sliding mode arrived condition $s\dot{s} < 0$.

1.2.2 Controller Design

1.2.2.1 System Description

The plant is

$$\ddot{\theta}(t) = -f(\theta, t) + bu(t) \tag{1.11}$$

where $f(\theta, t)$ and b are known and $b > 0$.

The sliding mode function is

$$s(t) = ce(t) + \dot{e}(t) \tag{1.12}$$

where c must satisfy Hurwitz condition $c > 0$.

The tracking error and its derivative value is

$$e(t) = r - \theta(t), \quad \dot{e}(t) = \dot{r} - \dot{\theta}(t)$$

where r is the ideal position signal.

Therefore, we have

$$\dot{s}(t) = c\dot{e}(t) + \ddot{e}(t) = c(\dot{r} - \dot{\theta}(t)) + (\ddot{r} - \ddot{\theta}(t)) \\ = c(\dot{r} - \dot{\theta}(t)) + (\ddot{r} + f(\theta,t) - bu(t)) \quad (1.13)$$

According to the exponential reaching law, we have

$$\dot{s} = -\varepsilon \operatorname{sgn} s - ks, \quad \varepsilon > 0, \quad k > 0 \quad (1.14)$$

From Eqs. (1.13) and (1.14), we have

$$c(\dot{r} - \dot{\theta}(t)) + (\ddot{r} + f(\theta,t) - bu(t)) = -\varepsilon \operatorname{sgn} s - ks$$

Then we can get the sliding mode controller as

$$u(t) = \frac{1}{b}(\varepsilon \operatorname{sgn}(s) + ks + c(\dot{r} - \dot{\theta}(t)) + \ddot{r} + f(\theta,t)) \quad (1.15)$$

1.2.2.2 Simulation Example

Consider the plant as

$$\ddot{\theta}(t) = -f(\theta,t) + bu(t)$$

where $\ddot{\theta}(t) = -25\dot{\theta}$, $b = 133$.

Choosing position ideal signal $r(t) = \sin t$, the initial state is set as [−0.15 −0.15], using controller Eq. (1.15), $c = 15$, $\varepsilon = 5$, $k = 10$, the results can be seen in Fig. 1.5 – Fig. 1.7.

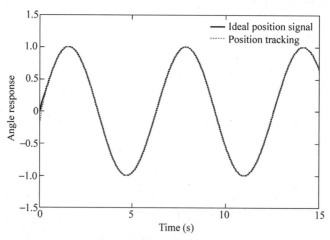

Figure 1.5 Position tracking

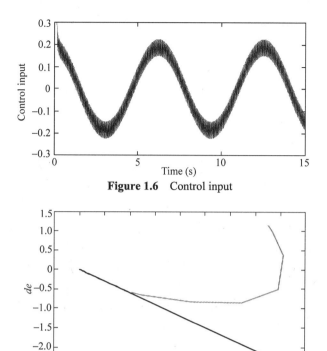

Figure 1.6 Control input

Figure 1.7 Phase trajectory

Simulation programs:

(1) Simulink main program: chap1_2sim.mdl

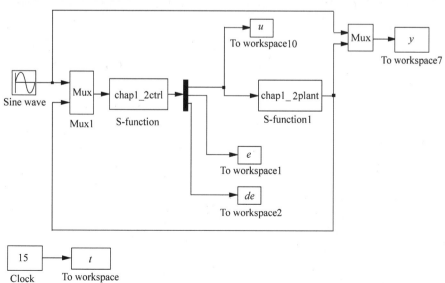

(2) Controller: chap1_2ctrl.m

```
function [sys,x0,str,ts] = spacemodel(t,x,u,flag)
switch flag,
case 0,
    [sys,x0,str,ts]=mdlInitializeSizes;
case 3,
    sys=mdlOutputs(t,x,u);
case {2,4,9}
    sys=[];
otherwise
    error(['Unhandled flag = ',num2str(flag)]);
end
function [sys,x0,str,ts]=mdlInitializeSizes
sizes = simsizes;
sizes.NumContStates  = 0;
sizes.NumDiscStates  = 0;
sizes.NumOutputs     = 3;
sizes.NumInputs      = 3;
sizes.DirFeedthrough = 1;
sizes.NumSampleTimes = 0;
sys = simsizes(sizes);
x0  = [];
str = [];
ts  = [];
function sys=mdlOutputs(t,x,u)
r=u(1);
dr=cos(t);
ddr=-sin(t);

th=u(2);
dth=u(3);

c=15;
e=r-th;
de=dr-dth;
s=c*e+de;

fx=25*dth;
b=133;

epc=5;k=10;
ut=1/b*(epc*sign(s)+k*s+c*de+ddr+fx);

sys(1)=ut;
sys(2)=e;
sys(3)=de;
```

(3) Plant: chap1_2plant.m

```
function [sys,x0,str,ts]=s_function(t,x,u,flag)
```

1 Introduction

```
switch flag,
case 0,
    [sys,x0,str,ts]=mdlInitializeSizes;
case 1,
    sys=mdlDerivatives(t,x,u);
case 3,
    sys=mdlOutputs(t,x,u);
case {2, 4, 9 }
    sys = [];
otherwise
    error(['Unhandled flag = ',num2str(flag)]);
end
function [sys,x0,str,ts]=mdlInitializeSizes
sizes = simsizes;
sizes.NumContStates  = 2;
sizes.NumDiscStates  = 0;
sizes.NumOutputs     = 2;
sizes.NumInputs      = 1;
sizes.DirFeedthrough = 0;
sizes.NumSampleTimes = 0;
sys=simsizes(sizes);
x0=[-0.15 -0.15];
str=[];
ts=[];
function sys=mdlDerivatives(t,x,u)
sys(1)=x(2);
sys(2)=-25*x(2)+133*u;
function sys=mdlOutputs(t,x,u)
sys(1)=x(1);
sys(2)=x(2);
```

(4) Plot program: chap1_2plot.m

```
close all;

figure(1);
plot(t,y(:,1),'k',t,y(:,2),'r:','linewidth',2);
legend('Ideal position signal','Position tracking');
xlabel('time(s)');ylabel('Angle response');

figure(2);
plot(t,u(:,1),'k','linewidth',0.01);
xlabel('time(s)');ylabel('Control input');

c=15;
figure(3);
plot(e,de,'r',e,-c'.*e,'k','linewidth',2);
xlabel('e');ylabel('de');
```

1.3 Robust Sliding Mode Control Based on Reaching Law

1.3.1 System Description

The plant is

$$\ddot{\theta}(t) = -f(\theta,t) + bu(t) + d(t) \tag{1.16}$$

where $f(\theta,t)$ and b are known and $b > 0$, $d(t)$ is the disturbance.

The sliding mode function is

$$s(t) = ce(t) + \dot{e}(t) \tag{1.17}$$

where c must satisfy Hurwitz condition $c > 0$.

The tracking error and its derivative value is

$$e(t) = r - \theta(t), \quad \dot{e}(t) = \dot{r} - \dot{\theta}(t)$$

where r is the ideal position signal.

Therefore, we have

$$
\begin{aligned}
\dot{s}(t) &= c\dot{e}(t) + \ddot{e}(t) = c(\dot{r} - \dot{\theta}(t)) + (\ddot{r} - \ddot{\theta}(t)) \\
&= c(\dot{r} - \dot{\theta}(t)) + (\ddot{r} + f - bu - d)
\end{aligned} \tag{1.18}
$$

Using the exponential reaching law, we have

$$\dot{s} = -\varepsilon \operatorname{sgn}(s) - ks, \quad \varepsilon > 0, \quad k > 0 \tag{1.19}$$

From Eqs. (1.18) and (1.19), we have

$$c(\dot{r} - \dot{\theta}) + (\ddot{r} + f - bu - d) = -\varepsilon \operatorname{sgn}(s) - ks$$

If we design the sliding mode controller as

$$u(t) = \frac{1}{b}(\varepsilon \operatorname{sgn}(s) + ks + c(\dot{r} - \dot{\theta}) + \ddot{r} + f - d) \tag{1.20}$$

Obviously, all quantities on the right-hand side of Eq. (1.20) are known except the disturbance d, which is unknown. Thus the control law Eq. (1.20) is incomplete. To solve this problem, d in Eq. (1.20) is replaced by a conservative known quantity d_c.

Then we can get the sliding mode controller as

$$u(t) = \frac{1}{b}(\varepsilon \operatorname{sgn}(s) + ks + c(\dot{r} - \dot{\theta}) + \ddot{r} + f - d_c) \tag{1.21}$$

where, d_c is chosen to guarantee the reaching condition.

Substituting Eq. (1.21) into Eq. (1.18) and simplifying the result, we get

$$\dot{s}(t) = -\varepsilon \operatorname{sgn}(s) - ks + d_c - d \tag{1.22}$$

The term d_c can be chosen to ensure the reaching condition. It is reasonable to assume that d is bounded, therefore, so is d_c. That is

$$d_L \leqslant d(t) \leqslant d_U \tag{1.23}$$

where the bounds d_L and d_U are known.

Referring to Eq. (1.22), d_c is chosen according to the following logic;

When $s(t) > 0$, $\dot{s}(t) = -\varepsilon - ks + d_c - d$, we want $\dot{s}(t) < 0$, so let $d_c = d_L$

When $s(t) < 0$, $\dot{s}(t) = \varepsilon - ks + d_c - d$, we want $\dot{s}(t) > 0$, so let $d_c = d_U$

Therefore, if we define $d_1 = \dfrac{d_U - d_L}{2}$, $d_2 = \dfrac{d_U + d_L}{2}$, then we can get

$$d_c = d_2 - d_1 \operatorname{sgn}(s) \tag{1.24}$$

1.3.2 Simulation Example

Consider the plant as

$$\ddot{\theta}(t) = -f(\theta, t) + bu(t) + d(t)$$

where $\ddot{\theta}(t) = -25\dot{\theta}$, $b = 133$, $d(t) = 10\sin(\pi t)$.

Choosing position ideal signal $r(t) = \sin t$, the initial state is set as $[-0.15 \quad -0.15]$, using controller Eq. (1.21), $c = 15$, $\varepsilon = 0.5$, $k = 10$, the results can be seen in Fig. 1.8 – Fig. 1.10.

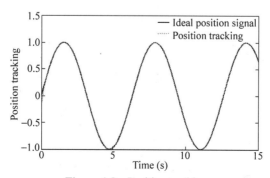

Figure 1.8 Position tracking

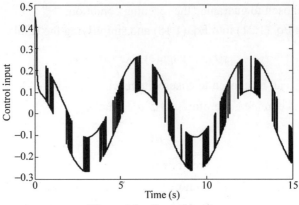

Figure 1.9 Control input

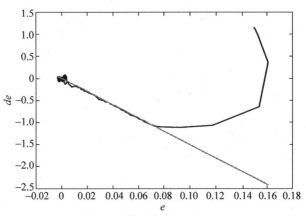

Figure 1.10 Phase trajectory

Simulation programs:

(1) Simulink main program: chap1_3sim.mdl

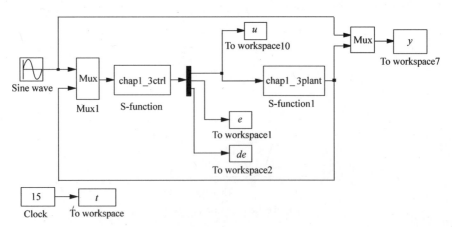

(2) Controller: chap1_3ctrl.m

```matlab
function [sys,x0,str,ts] = spacemodel(t,x,u,flag)
switch flag,
case 0,
    [sys,x0,str,ts]=mdlInitializeSizes;
case 3,
    sys=mdlOutputs(t,x,u);
case {2,4,9}
    sys=[];
otherwise
    error(['Unhandled flag = ',num2str(flag)]);
end
function [sys,x0,str,ts]=mdlInitializeSizes
sizes = simsizes;
sizes.NumContStates  = 0;
sizes.NumDiscStates  = 0;
sizes.NumOutputs     = 3;
sizes.NumInputs      = 3;
sizes.DirFeedthrough = 1;
sizes.NumSampleTimes = 0;
sys = simsizes(sizes);
x0  = [];
str = [];
ts  = [];
function sys=mdlOutputs(t,x,u)
r=u(1);
dr=cos(t);
ddr=-sin(t);

th=u(2);
dth=u(3);

c=15;
e=r-th;
de=dr-dth;
s=c*e+de;

fx=25*dth;
b=133;
dL=-10;dU=10;
d1=(dU-dL)/2;
d2=(dU+dL)/2;
dc=d2-d1*sign(s);

epc=0.5;k=10;
ut=1/b*(epc*sign(s)+k*s+c*de+ddr+fx-dc);

sys(1)=ut;
sys(2)=e;
sys(3)=de;
```

(3) Plant: chap1_3plant.m

```
function [sys,x0,str,ts]=s_function(t,x,u,flag)
switch flag,
case 0,
    [sys,x0,str,ts]=mdlInitializeSizes;
case 1,
    sys=mdlDerivatives(t,x,u);
case 3,
    sys=mdlOutputs(t,x,u);
case {2, 4, 9 }
    sys = [];
otherwise
    error(['Unhandled flag = ',num2str(flag)]);
end
function [sys,x0,str,ts]=mdlInitializeSizes
sizes = simsizes;
sizes.NumContStates  = 2;
sizes.NumDiscStates  = 0;
sizes.NumOutputs     = 2;
sizes.NumInputs      = 1;
sizes.DirFeedthrough = 0;
sizes.NumSampleTimes = 0;
sys=simsizes(sizes);
x0=[-0.15 -0.15];
str=[];
ts=[];
function sys=mdlDerivatives(t,x,u)
sys(1)=x(2);
sys(2)=-25*x(2)+133*u+10*sin(pi*t);
function sys=mdlOutputs(t,x,u)
sys(1)=x(1);
sys(2)=x(2);
```

(4) Plot program: chap1_3plot.m

```
close all;

figure(1);
plot(t,y(:,1),'k',t,y(:,2),'r:','linewidth',2);
legend('Ideal position signal','Position tracking');
xlabel('time(s)');ylabel('Position tracking');

figure(2);
plot(t,u(:,1),'k','linewidth',2);
xlabel('time(s)');ylabel('Control input');

c=15;
figure(3);
plot(e,de,'k',e,-c'.*e,'r','linewidth',2);
xlabel('e');ylabel('de');
```

1 Introduction

1.4 Sliding Mode Robust Control Based on Upper Bound

1.4.1 System Description

Consider a second-order nonlinear inverted pendulum as follows:

$$\ddot{\theta} = f(\theta,\dot{\theta}) + \Delta f(\theta,\dot{\theta}) + g(\theta,\dot{\theta})u + \Delta g(\theta,\dot{\theta})u + d_0(t) \tag{1.25}$$

where f and g are known nonlinear functions, $u \in R$ and $y = \theta \in R$ are the control input and measurement output respectively. $d_0(t)$ is the disturbance, and $|d(\theta,\dot{\theta},t)| \leqslant D$, D is a positive constant.

Let $d(\theta,\dot{\theta},t) = \Delta f(\theta,\dot{\theta}) + \Delta g(\theta,\dot{\theta})u + d_0(t)$, therefore, Eq. (1.25) can be written as

$$\ddot{\theta} = f(\theta,\dot{\theta}) + g(\theta,\dot{\theta})u + d(\theta,\dot{\theta},t) \tag{1.26}$$

1.4.2 Controller Design

Let desired position input be θ_d, and $e = \theta_d - \theta$. The sliding variable is selected as

$$s = \dot{e} + ce \tag{1.27}$$

where $c > 0$. Therefore,

$$\dot{s} = \ddot{e} + c\dot{e} = \ddot{\theta}_d - \ddot{\theta} + c\dot{e} = \ddot{\theta}_d - f - gu - d + c\dot{e}$$

The controller is adopted as

$$u = \frac{1}{g}[-f + \ddot{\theta}_d + c\dot{e} + \eta\,\mathrm{sgn}(s)] \tag{1.28}$$

Select the Lyapunov function as

$$L = \frac{1}{2}s^2$$

Therefore, we have

$$\dot{L} = s\dot{s} = s(\ddot{\theta}_d - f - gu - d + c\dot{e})$$
$$= s(\ddot{\theta}_d - f - (-f + \ddot{\theta}_d + c\dot{e} + \eta\,\mathrm{sgn}(s)) - d + c\dot{e})$$
$$= s(-d - \eta\,\mathrm{sgn}(s))$$
$$= -sd - \eta|s|$$

If $\eta \geqslant D$, then

$$\dot{L} = -sd - \eta|s| \leqslant 0$$

19

In order to restrain the chattering phenomenon, the saturated function sat(s) is adopted instead of sgn(s) in Eq. (1.29) as

$$\text{sat}(s) = \begin{cases} 1, & s > \Delta \\ ks, & |s| \leqslant \Delta, \ k = 1/\Delta \\ -1, & s < -\Delta \end{cases} \quad (1.29)$$

where Δ is the "boundary layer".

The nature of saturated function is: out of the boundary layer, switch control is selected, in the boundary layer, the usual feedback control is adopted. Therefore, the chattering phenomenon can be restrained thoroughly.

1.4.3 Simulation Example

The dynamic equation of inverted pendulum is

$$\begin{cases} \dot{x}_1 = x_2 \\ \dot{x}_2 = f(x) + g(x) \cdot u \end{cases}$$

where

$$f(x) = \frac{g \sin x_1 - m l x_2^2 \cos x_1 \sin x_1 / (m_c + m)}{l(4/3 - m \cos^2 x_1 / (m_c + m))}$$

$$g(x) = \frac{\cos x_1 / (m_c + m)}{l(4/3 - m \cos^2 x_1 / (m_c + m))}$$

where $x = [x_1 \ x_2]$, x_1 and x_2 are the oscillation angle and oscillation rate respectively, $g = 9.8 \ \text{m/s}^2$, m_c is the vehicle mass, $m_c = 1 \ \text{kg}$, m is the mass of pendulum bar, $m = 0.1 \ \text{kg}$, l is one half of pendulum length, $l = 0.5 \ \text{m}$, u is the control input.

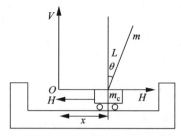

Figure 1.11 Inverted pendulum system

Let $x_1 = \theta$, and the desired trajectory is $\theta_d(t) = 0.1 \sin(t)$. The initial state of the inverted pendulum is $[\pi/60 \ 0]$, and $\eta = 0.20$. The controller is Eq. (1.28). M is a variable in the simulation program. $M=1$ indicates the controller with a switch function, and $M=2$ indicates the controller with a saturation function. The switch function is adopted firstly, and $M=1$. The simulation results are shown in Fig. 1.12 and Fig. 1.13. In order to restrain the chattering phenomenon, the saturated function is adopted instead of switch function, and let $M=2$ in the simulation program, and let $\Delta = 0.05$ in Eq. (1.29). The simulation results are shown in Fig. 1.14 and Fig. 1.15.

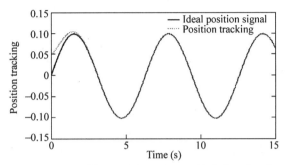

Figure 1.12 Position tracking using a switch function ($M=1$)

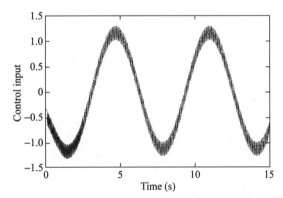

Figure 1.13 Control input using switch function ($M=1$)

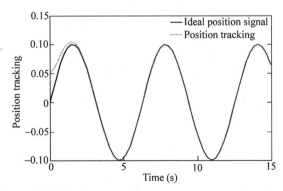

Figure 1.14 Position tracking using saturated function ($M=2$)

Advanced Sliding Mode Control for Mechanical Systems: Design, Analysis and MATLAB Simulation

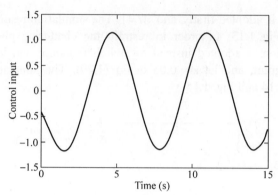

Figure 1.15 Control input using saturated function ($M=2$)

Simulation programs:

(1) Simulink main program: chap1_4sim.mdl

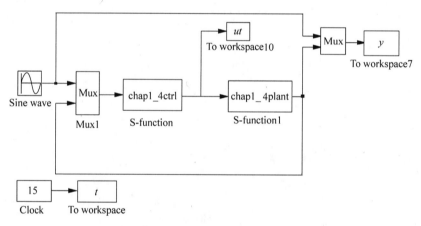

(2) S-function of controller: chap1_4ctrl.m

```
function [sys,x0,str,ts] = spacemodel(t,x,u,flag)
switch flag,
case 0,
    [sys,x0,str,ts]=mdlInitializeSizes;
case 3,
    sys=mdlOutputs(t,x,u);
case {1,2,4,9}
    sys=[];
otherwise
    error(['Unhandled flag = ',num2str(flag)]);
end
function [sys,x0,str,ts]=mdlInitializeSizes
sizes = simsizes;
sizes.NumContStates  = 0;
sizes.NumDiscStates  = 0;
```

1 Introduction

```matlab
sizes.NumOutputs       = 1;
sizes.NumInputs        = 3;
sizes.DirFeedthrough = 1;
sizes.NumSampleTimes = 0;
sys = simsizes(sizes);
x0  = [];
str = [];
ts  = [];
function sys=mdlOutputs(t,x,u)
r=0.1*sin(t);
dr=0.1*cos(t);
ddr=-0.1*sin(t);

x1=u(2);
x2=u(3);

e=r-x1;
de=dr-x2;

c=1.5;
s=c*e+de;

g=9.8;mc=1.0;m=0.1;l=0.5;
T=l*(4/3-m*(cos(x1))^2/(mc+m));

fx=g*sin(x1)-m*l*x2^2*cos(x1)*sin(x1)/(mc+m);
fx=fx/T;

gx=cos(x1)/(mc+m);
gx=gx/T;

xite=0.20;

M=2;
if M==1
   ut=1/gx*(-fx+ddr+c*de+xite*sign(s));
elseif M==2                   %Saturated function
      delta=0.05;
       kk=1/delta;
      if abs(s)>delta
        sats=sign(s);
      else
        sats=kk*s;
      end
   ut=1/gx*(-fx+ddr+c*de+xite*sats);
end
sys(1)=ut;
```

(3) S-function of the plant: chap1_4plant.m

```matlab
function [sys,x0,str,ts]=s_function(t,x,u,flag)
```

```
switch flag,
case 0,
    [sys,x0,str,ts]=mdlInitializeSizes;
case 1,
    sys=mdlDerivatives(t,x,u);
case 3,
    sys=mdlOutputs(t,x,u);
case {2, 4, 9 }
    sys = [];
otherwise
    error(['Unhandled flag = ',num2str(flag)]);
end
function [sys,x0,str,ts]=mdlInitializeSizes
sizes = simsizes;
sizes.NumContStates  = 2;
sizes.NumDiscStates  = 0;
sizes.NumOutputs     = 2;
sizes.NumInputs      = 1;
sizes.DirFeedthrough = 0;
sizes.NumSampleTimes = 0;
sys=simsizes(sizes);
x0=[pi/60 0];
str=[];
ts=[];
function sys=mdlDerivatives(t,x,u)
g=9.8;mc=1.0;m=0.1;l=0.5;
S=l*(4/3-m*(cos(x(1)))^2/(mc+m));
fx=g*sin(x(1))-m*l*x(2)^2*cos(x(1))*sin(x(1))/(mc+m);
fx=fx/S;
gx=cos(x(1))/(mc+m);
gx=gx/S;
%%%%%%%%%
dt=0*10*sin(t);
%%%%%%%%%

sys(1)=x(2);
sys(2)=fx+gx*u+dt;
function sys=mdlOutputs(t,x,u)
sys(1)=x(1);
sys(2)=x(2);
```

(4) plot program: chap1_4plot.m

```
close all;

figure(1);
plot(t,y(:,1),'k',t,y(:,2),'r:','linewidth',2);
legend('Ideal position signal','Position tracking');
xlabel('time(s)');ylabel('Position tracking');
```

```
figure(2);
plot(t,ut(:,1),'k','linewidth',2);
xlabel('time(s)');ylabel('Control input');
```

1.5 Sliding Mode Control Based on Quasi-Sliding Mode

1.5.1 Quasi-Sliding Mode

In practical engineering systems, the chattering of sliding mode control may cause damage to system components such as actuators. One way to alleviate the chattering is to use the quasi-sliding mode method which can make the state stay in a certain range at Δ neighborhood. Often we name Δ as the boundary layer.

In a continuous system, there are two common methods for the quasi-sliding mode design.

(1) Saturation function instead of sgn function

$$\mathrm{sat}(s) = \begin{cases} 1, & s > \Delta \\ ks, & |s| \leq \Delta \\ -1, & s < -\Delta \end{cases} \qquad k = \frac{1}{\Delta} \qquad (1.30)$$

where Δ is called "the boundary layer" which is shown in Fig. 1.16. Outside the boundary layer we use switch control and inside the boundary layer we use linear feedback control.

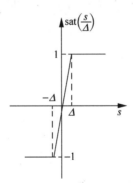

Figure 1.16 Saturation function

(2) Relay function instead of sgn function

$$\theta(s) = \frac{s}{|s| + \delta} \qquad (1.31)$$

where δ is a very small positive constant.

1.5.2 Simulation Example

Consider the plant as

$$\ddot{\theta}(t) = -f(\theta,t) + bu(t) + d(t)$$

where, $\ddot{\theta}(t) = -25\dot{\theta}$, $b = 133$, $d(t) = 50\sin t$.

Using the quasi-sliding mode, the chattering can be alleviated.

(1) Use upper bound based sliding mode control law (1.28), $M=1$ represents using sgn function. The simulation results are shown in Fig. 1.17 – Fig. 1.19.

(2) Use the quasi-sliding mode in the control law (1.28), $M=2$ represents using saturation function. Let $\Delta = 0.05$, the simulation results are shown in Fig. 1.20 and Fig. 1.21. $M=3$ represents using relay function, let $\delta = 0.05$, the simulation results are shown in Fig. 1.22 and Fig. 1.23.

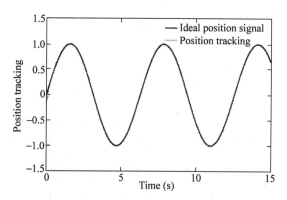

Figure 1.17 Position tracking ($M=1$)

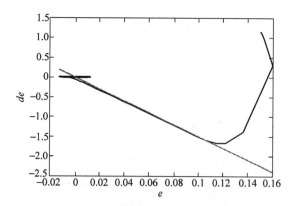

Figure 1.18 Phase trajectory ($M=1$)

1 Introduction

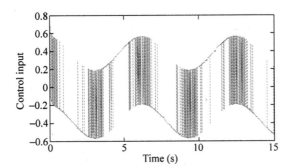

Figure 1.19 Control input ($M=1$)

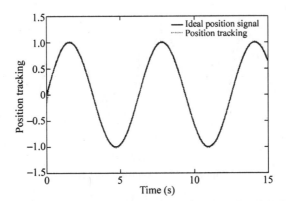

Figure 1.20 Position tracking ($M=2$)

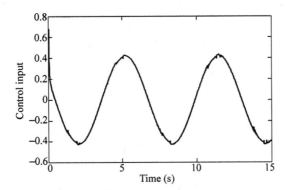

Figure 1.21 Control input ($M=2$)

Advanced Sliding Mode Control for Mechanical Systems: Design, Analysis and MATLAB Simulation

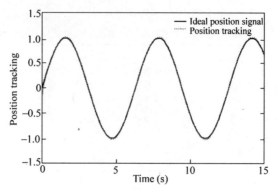

Figure 1.22 Position tracking ($M=3$)

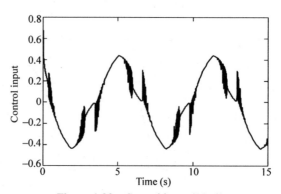

Figure 1.23 Control input ($M=3$)

Simulation programs:

(1) Simulink main program: chap1_5sim.mdl

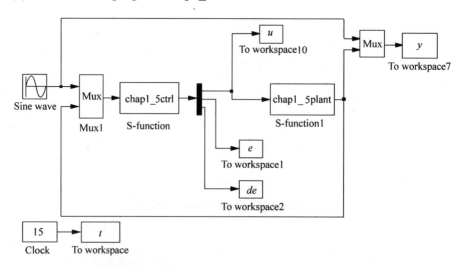

(2) Controller: chap1_5ctrl.m

```matlab
function [sys,x0,str,ts] = spacemodel(t,x,u,flag)
switch flag,
case 0,
    [sys,x0,str,ts]=mdlInitializeSizes;
case 3,
    sys=mdlOutputs(t,x,u);
case {2,4,9}
    sys=[];
otherwise
    error(['Unhandled flag = ',num2str(flag)]);
end
function [sys,x0,str,ts]=mdlInitializeSizes
sizes = simsizes;
sizes.NumContStates  = 0;
sizes.NumDiscStates  = 0;
sizes.NumOutputs     = 3;
sizes.NumInputs      = 3;
sizes.DirFeedthrough = 1;
sizes.NumSampleTimes = 0;
sys = simsizes(sizes);
x0  = [];
str = [];
ts  = [];
function sys=mdlOutputs(t,x,u)
r=u(1);
dr=cos(t);
ddr=-sin(t);

th=u(2);
dth=u(3);

c=15;
e=r-th;
de=dr-dth;
s=c*e+de;

D=50;
xite=1.50;

fx=25*dth;
b=133;

M=2;
if M==1           %Switch function
    ut=1/b*(c*(dr-dth)+ddr+fx+(D+xite)*sign(s));
elseif M==2       %Saturated function
    fai=0.20;
    if abs(s)<=fai
```

```
      sat=s/fai;
   else
      sat=sign(s);
   end
   ut=1/b*(c*(dr-dth)+ddr+fx+(D+xite)*sat);
elseif M==3        %Relay function
   delta=0.015;
   rs=s/(abs(s)+delta);
   ut=1/b*(c*(dr-dth)+ddr+fx+(D+xite)*rs);
end

sys(1)=ut;
sys(2)=e;
sys(3)=de;
```

(3) Plant: chap1_5plant.m

```
function [sys,x0,str,ts]=s_function(t,x,u,flag)
switch flag,
case 0,
    [sys,x0,str,ts]=mdlInitializeSizes;
case 1,
    sys=mdlDerivatives(t,x,u);
case 3,
    sys=mdlOutputs(t,x,u);
case {2, 4, 9 }
    sys = [];
otherwise
    error(['Unhandled flag = ',num2str(flag)]);
end
function [sys,x0,str,ts]=mdlInitializeSizes
sizes = simsizes;
sizes.NumContStates  = 2;
sizes.NumDiscStates  = 0;
sizes.NumOutputs     = 2;
sizes.NumInputs      = 1;
sizes.DirFeedthrough = 0;
sizes.NumSampleTimes = 0;
sys=simsizes(sizes);
x0=[-0.15 -0.15];
str=[];
ts=[];
function sys=mdlDerivatives(t,x,u)
dt=50*sin(t);
sys(1)=x(2);
sys(2)=-25*x(2)+133*u+dt;
function sys=mdlOutputs(t,x,u)
sys(1)=x(1);
sys(2)=x(2);
```

1 Introduction

(4) Plot program: chap1_5plot.m

```
close all;

figure(1);
plot(t,y(:,1),'k',t,y(:,2),'r:','linewidth',2);
legend('Ideal position signal','Position tracking');
xlabel('time(s)');ylabel('Position tracking');

figure(2);
plot(t,u(:,1),'k','linewidth',2);
xlabel('time(s)');ylabel('Control input');

c=15;
figure(3);
plot(e,de,'k',e,-c'.*e,'r','linewidth',2);
xlabel('e');ylabel('de');
```

1.6 Sliding Mode Control Based on the Equivalent Control

In the sliding mode controller, the control law usually consists of the equivalent control u_{eq} and the switching control u_{sw}. The equivalent control keeps the state of system on the sliding surface, while the switching control forces the system sliding on the sliding surface.

1.6.1 System Description

A n-order SISO nonlinear system can be described as

$$x^{(n)} = f(x,t) + bu(t) + d(t) \tag{1.32}$$

$$\boldsymbol{x} = [x \quad \dot{x} \quad \cdots \quad x^{(n-1)}]^{\mathrm{T}} \tag{1.33}$$

where $b > 0$, $x \in \mathbf{R}^n$, $u \in \mathbf{R}$, $d(t)$ denotes external disturbance and uncertainty while we assume $|d(t)| \leqslant D$.

1.6.2 Sliding Mode Controller Design

1.6.2.1 Equivalent Controller Design

Ignoring external disturbance and uncertainty, the plant can be described as

31

$$x^{(n)} = f(x,t) + bu(t) \tag{1.34}$$

The tracking error vector is

$$e = x_d - x = [e \quad \dot{e} \quad \cdots \quad e^{(n-1)}]^T \tag{1.35}$$

Then switch function is

$$s(x,t) = Ce = c_1 e + c_2 \dot{e} + \cdots + e^{(n-1)} \tag{1.36}$$

where $C = [c_1 \quad c_2 \quad \cdots \quad c_{n-1} \quad 1]$ is a $1 \times n$ vector.
Choose $\dot{s} = 0$, we get

$$\dot{s}(x,t) = c_1 \dot{e} + c_2 \ddot{e} + \cdots + e^{(n)} = c_1 \dot{e} + c_2 \ddot{e} + \cdots + c_{n-1} e^{(n-1)} + x_d^{(n)} - x^{(n)}$$

$$= \sum_{i=1}^{n-1} c_i e^{(i)} + x_d^{(n)} - f(x,t) - bu(t) = 0 \tag{1.37}$$

The control law is designed as

$$u_{eq} = \frac{1}{b}\left(\sum_{i=1}^{n-1} c_i e^{(i)} + x_d^{(n)} - f(x,t)\right) \tag{1.38}$$

1.6.2.2　Sliding Mode Controller Design

In order to satisfy reaching conditions of sliding mode control $s(x,t) \cdot \dot{s}(x,t) \leqslant -\eta |s|$, $\eta > 0$, we must choose switching control whose control law is

$$u_{sw} = \frac{1}{b} K \operatorname{sgn}(s) \tag{1.39}$$

where $K = D + \eta$.

The sliding mode controller include the equivalent control and the switching control, then we have

$$u = u_{eq} + u_{sw} \tag{1.40}$$

Stability proof:

$$\dot{s}(x,t) = \sum_{i=1}^{n-1} c_i e^{(i)} + x_d^{(n)} - f(x,t) - bu(t) - d(t) \tag{1.41}$$

Submitting Eqs. $(1.40) - (1.41)$, we can get:

$$\dot{s}(x,t) = \sum_{i=1}^{n-1} c_i e^{(i)} + x_d^{(n)} - f(x,t) - b\left(\frac{1}{b}\left(\sum_{i=1}^{n-1} c_i e^{(i)} + x_d^{(n)} - f(x,t)\right) + \frac{1}{b} K \operatorname{sgn}(s)\right) - d(t)$$

$$= -K \operatorname{sgn}(s) - d(t)$$

Therefore, we have

$$s\dot{s} = s(-K\operatorname{sgn}(s)) - s \cdot d(t) = -\eta|s| \leq 0 \quad (1.42)$$

1.6.3 Simulation Example

We choose a plant as follows:

$$\ddot{x} = -25\dot{x} + 133u(t) + d(t)$$

Therefore $f(x,t) = -25\dot{x}$, $b = 133$.

Let $d(t) = 50\sin(t)$, $\eta = 0.10$, ideal position signal is $r = \sin(2\pi t)$, choose $c = 25$, then we can get $D = 50$. Adapting controller (1.40), the simulation results are shown in Fig. 1.24 and Fig. 1.25.

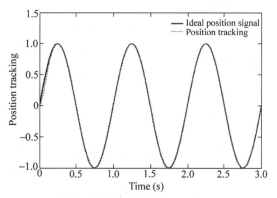

Figure 1.24 Position tracking

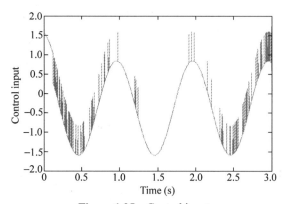

Figure 1.25 Control input

Simulation programs:

(1) Simulink main program: chap1_6sim.mdl

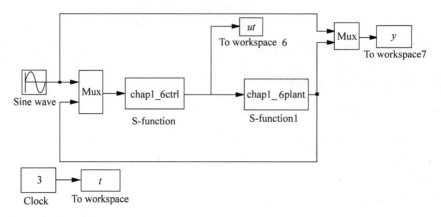

(2) Controller: chap1_6ctrl.m

```
function [sys,x0,str,ts]=s_function(t,x,u,flag)
switch flag,
case 0,
    [sys,x0,str,ts]=mdlInitializeSizes;
case 3,
    sys=mdlOutputs(t,x,u);
case {2, 4, 9 }
    sys = [];
otherwise
    error(['Unhandled flag = ',num2str(flag)]);
end
function [sys,x0,str,ts]=mdlInitializeSizes
sizes = simsizes;
sizes.NumContStates  = 0;
sizes.NumDiscStates  = 0;
sizes.NumOutputs     = 1;
sizes.NumInputs      = 3;
sizes.DirFeedthrough = 1;
sizes.NumSampleTimes = 0;
sys=simsizes(sizes);
x0=[];
str=[];
ts=[];
function sys=mdlOutputs(t,x,u)
r=u(1);
dr=2*pi*cos(2*pi*t);
ddr=-(2*pi)^2*sin(2*pi*t);
x=u(2);dx=u(3);
e=r-x;
de=dr-dx;
```

1 Introduction

```
c=25;
s=c*e+de;

f=-25*dx;
b=133;

ueq=1/b*(c*de+ddr-f);
D=50;
xite=0.10;
K=D+xite;
usw=1/b*K*sign(s);

ut=ueq+usw;

sys(1)=ut;
```

(3) Plant: chap1_6plant.m

```
function [sys,x0,str,ts]=s_function(t,x,u,flag)
switch flag,
case 0,
    [sys,x0,str,ts]=mdlInitializeSizes;
case 1,
    sys=mdlDerivatives(t,x,u);
case 3,
    sys=mdlOutputs(t,x,u);
case {2, 4, 9 }
    sys = [];
otherwise
    error(['Unhandled flag = ',num2str(flag)]);
end
function [sys,x0,str,ts]=mdlInitializeSizes
sizes = simsizes;
sizes.NumContStates  = 2;
sizes.NumDiscStates  = 0;
sizes.NumOutputs     = 2;
sizes.NumInputs      = 1;
sizes.DirFeedthrough = 0;
sizes.NumSampleTimes = 0;
sys=simsizes(sizes);
x0=[0,0];
str=[];
ts=[];
function sys=mdlDerivatives(t,x,u)
dt=50*sin(t);
sys(1)=x(2);
sys(2)=-25*x(2)+133*u+dt;
function sys=mdlOutputs(t,x,u)
sys(1)=x(1);
sys(2)=x(2);
```

35

(4) Plot program: chap1_6plot.m

```
close all;

figure(1);
plot(t,y(:,1),'k',t,y(:,2),'r:','linewidth',2);
legend('Ideal position signal','Position tracking');
xlabel('time(s)');ylabel('Position tracking');

figure(2);
plot(t,ut(:,1),'r','linewidth',2);
xlabel('time(s)');ylabel('Control input');
```

1.7 Digital Simulation of Sliding Mode Control

1.7.1 Basic Theory

In practical engineering we often use digital control. The digital control system structure is shown in Fig. 1.26, and the corresponding program diagram of the system is shown in Fig. 1.27.

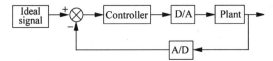

Figure 1.26 Digital control system structure

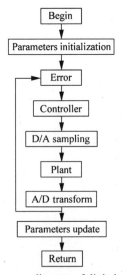

Figure 1.27 Program diagram of digital control algorithm

1.7.2 Simulation Example

We choose a plant as follow:

$$\ddot{x} = -25\dot{x} + 133u(t) + d(t)$$

Therefore $f(x,t) = -25\dot{x}$, $b = 133$. We choose sampling time $T = 0.001$. Let $d(t) = 3\sin(t)$, then $\eta = 3.1$. Choose ideal position signal as $r = \sin(t)$, and $c = 5$. Adapting controller Eq. (1.28) (in program $M=1$), the simulation results are shown in Fig. 1.28 – Fig. 1.30. Moreover, using saturation function (1.29) instead of switch function (in program $M=2$), the simulation results are shown in Fig. 1.31 – Fig. 1.33.

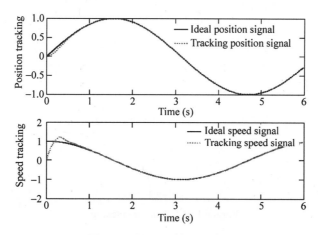

Figure 1.28 Position tracking

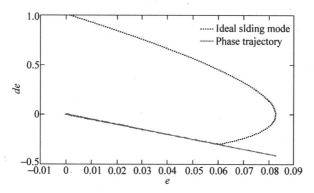

Figure 1.29 Phase trajectory

Advanced Sliding Mode Control for Mechanical Systems: Design, Analysis and MATLAB Simulation

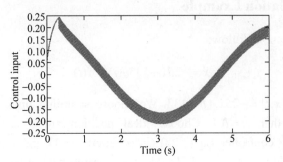

Figure 1.30 Control input

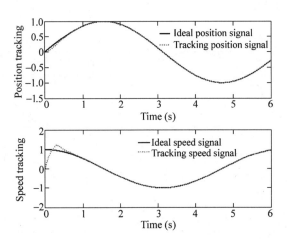

Figure 1.31 Position tracking

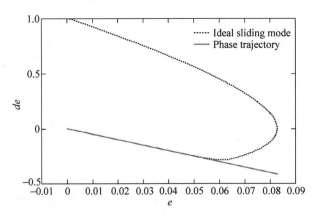

Figure 1.32 Phase trajectory

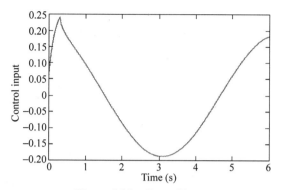

Figure 1.33 Control input

Simulation programs:

(1) Main program: chap1_7.m

```
clear all;
close all;
a=25;b=133;
xk=zeros(2,1);
ut_1=0;
c=5;
T=0.001;
for k=1:1:6000
time(k)=k*T;
thd(k)=sin(k*T);
dthd(k)=cos(k*T);
ddthd(k)=-sin(k*T);

tSpan=[0 T];

para=ut_1;       % D/A
[tt,xx]=ode45('chap1_7plant',tSpan,xk,[],para);
xk=xx(length(xx),:);    % A/D
th(k)=xk(1);
dth(k)=xk(2);

e(k)=thd(k)-th(k);
de(k)=dthd(k)-dth(k);
s(k)=c*e(k)+de(k);

xite=3.1;  % xite>max(dt)
M=1;
if M==1
   ut(k)=1/b*(a*dth(k)+ddthd(k)+c*de(k)+xite*sign(s(k)));
elseif M==2              %Saturated function
       delta=0.05;
        kk=1/delta;
```

Advanced Sliding Mode Control for Mechanical Systems: Design, Analysis and MATLAB Simulation

```
        if abs(s(k))>delta
          sats=sign(s(k));
        else
          sats=kk*s(k);
        end
    ut(k)=1/b*(a*dth(k)+ddthd(k)+c*de(k)+xite*sats);
  end
  ut_1=ut(k);
  end
  figure(1);
  subplot(211);
  plot(time,thd,'k',time,th,'r:','linewidth',2);
  xlabel('time(s)');ylabel('position tracking');
  legend('ideal position signal','tracking position signal');
  subplot(212);
  plot(time,dthd,'k',time,dth,'r:','linewidth',2);
  xlabel('time(s)');ylabel('speed tracking');
  legend('ideal speed signal','tracking speed signal');
  figure(2);
  plot(thd-th,dthd-dth,'k:',thd-th,-c*(thd-th),'r','linewidth',2);
      %Draw line(s=0)
  xlabel('e');ylabel('de');
  legend('ideal sliding mode','phase trajectory');
  figure(3);
  plot(time,ut,'r','linewidth',2);
  xlabel('time(s)');ylabel('Control input');
```

(2) Plant program: chap1_7plant.m

```
function dx=Plant(t,x,flag,para)
dx=zeros(2,1);
a=25;b=133;
ut=para(1);
dt=3.0*sin(t);
dx(1)=x(2);
dx(2)=-a*x(2)+b*ut+dt;
```

References

[1] Itkis U. Control System of Variable Structure. New York: Wiley, 1976

[2] Hung JY, Gao W, Hung JC. Variable Structure Control: A Survey, IEEE Transaction on Industrial Electronics, 1993,40(1): 2 − 22

[3] Edwards C, Spurgeon S. Sliding Mode Control: Theory and Applications, London: Taylor and Francis, 1998

2 Normal Sliding Mode Control

Jinkun Liu
Beijing University of Aeronautics and Astronautics
P.R.China
E-mail: ljk@buaa.edu.cn

Xinhua Wang
National University of Singapore
Singapore
E-mail: wangxinhua04@gmail.com

Abstract   This chapter introduces several normal sliding mode controllers design, including sliding mode control based on nominal model, global sliding mode control, sliding mode control based on linearization feedback technology and sliding mode control based on low pass filter.

Keywords   sliding mode control, nominal model, global sliding mode, linearization feedback control, low pass filter

2.1   Sliding Mode Control Based on Nominal Model

2.1.1   System Description

Consider the servo system as under:

$$J\ddot{\theta} + B\dot{\theta} = u - d \qquad (2.1)$$

where J is the moment of inertia, B is the damping coefficient, u is the control input, d is the disturbance, and θ the rolling angle. also, $J > 0$, $B > 0$.

In practice, J is the time-variant, and disturbances and uncertainties exist. We let the nominal model be

$$J_n\ddot{\theta}_n + B_n\dot{\theta}_n = \mu \qquad (2.2)$$

where J_n is the nominal moment of inertia, B_n is the nominal sampling coefficient, μ is the nominal control input, θ_n the nominal rolling angle, and $J_n > 0$, $B_n > 0$.

2.1.2 The Structure of Control System

From Fig. 2.1, the control consists of two controllers: sliding mode controller with respect to system Eq. (2.1) and $\theta \to \theta_n$ is expected to be obtained. For model Eq. (2.2), a sliding mode controller is designed to obtain $\theta_n \to \theta_d$, and $\theta \to \theta_d$. θ_d denotes a desired angle and θ_n denotes a nominal rolling angle.

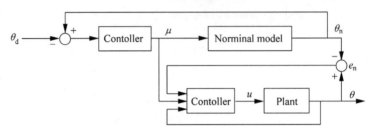

Figure 2.1 Structure of control system

2.1.3 Design of Nominal Model

Suppose the desired trajectory is θ_d, and the nominal-model tracking error is $e = \theta_n - \theta_d$. Therefore, $\dot{\theta}_n = \dot{e} + \dot{\theta}_d$, $\ddot{\theta}_n = \ddot{e} + \ddot{\theta}_d$, and

$$J_n(\ddot{e} + \ddot{\theta}_d) + B_n(\dot{e} + \dot{\theta}_d) = \mu$$

i.e.

$$\ddot{e} + \ddot{\theta}_d = -\frac{B_n}{J_n}(\dot{e} + \dot{\theta}_d) + \frac{1}{J_n}\mu \quad (2.3)$$

The controller is designed for the nominal model as

$$\mu = J_n\left(-h_1 e - h_2 \dot{e} + \frac{B_n}{J_n}\dot{\theta}_d + \ddot{\theta}_d\right) \quad (2.4)$$

From Eqs. (2.3) and (2.4), we have the closed-loop system as

$$\ddot{e} + \ddot{\theta}_d = -\frac{B_n}{J_n}(\dot{e} + \dot{\theta}_d) + \left(-h_1 e - h_2 \dot{e} + \frac{B_n}{J_n}\dot{\theta}_d + \ddot{\theta}_d\right)$$

Therefore, we get

$$\ddot{e} + \left(h_2 + \frac{B_n}{J_n}\right)\dot{e} + h_1 e = 0$$

In order to make the system stable, $s^2 + \left(h_2 + \dfrac{B_n}{J_n}\right)s + h_1$ must be Hurwitz.

For $k > 0$, let the eigenvalue be $-k$. From $(s+k)^2 = 0$, we have $s^2 + 2ks + k^2 = 0$, therefore, $h_2 + \dfrac{B_n}{J_n} = 2k$, $h_1 = k^2$, i.e. $h_2 = 2k - \dfrac{B_n}{J_n}$, $h_1 = k^2$. Therefore, we can get h_1 and h_2.

2.1.4 Sliding Mode Controller Design for Actual Plant

Suppose the following relations are stratified:

$$J_m \leqslant J \leqslant J_M, \quad B_m \leqslant B \leqslant B_M, \quad |d| \leqslant d_M \tag{2.5}$$

where J_m is the minimum value of J, J_M is the maximum value of J, B_m is the minimum value of B, B_M is the maximum value of B, and d_M is the maximum value of d.

Let:

$$e_n = \theta - \theta_n \tag{2.6}$$

Define the sliding variable as

$$s = \dot{e}_n + \lambda e_n \tag{2.7}$$

where $\lambda > 0$, and λ is defined as

$$\lambda = \frac{B_n}{J_n} \tag{2.8}$$

Denote:

$$J_a = \frac{1}{2}(J_m + J_M) \tag{2.9}$$

$$B_a = \frac{1}{2}(B_m + B_M) \tag{2.10}$$

Select the controller as

$$u = -Ks - h \cdot \mathrm{sgn}(s) + J_a\left(\frac{1}{J_n}\mu - \lambda\dot{\theta}\right) + B_a\dot{\theta} \tag{2.11}$$

where $K > 0$.

Define

$$h = d_M + \frac{1}{2}(J_M - J_m)\left|\frac{1}{J_n}\mu - \lambda\dot{\theta}\right| + \frac{1}{2}(B_M - B_m)|\dot{\theta}| \tag{2.12}$$

Let the Lyapunov function be

$$V = \frac{1}{2}Js^2$$

Therefore, we have

$$
\begin{aligned}
J\dot{s} &= J\left[(\ddot{\theta} - \ddot{\theta}_n) + \lambda(\dot{\theta} - \dot{\theta}_n)\right] \\
&= (J\ddot{\theta} + B\dot{\theta}) - B\dot{\theta} - \frac{J}{J_n}J_n\ddot{\theta}_n - \frac{J}{J_n}B_n\dot{\theta}_n + \frac{J}{J_n}B_n\dot{\theta}_n + J\lambda(\dot{\theta} - \dot{\theta}_n) \\
&= (J\ddot{\theta} + B\dot{\theta}) - \frac{J}{J_n}(J_n\ddot{\theta}_n + B_n\dot{\theta}_n) - B\dot{\theta} + \lambda J\dot{\theta} \\
&= u - d - \frac{J}{J_n}\mu - B\dot{\theta} + \lambda J\dot{\theta}
\end{aligned}
$$

From Eq. (2.11), we get

$$
\begin{aligned}
J\dot{s} &= -Ks - h\,\mathrm{sgn}(s) + J_a\left(\frac{1}{J_n}\mu - \lambda\dot{\theta}\right) + B_a\dot{\theta} - d - \frac{J}{J_n}\mu - B\dot{\theta} + \lambda J\dot{\theta} \\
&= -Ks - h\,\mathrm{sgn}(s) - d + (J_a - J)\left(\frac{1}{J_n}\mu - \lambda\dot{\theta}\right) + (B_a - B)\dot{\theta}
\end{aligned}
$$

Therefore,

$$
\begin{aligned}
\dot{V} = Js\dot{s} &= -Ks^2 - h\,|s| + s\left[-d + (J_a - J)\left(\frac{1}{J_n}\mu - \lambda\dot{\theta}\right) + (B_a - B)\dot{\theta}\right] \\
&\leqslant -Ks^2 - h\,|s| + |s|\left[|d| + |J_a - J|\left|\frac{1}{J_n}\mu - \lambda\dot{\theta}\right| + |B_a - B||\dot{\theta}|\right]
\end{aligned}
$$

From Eqs. (2.9) and (2.10), we have

$$\frac{1}{2}(J_M - J_m) \geqslant |J_a - J|$$

$$\frac{1}{2}(B_M - B_m) \geqslant |B_a - B|$$

Therefore,

$$h \geqslant |d| + |J_a - J|\left|\frac{1}{J_n}\mu - \lambda\dot{\theta}\right| + |B_a - B||\dot{\theta}|$$

Then,

$$\dot{V} \leqslant -Ks^2$$

From $V = \frac{1}{2}Js^2$, we get $Js\dot{s} \leqslant -Ks^2$, i.e. $s\dot{s} \leqslant -\frac{K}{J}s^2$. Therefore, we have

$$s(t) \leqslant |s(0)| \exp\left(-\frac{K}{J}t\right)$$

Finally, we can find that $s(t)$ is exponentially convergent.

2.1.5 Simulation

Consider the system as follows:

$$J\ddot{\theta} + B\dot{\theta} = u - d$$

where $B = 10 + 3\sin(2\pi t)$, $J = 3 + 0.5\sin(2\pi t)$, and $d(t) = 10\sin t$.

Let $B_n = 10$, $J_n = 3$, and we get $B_m = 7$, $B_M = 13$, $J_m = 2.5$, $J_M = 3.5$, $d_M = 10$.

We select $k = 1.0$, therefore, $h_2 = 2k - \frac{B_n}{J_n}$, $h_1 = k^2$. In Eq. (2.11), select $\lambda = \frac{B_n}{J_n} = \frac{10}{3}$, $K = 10$, and the desired trajectory is $\theta_d(t) = \sin t$, the initial state vector is [0.5 0]. The simulation results are shown in Fig. 2.2 – Fig. 2.4.

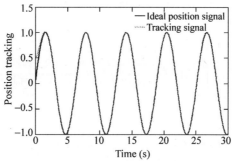

Figure 2.2 Position tracking

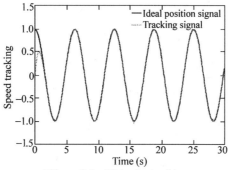

Figure 2.3 Velocity tracking

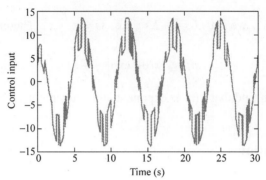

Figure 2.4 Control input

Simulation programs:

(1) Simulink main program: chap2_1sim.mdl

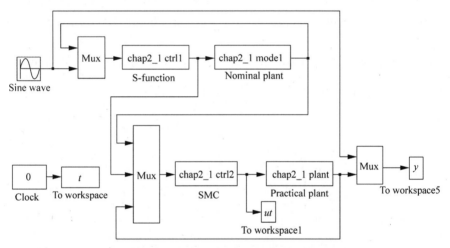

(2) S-function of controller for the nominal model: chap2_1ctrl1.m

```
function [sys,x0,str,ts]=s_function(t,x,u,flag)
switch flag,
case 0,
    [sys,x0,str,ts]=mdlInitializeSizes;
case 3,
    sys=mdlOutputs(t,x,u);
case {2, 4, 9 }
    sys = [];
otherwise
    error(['Unhandled flag = ',num2str(flag)]);
end
function [sys,x0,str,ts]=mdlInitializeSizes
sizes = simsizes;
sizes.NumContStates  = 0;
sizes.NumDiscStates  = 0;
```

2 Normal Sliding Mode Control

```
sizes.NumOutputs      = 1;
sizes.NumInputs       = 3;
sizes.DirFeedthrough = 1;
sizes.NumSampleTimes = 0;
sys=simsizes(sizes);
x0=[];
str=[];
ts=[];
function sys=mdlOutputs(t,x,u)
thn=u(1);
dthn=u(2);
thd=u(3);dthd=cos(t);ddthd=-sin(t);

e=thn-thd;
de=dthn-dthd;

k=3;
Bn=10;Jn=3;
h1=k^2;
h2=2*k-Bn/Jn;

ut=Jn*(-h1*e-h2*de+Bn/Jn*dthd+ddthd);

sys(1)=ut;
```

(3) S-function of nominal model: chap2_1model.m

```
function [sys,x0,str,ts]=s_function(t,x,u,flag)
switch flag,
case 0,
    [sys,x0,str,ts]=mdlInitializeSizes;
case 1,
    sys=mdlDerivatives(t,x,u);
case 3,
    sys=mdlOutputs(t,x,u);
case {2, 4, 9 }
    sys = [];
otherwise
    error(['Unhandled flag = ',num2str(flag)]);
end
function [sys,x0,str,ts]=mdlInitializeSizes
sizes = simsizes;
sizes.NumContStates  = 2;
sizes.NumDiscStates  = 0;
sizes.NumOutputs      = 2;
sizes.NumInputs       = 1;
sizes.DirFeedthrough = 0;
sizes.NumSampleTimes = 0;
sys=simsizes(sizes);
x0=[0.5,0];
str=[];
ts=[];
function sys=mdlDerivatives(t,x,u)
```

```
Bn=10;
Jn=3;
sys(1)=x(2);
sys(2)=1/Jn*(u-Bn*x(2));
function sys=mdlOutputs(t,x,u)
sys(1)=x(1);
sys(2)=x(2);
```

(4) S-function of sliding mode controller for the actual plant: chap2_1ctrl2.m

```
function [sys,x0,str,ts]=s_function(t,x,u,flag)
switch flag,
case 0,
    [sys,x0,str,ts]=mdlInitializeSizes;
case 3,
    sys=mdlOutputs(t,x,u);
case {2, 4, 9 }
    sys = [];
otherwise
    error(['Unhandled flag = ',num2str(flag)]);
end
function [sys,x0,str,ts]=mdlInitializeSizes
sizes = simsizes;
sizes.NumContStates  = 0;
sizes.NumDiscStates  = 0;
sizes.NumOutputs     = 1;
sizes.NumInputs      = 5;
sizes.DirFeedthrough = 1;
sizes.NumSampleTimes = 0;
sys=simsizes(sizes);
x0=[];
str=[];
ts=[];
function sys=mdlOutputs(t,x,u)
Bn=10;Jn=3;
lamt=Bn/Jn;

Jm=2.5;JM=3.5;
Bm=7;BM=13;

dM=0.10;
K=10;

thn=u(1);dthn=u(2);
nu=u(3);
th=u(4);dth=u(5);

en=th-thn;
den=dth-dthn;

s=den+lamt*en;

temp0=(1/Jn)*nu-lamt*dth;
```

48

2 Normal Sliding Mode Control

```
Ja=1/2*(JM+Jm);
Ba=1/2*(BM+Bm);

h=dM+1/2*(JM-Jm)*abs(temp0)+1/2*(BM-Bm)*abs(dth);

ut=-K*s-h*sign(s)+Ja*((1/Jn)*nu-lamt*dth)+Ba*dth;

sys(1)=ut;
```

(5) S-function of the actual plant: chap2_1plant.m

```
function [sys,x0,str,ts]=s_function(t,x,u,flag)
switch flag,
case 0,
    [sys,x0,str,ts]=mdlInitializeSizes;
case 1,
    sys=mdlDerivatives(t,x,u);
case 3,
    sys=mdlOutputs(t,x,u);
case {2, 4, 9 }
    sys = [];
otherwise
    error(['Unhandled flag = ',num2str(flag)]);
end
function [sys,x0,str,ts]=mdlInitializeSizes
sizes = simsizes;
sizes.NumContStates  = 2;
sizes.NumDiscStates  = 0;
sizes.NumOutputs     = 2;
sizes.NumInputs      = 1;
sizes.DirFeedthrough = 0;
sizes.NumSampleTimes = 0;
sys=simsizes(sizes);
x0=[0.5,0];
str=[];
ts=[];
function sys=mdlDerivatives(t,x,u)
d=0.10*sin(t);
B=10+3*sin(2*pi*t);
J=3+0.5*sin(2*pi*t);

sys(1)=x(2);
sys(2)=1/J*(u-B*x(2)-d);
function sys=mdlOutputs(t,x,u)
sys(1)=x(1);
sys(2)=x(2);
```

(6) Plot program: chap2_1plot.m

```
close all;

figure(1);
plot(t,sin(t),'k',t,y(:,2),'r:','linewidth',2);
```

Advanced Sliding Mode Control for Mechanical Systems: Design, Analysis and MATLAB Simulation

```
xlabel('time(s)');ylabel('Position tracking');
legend('Ideal position signal','tracking signal');

figure(2);
plot(t,cos(t),'k',t,y(:,3),'r:','linewidth',2);
xlabel('time(s)');ylabel('Speed tracking');
legend('Ideal speed signal','tracking signal');

figure(3);
plot(t,ut,'r','linewidth',2);
xlabel('time(s)');ylabel('control input');
```

2.2 Global Sliding Mode Control for an Uncertain System

The tending mode and the sliding mode are the conclusions drawn from the responses of the traditional sliding mode variable structure control. The robustness of this control to parameter uncertainties and disturbances exists only in the phase of sliding mode. However, the kinetic characteristic of this system is robust during the whole response.

Global sliding mode control can be obtained by designing an equation of dynamic nonlinear sliding surface. Global sliding mode control eliminates the attaining motion phase and ensures that the whole process of system response is robust. Thus, the drawback of the traditional sliding mode variable structure which has no robustness in the attaining mode is overcome.

2.2.1 System Description

Consider a second-order uncertain system as follows:

$$J\ddot{\theta} = u(t) - d(t) \tag{2.13}$$

We can get

$$\ddot{\theta}(t) = b(u(t) - d(t))$$

where J is the moment of inertia, $b = \dfrac{1}{J} > 0$, $d(t)$ is the disturbance.

Suppose:

$$J_{min} \leqslant J \leqslant J_{max} \tag{2.14}$$

$$|d(t)| < D \tag{2.15}$$

2.2.2 Global Sliding Mode Design

Let the desired trajectory be θ_d and the tracking error be:

$$e = \theta - \theta_d \qquad (2.16)$$

The global dynamic sliding mode variable is designed as

$$s = \dot{e} + ce - f(t) \qquad (2.17)$$

where $c > 0$, $f(t)$ is a function to be designed so as to attain at the sliding surface, and $f(t)$ is satisfied with the following conditions[1]: (1) $f(0) = \dot{e}_0 + ce_0$; (2) $f(t) \to 0$ as $t \to \infty$; and (3) $f(t)$ is derivable.

From the above three conditions, $f(t)$ can be designed as

$$f(t) = f(0)e^{-kt} \qquad (2.18)$$

2.2.3 Sliding Mode Controller Design

The global sliding mode controller is designed as

$$u = -\hat{J}(c\dot{\theta} - \dot{f}) + \hat{J}(\ddot{\theta}_d + c\dot{\theta}_d) - (\Delta J \,|\, c\dot{\theta} - \dot{f} \,| + D + \Delta J \,|\, \ddot{\theta}_d + c\dot{\theta}_d \,|) \mathrm{sgn}(s) \qquad (2.19)$$

where,

$$\hat{J} = \frac{J_{\max} + J_{\min}}{2}, \qquad \Delta J = \frac{J_{\max} - J_{\min}}{2} \qquad (2.20)$$

Let the Lyapunov function be

$$V = \frac{1}{2}s^2 \qquad (2.21)$$

From Eq. (2.17), we have

$$\dot{s} = \ddot{e} + c\dot{e} - \dot{f} = \ddot{\theta} - \ddot{\theta}_d + c(\dot{\theta} - \dot{\theta}_d) - \dot{f}$$
$$= bu - bd + (c\dot{\theta} - \dot{f}) - (\ddot{\theta}_d + c\dot{\theta}_d)$$
$$= b(b^{-1}(c\dot{\theta} - \dot{f}) - b^{-1}(\ddot{\theta}_d + c\dot{\theta}_d) + u - d)$$

and from Eq. (2.19), we have

$$b^{-1}\dot{s} = b^{-1}(c\dot{\theta} - \dot{f}) - b^{-1}(\ddot{\theta}_d + c\dot{\theta}_d) - \hat{J}(c\dot{\theta} - \dot{f}) + \hat{J}(\ddot{\theta}_d + c\dot{\theta}_d)$$
$$- (\Delta J \,|\, c\dot{\theta} - \dot{f} \,| + D + \Delta J \,|\, \ddot{\theta}_d + c\dot{\theta}_d \,|) \mathrm{sgn}(s) - d$$
$$= (b^{-1} - \hat{J})(c\dot{\theta} - \dot{f}) - \Delta J \,|\, c\dot{\theta} - \dot{f} \,| \mathrm{sgn}(s) - (b^{-1} - \hat{J})(\ddot{\theta}_d + c\dot{\theta}_d)$$
$$- \Delta J \,|\, \ddot{\theta}_d + c\dot{\theta}_d \,| \mathrm{sgn}(s) - d - D\mathrm{sgn}(s)$$

Therefore,

$$b^{-1}\dot{V} = b^{-1}s\dot{s} = (b^{-1} - \hat{J})(c\dot{\theta} - \dot{f})s - \Delta J \mid c\dot{\theta} - \dot{f} \parallel s \mid -(b^{-1} - \hat{J})(\ddot{\theta}_d + c\dot{\theta}_d)s$$
$$- \Delta J \mid \ddot{\theta}_d + c\dot{\theta}_d \parallel s \mid -ds - D \mid s \mid$$

From Eq. (2.20), we get

$$b^{-1} - \hat{J} = J - \frac{J_{max} + J_{min}}{2} \leqslant \frac{J_{max} - J_{min}}{2} = \Delta J > 0$$

Therefore,

$$b^{-1}\dot{V} < -ds - D \mid s \mid < 0$$

i.e.,

$$\dot{V} < 0$$

In order to reduce the chattering phenomenon, the saturated function can be used, i.e.

$$\text{sat}\left(\frac{\sigma}{\varphi}\right) = \begin{cases} 1, & \dfrac{\sigma}{\varphi} > 1 \\ \dfrac{\sigma}{\varphi}, & \left|\dfrac{\sigma}{\varphi}\right| \leqslant 1 \\ -1, & \dfrac{\sigma}{\varphi} < -1 \end{cases} \tag{2.22}$$

2.2.4 Simulation Example

Let the plant be

$$J\ddot{\theta} = u(t) - d(t)$$

where $J = 1.0 + 0.2\sin t$, $d(t) = 0.1\sin(2\pi t)$.

We can get: $J_{min} = 0.80$, $J_{max} = 1.2$, $D = 0.10$. From Eq. (2.20), we have:
$\hat{J} = \dfrac{J_{max} + J_{min}}{2} = 1.0$, $\Delta J = \dfrac{J_{max} - J_{min}}{2} = 0.20$.

Let the desired position trajectory be $\theta_d = \sin t$. The controller is given in Eq. (2.19), and $c = 10$, $f(t) = s(0)e^{-130t}$. $M = 1$ and $M = 2$ denote the saturated function and the switch function respectively. Let $M = 2$, $\varphi = 0.05$, and the simulation results are shown in Fig. 2.5 – Fig. 2.7. The use of saturated function can reduce the chattering phenomenon effectively.

2 Normal Sliding Mode Control

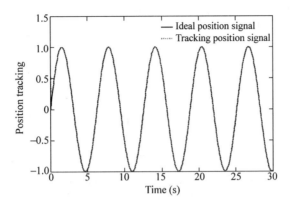

Figure 2.5 Position tracking

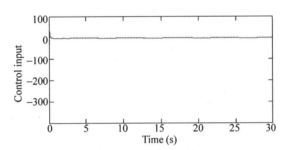

Figure 2.6 Control input

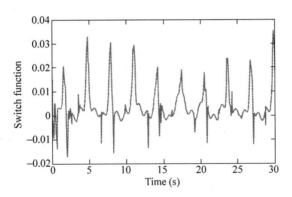

Figure 2.7 Switch function

Advanced Sliding Mode Control for Mechanical Systems: Design, Analysis and MATLAB Simulation

Simulation programs:

(1) Simulink main program: chap2_2sim.mdl

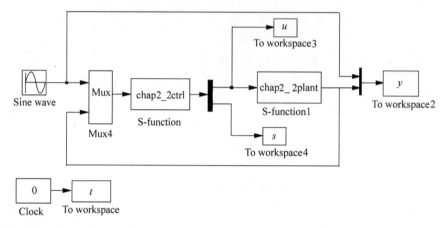

(2) S-function of controller: chap2_2ctrl.m

```
function [sys,x0,str,ts] = spacemodel(t,x,u,flag)

switch flag,
case 0,
    [sys,x0,str,ts]=mdlInitializeSizes;
case 3,
    sys=mdlOutputs(t,x,u);
case {2,4,9}
    sys=[];
otherwise
    error(['Unhandled flag = ',num2str(flag)]);
end

function [sys,x0,str,ts]=mdlInitializeSizes
sizes = simsizes;
sizes.NumContStates  = 0;
sizes.NumDiscStates  = 0;
sizes.NumOutputs     = 2;
sizes.NumInputs      = 3;
sizes.DirFeedthrough = 1;
sizes.NumSampleTimes = 1;
sys = simsizes(sizes);
x0  = [];
str = [];
ts  = [0 0];

function sys=mdlOutputs(t,x,u)
thd=u(1);
dthd=cos(t);
```

2 Normal Sliding Mode Control

```
ddthd=-sin(t);
th=u(2);
dth=u(3);

c=10;
e=th-thd;
de=dth-dthd;

dt=0.10*sin(2*pi*t);
D=0.10;

e0=pi/6;
de0=0-1.0;
s0=de0+c*e0;
ft=s0*exp(-130*t);
df=-130*s0*exp(-130*t);

s=de+c*e-ft;
R=ddthd+c*dthd;

J_min=0.80;
J_max=1.20;

aJ=(J_min+J_max)/2;
dJ=(J_max-J_min)/2;

M=2;
if M==1
    ut=-aJ*(c*dth-df)+aJ*R-[dJ*abs(c*dth-df)+D+dJ*abs(R)]*sign(s);
elseif M==2
    fai=0.05;
    if s/fai>1
      sat=1;
    elseif abs(s/fai)<=1
       sat=s/fai;
    elseif s/fai<-1
       sat=-1;
    end
    ut=-aJ*(c*dth-df)+aJ*R-[dJ*abs(c*dth-df)+D+dJ*abs(R)]*sat;
end
sys(1)=ut;
sys(2)=s;
```

(3) S-function of the plant: chap2_2plant.m

```
function [sys,x0,str,ts] = spacemodel(t,x,u,flag)

switch flag,
case 0,
    [sys,x0,str,ts]=mdlInitializeSizes;
```

Advanced Sliding Mode Control for Mechanical Systems: Design, Analysis and MATLAB Simulation

```
case 1,
    sys=mdlDerivatives(t,x,u);
case 3,
    sys=mdlOutputs(t,x,u);
case {2,4,9}
    sys=[];
otherwise
    error(['Unhandled flag = ',num2str(flag)]);
end

function [sys,x0,str,ts]=mdlInitializeSizes
sizes = simsizes;
sizes.NumContStates  = 2;
sizes.NumDiscStates  = 0;
sizes.NumOutputs     = 2;
sizes.NumInputs      = 1;
sizes.DirFeedthrough = 0;
sizes.NumSampleTimes = 0;
sys = simsizes(sizes);
x0 = [pi/6;0];
str = [];
ts = [];
function sys=mdlDerivatives(t,x,u)
J=1.0+0.2*sin(t);
dt=0.10*sin(2*pi*t);

sys(1)=x(2);
sys(2)=1/J*(u-dt);
function sys=mdlOutputs(t,x,u)
sys(1)=x(1);
sys(2)=x(2);
```

(4) Plot program: chap2_2plot.m

```
close all;

figure(1);
figure(1);
plot(t,y(:,1),'k',t,y(:,2),'r:','linewidth',2);
xlabel('time(s)');ylabel('Position tracking');
legend('ideal position signal','tracking position signal');

figure(2);
plot(t,u(:,1),'r','linewidth',2);
xlabel('time(s)');ylabel('Control input');

figure(3);
plot(t,s(:,1),'r','linewidth',2);
xlabel('time(s)');ylabel('Switch function');
```

2.3 Sliding Mode Control Based on Linearization Feedback Control

2.3.1 Linearization Feedback Control

Consider the following second-order SISO nonlinear system:

$$\ddot{x} = f(x,t) + g(x,t)u \tag{2.23}$$

where f and g are known nonlinear functions.

Let x_d denote the desired trajectory, and $e = x_d - x$. Based on linearization feedback technique, sliding mode controller is designed as

$$u = \frac{v - f(x,t)}{g(x,t)} \tag{2.24}$$

where v is the auxiliary controller and will be designed in the following.

From Eqs. (2.24) and (2.23), we have

$$\ddot{x} = v \tag{2.25}$$

We design v as

$$v = \ddot{x}_d + k_1 e + k_2 \dot{e} \tag{2.26}$$

where k_1 and k_2 are all positive constants.

From Eqs. (2.26) and (2.25), we get

$$\ddot{e} + k_1 e + k_2 \dot{e} = 0 \tag{2.27}$$

Therefore, $e_1 \to 0$ and $e_2 \to 0$ as $t \to \infty$.

The shortcoming of this method is: In designing controller Eq. (2.24), f and g must be known. The solution is that the robustness can be introduced in the controller.

2.3.2 Simulation Example

The dynamic equation of the inverted pendulum is

$$\begin{cases} \dot{x}_1 = x_2 \\ \dot{x}_2 = \dfrac{g \sin x_1 - mlx_2^2 \cos x_1 \sin x_1 /(m_c + m)}{l(4/3 - m\cos^2 x_1 /(m_c + m))} + \dfrac{\cos x_1 /(m_c + m)}{l(4/3 - m\cos^2 x_1 /(m_c + m))} u \end{cases}$$

where x_1 and x_2 are the oscillation angle and the oscillation rate respectively. $g = 9.8 \text{ m/s}^2$, m_c is the vehicle mass, $m_c = 1 \text{ kg}$, m is the mass of pendulum bar, $m = 0.1 \text{ kg}$, l is one half of pendulum length, $l = 0.5 \text{ m}$, u is the control input.

The desired trajectory is $x_d(t) = 0.1\sin(\pi t)$. Controller is Eq. (2.24), $k_1 = k_2 = 5$, The initial state of the inverted pendulum is $[\pi/60 \ \ 0]$. The simulation results are shown in Fig. 2.8 and Fig. 2.9.

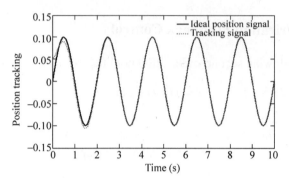

Figure 2.8   Position tracking

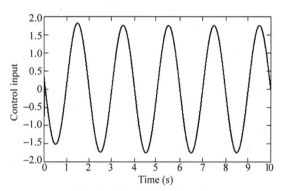

Figure 2.9   Control input

Simulation programs:

(1) Simulink main program: chap2_3sim.mdl

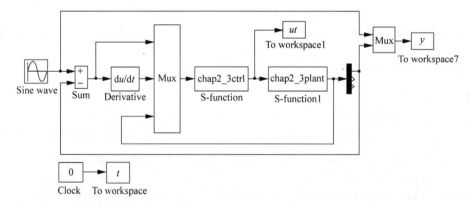

2 Normal Sliding Mode Control

(2) S-function of controller: chap2_3ctrl.m

```
function [sys,x0,str,ts] = spacemodel(t,x,u,flag)
switch flag,
case 0,
    [sys,x0,str,ts]=mdlInitializeSizes;
case 1,
    sys=mdlDerivatives(t,x,u);
case 3,
    sys=mdlOutputs(t,x,u);
case {1,2,4,9}
    sys=[];
otherwise
    error(['Unhandled flag = ',num2str(flag)]);
end
function [sys,x0,str,ts]=mdlInitializeSizes
sizes = simsizes;
sizes.NumContStates  = 0;
sizes.NumDiscStates  = 0;
sizes.NumOutputs     = 1;
sizes.NumInputs      = 5;
sizes.DirFeedthrough = 1;
sizes.NumSampleTimes = 0;
sys = simsizes(sizes);
x0  = [];
str = [];
ts  = [];
function sys=mdlOutputs(t,x,u)
r=0.1*sin(pi*t);
dr=0.1*pi*cos(pi*t);
ddr=-0.1*pi*pi*sin(pi*t);

e=u(1);
de=u(2);
fx=u(4);
gx=u(5);

k1=5;k2=5;
v=ddr+k1*e+k2*de;
ut=(v-fx)/(gx+0.002);

sys(1)=ut;
```

(3) S-function of the plant: chap2_3plant.m

```
function [sys,x0,str,ts]=s_function(t,x,u,flag)
switch flag,
case 0,
    [sys,x0,str,ts]=mdlInitializeSizes;
case 1,
```

```
    sys=mdlDerivatives(t,x,u);
case 3,
    sys=mdlOutputs(t,x,u);
case {2, 4, 9 }
    sys = [];
otherwise
    error(['Unhandled flag = ',num2str(flag)]);
end
function [sys,x0,str,ts]=mdlInitializeSizes
sizes = simsizes;
sizes.NumContStates  = 2;
sizes.NumDiscStates  = 0;
sizes.NumOutputs     = 3;
sizes.NumInputs      = 1;
sizes.DirFeedthrough = 0;
sizes.NumSampleTimes = 0;
sys=simsizes(sizes);
x0=[pi/60 0];
str=[];
ts=[];
function sys=mdlDerivatives(t,x,u)
g=9.8;mc=1.0;m=0.1;l=0.5;
S=l*(4/3-m*(cos(x(1)))^2/(mc+m));
fx=g*sin(x(1))-m*l*x(2)^2*cos(x(1))*sin(x(1))/(mc+m);
fx=fx/S;
gx=cos(x(1))/(mc+m);
gx=gx/S;

sys(1)=x(2);
sys(2)=fx+gx*u;
function sys=mdlOutputs(t,x,u)
g=9.8;mc=1.0;m=0.1;l=0.5;
S=l*(4/3-m*(cos(x(1)))^2/(mc+m));
fx=g*sin(x(1))-m*l*x(2)^2*cos(x(1))*sin(x(1))/(mc+m);
fx=fx/S;
gx=cos(x(1))/(mc+m);
gx=gx/S;

sys(1)=x(1);
sys(2)=fx;
sys(3)=gx;
```

(4) Plot program: chap2_3plot.m

```
close all;
figure(1);
plot(t,y(:,1),'k',t,y(:,2),'r:','linewidth',2);
xlabel('time(s)');ylabel('Position tracking');
legend('Ideal position signal','tracking signal');
```

```
figure(2);
plot(t,ut(:,1),'k','linewidth',2);
xlabel('time(s)');ylabel('Control input');
```

2.3.3 Sliding Mode Control Based on Linearization Feedback

Consider the following second-order SISO uncertain nonlinear system:

$$\ddot{x} = f(x,t) + g(x,t)u + d(t) \tag{2.28}$$

where f and g are known nonlinear functions, $d(t)$ is the uncertainty, and $|d(t)| \leqslant D$.

Let the desired trajectory be x_d, therefore, we denote:

$$e = x - x_d = [e \quad \dot{e}]^T \tag{2.29}$$

Sliding variable is selected as

$$s(x,t) = ce \tag{2.30}$$

where $c = [c \quad 1]$.

Based on linearization feedback technique, the sliding mode controller is designed as

$$u = \frac{v - f(x,t)}{g(x,t)} \tag{2.31}$$

$$v = \ddot{x}_d - c\dot{e} - \eta \, \mathrm{sgn}(s), \quad \eta > D \tag{2.32}$$

We select the Lyapunov function is

$$V = \frac{1}{2}s^2$$

therefore, we have

$$\dot{V} = s\dot{s} = s(\ddot{e} + c\dot{e}) = s(\ddot{x} - \ddot{x}_d + c\dot{e})$$
$$= s(f(x,t) + g(x,t)u + d(t) - \ddot{x}_d + c\dot{e})$$

From Eq. (2.31), we get

$$\dot{V} = s(v + d(t) - \ddot{x}_d + c\dot{e})$$
$$= s(\ddot{x}_d - c\dot{e} - \eta \, \mathrm{sgn}(s) + d(t) - \ddot{x}_d + c\dot{e})$$
$$= s(-\eta \, \mathrm{sgn}(s) + d(t)) = -\eta |s| + d(t)s \leqslant 0$$

2.3.4 Simulation Example

The dynamic equation of the inverted pendulum is

$$\begin{cases} \dot{x}_1 = x_2 \\ \dot{x}_2 = \dfrac{g\sin x_1 - mlx_2^2 \cos x_1 \sin x_1/(m_c + m)}{l(4/3 - m\cos^2 x_1/(m_c + m))} + \dfrac{\cos x_1/(m_c + m)}{l(4/3 - m\cos^2 x_1/(m_c + m))} u + d(t) \end{cases}$$

where x_1 and x_2 are the oscillation angle and the oscillation rate respectively. $g = 9.8 \text{ m/s}^2$, m_c is the vehicle mass, $m_c = 1$ kg, m is the mass of pendulum bar, $m = 0.1$ kg, l is one half of pendulum length, $l = 0.5$ m, u is the control input. $d(t)$ is the disturbance.

The desired trajectory is $x_d(t) = 0.1\sin(\pi t)$. The sliding variable is $s = ce + \dot{e}$, where $c = 10$. Controller is Eq. (2.31). The initial state of the inverted pendulum is $[-\pi/60 \ 0]$. In the simulation program, $M=1$ denoes the sgn function is adopted, and $M=2$ denotes the saturated function is adopted, and let $M=2$, $\delta_0 = 0.03$, $\delta_1 = 5$, $\delta = \delta_0 + \delta_1 |e|$, $k = 5$. The simulation results are shown in Fig. 2.10 and Fig. 2.11.

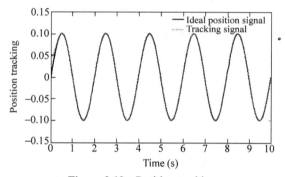

Figure 2.10 Position tracking

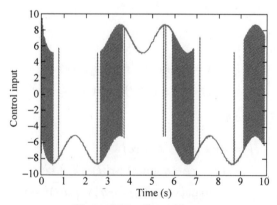

Figure 2.11 Control input

Simulation programs:

(1) Simulink main program: chap2_4sim.mdl

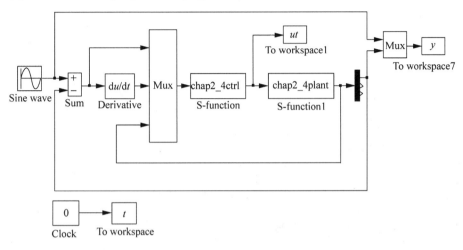

(2) S-function of controller: chap2_4ctrl.m

```
function [sys,x0,str,ts] = spacemodel(t,x,u,flag)
switch flag,
case 0,
    [sys,x0,str,ts]=mdlInitializeSizes;
case 1,
    sys=mdlDerivatives(t,x,u);
case 3,
    sys=mdlOutputs(t,x,u);
case {1,2,4,9}
    sys=[];
otherwise
    error(['Unhandled flag = ',num2str(flag)]);
end
function [sys,x0,str,ts]=mdlInitializeSizes
sizes = simsizes;
sizes.NumContStates  = 0;
sizes.NumDiscStates  = 0;
sizes.NumOutputs     = 1;
sizes.NumInputs      = 5;
sizes.DirFeedthrough = 1;
sizes.NumSampleTimes = 0;
sys = simsizes(sizes);
x0  = [];
str = [];
ts  = [];
function sys=mdlOutputs(t,x,u)
r=0.1*sin(pi*t);
dr=0.1*pi*cos(pi*t);
```

```matlab
ddr=-0.1*pi*pi*sin(pi*t);

e=u(1);
de=u(2);
fx=u(4);
gx=u(5);

c=10;
s=de+c*e;

M=1;
if M==1
    xite=10;
    v=ddr-c*de-xite*sign(s);
elseif M==2
    xite=30;
    delta0=0.03;
    delta1=5;
    delta=delta0+delta1*abs(e);
    v=ddr-c*de-xite*s/(abs(s)+delta);
end

xx(1)=r+e;
xx(2)=dr+de;

ut=(-fx+v)/(gx+0.002);

sys(1)=ut;
```

(3) S-function of the plant: chap2_4plant.m

```matlab
function [sys,x0,str,ts]=s_function(t,x,u,flag)
switch flag,
case 0,
    [sys,x0,str,ts]=mdlInitializeSizes;
case 1,
    sys=mdlDerivatives(t,x,u);
case 3,
    sys=mdlOutputs(t,x,u);
case {2, 4, 9 }
    sys = [];
otherwise
    error(['Unhandled flag = ',num2str(flag)]);
end
function [sys,x0,str,ts]=mdlInitializeSizes
sizes = simsizes;
sizes.NumContStates  = 2;
sizes.NumDiscStates  = 0;
sizes.NumOutputs     = 3;
sizes.NumInputs      = 1;
sizes.DirFeedthrough = 0;
```

2 Normal Sliding Mode Control

```
sizes.NumSampleTimes = 0;
sys=simsizes(sizes);
x0=[pi/60 0];
str=[];
ts=[];
function sys=mdlDerivatives(t,x,u)
g=9.8;mc=1.0;m=0.1;l=0.5;
S=l*(4/3-m*(cos(x(1)))^2/(mc+m));
fx=g*sin(x(1))-m*l*x(2)^2*cos(x(1))*sin(x(1))/(mc+m);
fx=fx/S;
gx=cos(x(1))/(mc+m);
gx=gx/S;
dt=10*sin(t);

sys(1)=x(2);
sys(2)=fx+gx*u+dt;
function sys=mdlOutputs(t,x,u)
g=9.8;mc=1.0;m=0.1;l=0.5;
S=l*(4/3-m*(cos(x(1)))^2/(mc+m));
fx=g*sin(x(1))-m*l*x(2)^2*cos(x(1))*sin(x(1))/(mc+m);
fx=fx/S;
gx=cos(x(1))/(mc+m);
gx=gx/S;

sys(1)=x(1);
sys(2)=fx;
sys(3)=gx;
```

(4) Plot program: chap2_4plot.m

```
close all;

figure(1);
plot(t,y(:,1),'k',t,y(:,2),'r:','linewidth',2);
xlabel('time(s)');ylabel('Position tracking');
legend('Ideal position signal','tracking signal');

figure(2);
plot(t,ut(:,1),'r','linewidth',2);
xlabel('time(s)');ylabel('Control input');
```

2.4 Input-Output Feedback Linearization Control

2.4.1 System Description

Consider the following system:

65

$$
\left.\begin{aligned}
\dot{x}_1 &= \sin x_2 + (x_2 + 1)x_3 \\
\dot{x}_2 &= x_1^5 + x_3 \\
\dot{x}_3 &= x_1^2 + u \\
y &= x_1
\end{aligned}\right\} \tag{2.33}
$$

Problem statement: to make the output y track the desired trajectory y_d. From Eq. (2.33), the output y is connected with u indirectly through x. It is difficult to design the controller.

2.4.2 Controller Design

In order to obtain the relation of y and u, we differentiate y as follows:

$$
\dot{y} = \dot{x}_1 = \sin x_2 + (x_2 + 1)x_3 \tag{2.34}
$$

From Eq. (2.34), we can find that $\dot{y}$ and u have no direct relation, thus, differentiating $\dot{y}$

$$
\begin{aligned}
\ddot{y} = \ddot{x}_1 &= \dot{x}_2 \cos x_2 + \dot{x}_2 x_3 + (x_2 + 1)\dot{x}_3 \\
&= (x_1^5 + x_3)\cos x_2 + (x_1^5 + x_3)x_3 + (x_2 + 1)(x_1^2 + u) \\
&= (x_1^5 + x_3)(\cos x_2 + x_3) + (x_2 + 1)x_1^2 + (x_2 + 1)u
\end{aligned} \tag{2.35}
$$

Let $f(x) = (x_1^5 + x_3)(\cos x_2 + x_3) + (x_2 + 1)x_1^2$, therefore, we have

$$
\ddot{y} = (x_2 + 1)u + f(x) \tag{2.36}
$$

Equation (2.36) denotes the visible relation of the output y and the input u. We select:

$$
u = \frac{1}{x_2 + 1}(v - f) \tag{2.37}
$$

where v is the auxiliary controller and will be designed in the following.
From Eqs. (2.37) and (2.36), we get

$$
\ddot{y} = v \tag{2.38}
$$

Denote $e = y_d - y$, We design v with PD and feedforward forms:

$$
v = \ddot{y}_d + k_1 e + k_2 \dot{e} \tag{2.39}
$$

where k_1 and k_2 are positive constants.

From Eqs. (2.39) and (2.38), we can get

$$\ddot{e} + k_2\dot{e} + k_1 e = 0 \qquad (2.40)$$

Therefore, $e_1 \to 0$ and $e_2 \to 0$ as $t \to \infty$.

The shortcoming of this method is: The model of the plant must be precise. The solution is that the robustness can be introduced in the controller.

2.4.3 Simulation Example

The desired trajectory is $y_d = \sin t$. Let $k_1 = k_2 = 10$. The controller is Eq. (2.37). The simulation results are shown in Fig. 2.12 and Fig. 2.13. From the simulation, we can see that using linearization feedback control, high-precise position tracking can be realized, and relative smaller controller is needed.

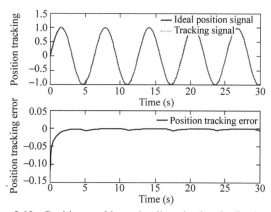

Figure 2.12 Position tracking using linearization feedback method

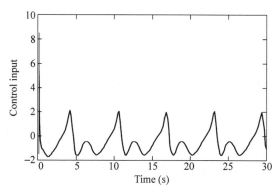

Figure 2.13 Control input using linearization feedback method

Simulation programs:

(1) Simulink main program: chap2_5sim.mdl

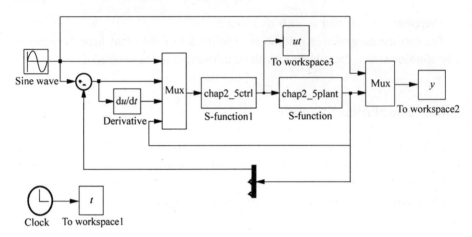

(2) Sub-program of controller: chap2_5ctrl.m

```
function [sys,x0,str,ts]=obser(t,x,u,flag)
switch flag,
case 0,
    [sys,x0,str,ts]=mdlInitializeSizes;
case 1,
    sys=mdlDerivatives(t,x,u);
case 3,
    sys=mdlOutputs(t,x,u);
case {1, 2, 4, 9 }
    sys = [];
otherwise
    error(['Unhandled flag = ',num2str(flag)]);
end
function [sys,x0,str,ts]=mdlInitializeSizes
sizes = simsizes;
sizes.NumDiscStates  = 0;
sizes.NumOutputs     = 1;
sizes.NumInputs      = 6;
sizes.DirFeedthrough = 1;
sizes.NumSampleTimes = 0;
sys=simsizes(sizes);
x0=[];
str=[];
ts=[];
function sys=mdlOutputs(t,x,u)
yd=u(1);
dyd=cos(t);
ddyd=-sin(t);
```

2 Normal Sliding Mode Control

```
e=u(2);
de=u(3);
x1=u(4);
x2=u(5);
x3=u(6);

f=(x1^5+x3)*(x3+cos(x2))+(x2+1)*x1^2;

k1=10;k2=10;
v=ddyd+k1*e+k2*de;
ut=1.0/(x2+1)*(v-f);
sys(1)=ut;
```

(3) Sub-program of the plant: chap2_5plant.m

```
function [sys,x0,str,ts]=obser(t,x,u,flag)
switch flag,
case 0,
    [sys,x0,str,ts]=mdlInitializeSizes;
case 1,
    sys=mdlDerivatives(t,x,u);
case 3,
    sys=mdlOutputs(t,x,u);
case {2, 4, 9 }
    sys = [];
otherwise
    error(['Unhandled flag = ',num2str(flag)]);
end
function [sys,x0,str,ts]=mdlInitializeSizes
sizes = simsizes;
sizes.NumContStates  = 3;
sizes.NumDiscStates  = 0;
sizes.NumOutputs     = 3;
sizes.NumInputs      = 1;
sizes.DirFeedthrough = 1;
sizes.NumSampleTimes = 0;
sys=simsizes(sizes);
x0=[0.15 0 0];
str=[];
ts=[];
function sys=mdlDerivatives(t,x,u)
ut=u(1);
sys(1)=sin(x(2))+(x(2)+1)*x(3);
sys(2)=x(1)^5+x(3);
sys(3)=x(1)^2+ut;
function sys=mdlOutputs(t,x,u)
sys(1)=x(1);
sys(2)=x(2);
sys(3)=x(3);
```

(4) Plot program: chap2_5plot.m

```
close all;

figure(1);
subplot(211);
plot(t,y(:,1),'k',t,y(:,2),'r:','linewidth',2);
xlabel('time(s)');ylabel('Position tracking');
legend('Ideal position signal','tracking signal');
subplot(212);
plot(t,y(:,1)-y(:,2),'k','linewidth',2);
xlabel('time');ylabel('position tracking error');
legend('position tracking error');

figure(2);
plot(t,ut(:,1),'k','linewidth',2);
xlabel('time');ylabel('control input');
```

2.5 Sliding Mode Control Based on Input-Output Feedback Linearization

Sliding mode robust item is introduced into the controller to overcome the faults in the usual input-output feedback linearization sliding mode control. Then, the input-output feedback linearization sliding mode control is designed.

2.5.1 System Description

Consider the following uncertain system:

$$\left.\begin{aligned}
\dot{x}_1 &= \sin x_2 + (x_2 + 1)x_3 + d_1 \\
\dot{x}_2 &= x_1^5 + x_3 + d_2 \\
\dot{x}_3 &= x_1^2 + u + d_3 \\
y &= x_1
\end{aligned}\right\} \tag{2.41}$$

where d_1, d_2 and d_3 are the uncertainties in the three sub-systems respectively.

Problem statement: to make the output y track the desired trajectory y_d. From Eq. (2.41), the output y is connected with u indirectly through x. It is difficult to design the controller.

2.5.2 Controller Design

In order to obtain the relation of y and u, we differentiate y as follows:

$$\dot{y} = \dot{x}_1 = \sin x_2 + (x_2 + 1)x_3 + d_1 \tag{2.42}$$

From Eq. (2.42), we can find that $\dot{y}$ and u have no direct relation, thus, differentiate $\dot{y}$:

$$\begin{aligned}
\ddot{y} = \ddot{x}_1 &= \dot{x}_2 \cos x_2 + \dot{x}_2 x_3 + (x_2 + 1)\dot{x}_3 + \dot{d}_1 \\
&= (x_1^5 + x_3 + d_2)\cos x_2 + (x_1^5 + x_3 + d_2)x_3 + (x_2 + 1)(x_1^2 + u + d_3) + \dot{d}_1 \\
&= (x_1^5 + x_3)(\cos x_2 + x_3) + (x_2 + 1)x_1^2 + (x_2 + 1)u + d \tag{2.43}
\end{aligned}$$

where $d = d_2 \cos x_2 + d_2 x_3 + (x_2 + 1)d_3 + \dot{d}_1$. We assume $|d| \leqslant D$.

Let $f(x) = (x_1^5 + x_3)(\cos x_2 + x_3) + (x_2 + 1)x_1^2$, therefore, equation (2.43) can be transferred to

$$\ddot{y} = (x_2 + 1)u + f(x) + d \tag{2.44}$$

Denote $e = y_d - y$, and the sliding variable is selected as

$$s(x,t) = ce \tag{2.45}$$

where $c = [c \ \ 1]$, $c > 0$, $e = [e \ \ \dot{e}]^{\mathrm{T}}$.

Equation (2.44) denotes the visible relation of the output y and the input u. We select:

$$u = \frac{1}{x_2 + 1}(v - f + \eta \operatorname{sgn}(s)) \tag{2.46}$$

where v is the auxiliary controller and will be designed in the following. $\eta \geqslant D$.

Select Lyapunov function as

$$V = \frac{1}{2}s^2$$

We have

$$\begin{aligned}
\dot{V} = s\dot{s} = s(\ddot{e} + c\dot{e}) &= s(\ddot{y}_d - \ddot{y} + c\dot{e}) \\
&= s(\ddot{y}_d - (x_2 + 1)u - f(x) - d + c\dot{e})
\end{aligned}$$

From Eq. (2.46), we have

$$\begin{aligned}
\dot{V} &= s(\ddot{y}_d - (v - f(x) + \eta \operatorname{sgn}(s)) - f(x) - d + c\dot{e}) \\
&= s(\ddot{y}_d - v + f(x) - \eta \operatorname{sgn}(s) - f(x) - d + c\dot{e}) \tag{2.47}
\end{aligned}$$

Select v be

$$v = \ddot{y}_d + c\dot{e} \tag{2.48}$$

From Eqs. (2.47) and (2.48), we get

$$\dot{V} = s(-\eta \operatorname{sgn}(s) - d) = ds - \eta|s| \leqslant (D-\eta)|s| \leqslant 0$$

2.5.3 Simulation Example

Let the desired trajectory be $y_d = \sin t$. $c = 10$, $\eta = 3.0$. The controller is Eq. (2.46). The simulation results are shown in Fig. 2.14 and Fig. 2.15. From the simulation, we can see that the linearization feedback sliding mode control can realize the high-precise position tracking for the uncertain systems.

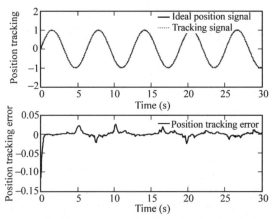

Figure 2.14 Position tracking using linearization feedback method

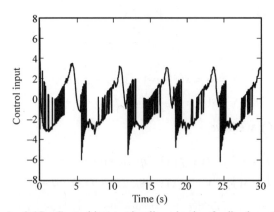

Figure 2.15 Control input using linearization feedback method

2 Normal Sliding Mode Control

Simulation programs:

(1) Simulink main program: chap2_6sim.mdl

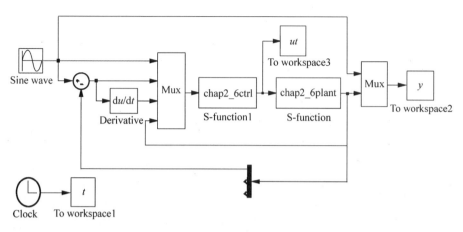

(2) Controller program: chap2_6ctrl.m

```
function [sys,x0,str,ts]=obser(t,x,u,flag)
switch flag,
case 0,
    [sys,x0,str,ts]=mdlInitializeSizes;
case 1,
    sys=mdlDerivatives(t,x,u);
case 3,
    sys=mdlOutputs(t,x,u);
case {1, 2, 4, 9 }
    sys = [];
otherwise
    error(['Unhandled flag = ',num2str(flag)]);
end
function [sys,x0,str,ts]=mdlInitializeSizes
sizes = simsizes;
sizes.NumDiscStates  = 0;
sizes.NumOutputs     = 1;
sizes.NumInputs      = 6;
sizes.DirFeedthrough = 1;
sizes.NumSampleTimes = 0;
sys=simsizes(sizes);
x0=[];
str=[];
ts=[];
function sys=mdlOutputs(t,x,u)
yd=u(1);
dyd=cos(t);
ddyd=-sin(t);
```

```
e=u(2);
de=u(3);
x1=u(4);
x2=u(5);
x3=u(6);

f=(x1^5+x3)*(x3+cos(x2))+(x2+1)*x1^2;
c=10;
s=de+c*e;
v=ddyd+c*de;
xite=3.0;
ut=1.0/(x2+1)*(v-f+xite*sign(s));
sys(1)=ut;
```

(3) The program of the plant: chap2_6plant.m

```
function [sys,x0,str,ts]=obser(t,x,u,flag)
switch flag,
case 0,
    [sys,x0,str,ts]=mdlInitializeSizes;
case 1,
    sys=mdlDerivatives(t,x,u);
case 3,
    sys=mdlOutputs(t,x,u);
case {2, 4, 9 }
    sys = [];
otherwise
    error(['Unhandled flag = ',num2str(flag)]);
end
function [sys,x0,str,ts]=mdlInitializeSizes
sizes = simsizes;
sizes.NumContStates  = 3;
sizes.NumDiscStates  = 0;
sizes.NumOutputs     = 3;
sizes.NumInputs      = 1;
sizes.DirFeedthrough = 1;
sizes.NumSampleTimes = 0;
sys=simsizes(sizes);
x0=[0.15 0 0];
str=[];
ts=[];
function sys=mdlDerivatives(t,x,u)
ut=u(1);
d1=sin(t);
d2=sin(t);
d3=sin(t);
sys(1)=sin(x(2))+(x(2)+1)*x(3)+d1;
sys(2)=x(1)^5+x(3)+d2;
sys(3)=x(1)^2+ut+d3;
function sys=mdlOutputs(t,x,u)
```

```
sys(1)=x(1);
sys(2)=x(2);
sys(3)=x(3);
```

(4) Plot program: chap2_6plot.m

```
close all;

figure(1);
subplot(211);
plot(t,y(:,1),'k',t,y(:,2),'r:','linewidth',2);
xlabel('time(s)');ylabel('Position tracking');
legend('Ideal position signal','tracking signal');
subplot(212);
plot(t,y(:,1)-y(:,2),'k','linewidth',2);
xlabel('time');ylabel('position tracking error');
legend('position tracking error');

figure(2);
plot(t,ut(:,1),'k','linewidth',2);
xlabel('time');ylabel('control input');
```

2.6 Sliding Mode Control Based on Low Pass Filter

2.6.1 System Description

Consider the following second servo system:

$$J\ddot{\theta} = \tau - d(t) \tag{2.49}$$

where J is the initial moment, τ is the control input, $d(t)$ is the disturbance.

2.6.2 Sliding Mode Controller Design

Sliding mode control system with low pass filter is shown in Fig. 2.16.

Figure 2.16 Sliding mode control system with low pass filter

In Fig. 2.16, $u(t)$ is the virtual control input and $\tau(t)$ is the practical control input. To decrease control chattering, low pass filter is designed as[2]

$$Q(s) = \frac{\lambda}{s + \lambda} \qquad (2.50)$$

where $\lambda > 0$.

From Fig. 2.16, we have

$$\dot{\tau} + \lambda\tau = \lambda u \qquad (2.51)$$

where $\lambda > 0$.

From Eq. (2.51), we have

$$\tau = J\ddot{\theta} + d(t)$$

$$J\dddot{\theta} + \dot{d} + \lambda(J\ddot{\theta} + d) = \lambda u$$

and

$$J\dddot{\theta} = \lambda u - \dot{d} - \lambda(J\ddot{\theta} + d)$$

We assume ideal position signal is $\theta_{\mathrm{d}}(t)$, the tracking error is

$$e(t) = \theta(t) - \theta_{\mathrm{d}}(t) \qquad (2.52)$$

Sliding function is designed as

$$s(t) = \ddot{e} + \lambda_1\dot{e} + \lambda_2 e \qquad (2.53)$$

where $\lambda_1 > 0$, $\lambda_2 > 0$.

Then

$$J\dot{s}(t) = J(\dddot{e} + \lambda_1\ddot{e} + \lambda_2\dot{e}) = J\dddot{\theta} + J(-\dddot{\theta}_{\mathrm{d}} + \lambda_1\ddot{e} + \lambda_2\dot{e})$$
$$= \lambda u - \dot{d} - \lambda(J\ddot{\theta} + d) + J(-\dddot{\theta}_{\mathrm{d}} + \lambda_1\ddot{e} + \lambda_2\dot{e})$$

Define Lyapunov function as

$$V = \frac{1}{2}Js^2 \qquad (2.54)$$

Then

$$\dot{V} = Js\dot{s} = s(\lambda u - \dot{d} - \lambda(J\ddot{\theta} + d) + J(-\dddot{\theta}_{\mathrm{d}} + \lambda_1\ddot{e} + \lambda_2\dot{e}))$$
$$= s(\lambda u - \dot{d} - \lambda d - \lambda J\ddot{\theta} + J(-\dddot{\theta}_{\mathrm{d}} + \lambda_1\ddot{e} + \lambda_2\dot{e}))$$

Sliding mode controller is designed as

$$u = -\frac{1}{\lambda}(-\lambda J\ddot{\theta} + J(-\dddot{\theta}_{\mathrm{d}} + \lambda_1\ddot{e} + \lambda_2\dot{e}) + \eta\,\mathrm{sgn}(s)) \qquad (2.55)$$

where $\eta > |\dot{d} + \lambda d|$.

Then

$$\dot{V} = s(-\eta\,\mathrm{sgn}(s) - \dot{d} - \lambda d) = -s(\dot{d} + \lambda d) - \eta s\,\mathrm{sgn}(s) = -s(\dot{d} + \lambda d) - \eta|s| < 0$$

2.6.3 Simulation Example

The plant is

$$J\ddot{\theta} = \tau - d(t)$$

where $J = \dfrac{1}{133}$, $d(t) = 10\sin t$.

Choose ideal position signal as $r = \sin t$, and the initial plant state is $(0.5 \ \ 0)^T$. Using the controller (2.55) with low pass filter (2.50), design $\lambda = 25$, $\lambda_1 = 30$, $\lambda_2 = 50$, $\eta = 50$. The simulation results are shown in Fig. 2.17 – Fig. 2.19.

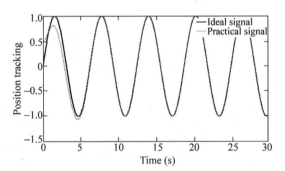

Figure 2.17 Position tracking

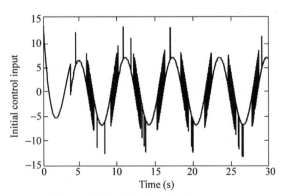

Figure 2.18 Virtual control input u

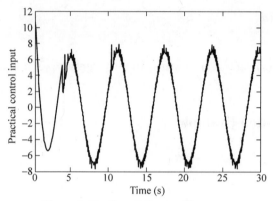

Figure 2.19 Practical control input τ

Simulation programs:

(1) Main Simulink program: chap2_7sim.mdl

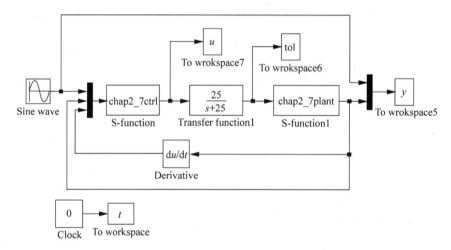

(2) Control law program: chap2_7ctrl.m

```
function [sys,x0,str,ts] = spacemodel(t,x,u,flag)
switch flag,
case 0,
    [sys,x0,str,ts]=mdlInitializeSizes;
case 3,
    sys=mdlOutputs(t,x,u);
case {2,4,9}
    sys=[];
otherwise
    error(['Unhandled flag = ',num2str(flag)]);
end
function [sys,x0,str,ts]=mdlInitializeSizes
```

2 Normal Sliding Mode Control

```
sizes = simsizes;
sizes.NumContStates  = 0;
sizes.NumDiscStates  = 0;
sizes.NumOutputs     = 1;
sizes.NumInputs      = 5;
sizes.DirFeedthrough = 1;
sizes.NumSampleTimes = 1;
sys = simsizes(sizes);
x0  = [];
str = [];
ts  = [0 0];
function sys=mdlOutputs(t,x,u)
tol=u(1);
th=u(2);
d_th=u(3);
dd_th=u(5);

J=10;
thd=sin(t);
d_thd=cos(t);
dd_thd=-sin(t);
ddd_thd=-cos(t);
e=th-thd;
de=d_th-d_thd;
dde=dd_th-dd_thd;

n1=30;n2=30;
n=25;
s=dde+n1*de+n2*e;

xite=80;   %dot(d)+n*dmax,dmax=3
ut=-1/n*(-n*J*dd_th+J*(-ddd_thd+n1*dde+n2*de)+xite*sign(s));

sys(1)=ut;
```

(3) Plant S function: chap2_7plant.m

```
function [sys,x0,str,ts] = spacemodel(t,x,u,flag)
switch flag,
case 0,
    [sys,x0,str,ts]=mdlInitializeSizes;
case 1,
    sys=mdlDerivatives(t,x,u);
case 3,
    sys=mdlOutputs(t,x,u);
case {2,4,9}
    sys=[];
otherwise
    error(['Unhandled flag = ',num2str(flag)]);
end
```

```
function [sys,x0,str,ts]=mdlInitializeSizes
sizes = simsizes;
sizes.NumContStates  = 2;
sizes.NumDiscStates  = 0;
sizes.NumOutputs     = 2;
sizes.NumInputs      = 1;
sizes.DirFeedthrough = 1;
sizes.NumSampleTimes = 1; % At least one sample time is needed
sys = simsizes(sizes);
x0  = [0.5;0];
str = [];
ts  = [0 0];
function sys=mdlDerivatives(t,x,u)   %Time-varying model
J=10;
ut=u(1);
d=3.0*sin(t);
sys(1)=x(2);
sys(2)=1/J*(ut-d);
function sys=mdlOutputs(t,x,u)
sys(1)=x(1);
sys(2)=x(2);
```

(4) Plot program: chap2_7plot.m

```
close all;

figure(1);
plot(t,y(:,1),'k',t,y(:,2),'r:','linewidth',2);
xlabel('time(s)');ylabel('Position tracking');
legend('ideal signal','practical signal');

figure(2);
plot(t,u,'k','linewidth',2);
xlabel('time(s)');ylabel('initial control input');

figure(3);
plot(t,tol,'k','linewidth',2);
xlabel('time(s)');ylabel('practical control input');
```

References

[1] Choi HS, Park YH, Cho Y, Lee M. Global sliding mode control. IEEE Control Magazine, 2001, 21(3): 27–35

[2] Kang BP, Ju JL. Sliding mode controller with filtered signal for robot manipulators using virtual plant/controller, Mechatronics, 1997, 7(3): 277–286

3 Advanced Sliding Mode Control

Jinkun Liu

Beijing University of Aeronautics and Astronautics

P.R.China

E-mail: ljk@buaa.edu.cn

Xinhua Wang

National University of Singapore

Singapore

E-mail: wangxinhua04@gmail.com

Abstract This chapter introduces two kinds of advanced sliding mode controllers design, including sliding mode control based on LMI technology and sliding mode control based on back-stepping technology.

Keywords sliding mode control, LMI, back-stepping

3.1 Sliding Mode Control Based on a Linear Matrix Inequality for Inverted Pendulum

3.1.1 System Description

The kinetic equation of the inverted pendulum is given as follows:

$$
\left.
\begin{aligned}
\ddot{\theta} &= \frac{m(m+M)gl}{(M+m)I+Mml^2}\theta - \frac{ml}{(M+m)I+Mml^2}u \\
\ddot{x} &= -\frac{m^2gl^2}{(M+m)I+Mml^2}\theta + \frac{I+ml^2}{(M+m)I+Mml^2}u
\end{aligned}
\right\}
\tag{3.1}
$$

where $I = \frac{1}{12}mL^2$, $l = \frac{1}{2}L$, θ and x are pendulum swing angle and vehicle position respectively, $g=9.8$ m/s^2, M is vehicle mass, m is pendulum mass, e is one half of the pendulum length, and u is control input.

Control object: rolling angle $\theta \to 0$, rolling rate $\dot{\theta} \to 0$, the position of vehicle

$x \to 0$ and the velocity of vehicle $\dot{x} \to 0$.

Let $x(1) = \theta$, $x(2) = \dot{\theta}$, $x(3) = x$, $x(4) = \dot{x}$, therefore, Eq. (3.1) can be written as

$$\dot{x} = Ax + Bu \tag{3.2}$$

where $A = \begin{bmatrix} 0 & 1 & 0 & 0 \\ t_1 & 0 & 0 & 0 \\ 0 & 0 & 0 & 1 \\ t_2 & 0 & 0 & 0 \end{bmatrix}$, $B = \begin{bmatrix} 0 \\ t_3 \\ 0 \\ t_4 \end{bmatrix}$, $t_1 = \dfrac{m(m+M)gl}{(M+m)I+Mml^2}$,

$t_2 = -\dfrac{m^2gl^2}{(M+m)I+Mml^2}$, $t_3 = -\dfrac{ml}{(M+m)I+Mml^2}$, $t_4 = \dfrac{I+ml^2}{(M+m)I+Mml^2}$.

Considering the uncertainties and the disturbances, Eq. (3.2) can be written as

$$\dot{x}(t) = Ax(t) + B(u + f(t)) \tag{3.3}$$

where $x = (\theta \quad \dot{\theta} \quad x \quad \dot{x})^{\mathrm{T}}$, $x(1) = \theta$, $x(2) = \dot{\theta}$, $x(3) = x$, $x(4) = \dot{x}$, $|f(t)| \leqslant \delta_f$, δ_f is upper bound of $f(t)$, and $\varepsilon_0 > 0$.

3.1.2 Equivalent Sliding Mode Control

The sliding variable is selected as

$$s = B^{\mathrm{T}} Px \tag{3.4}$$

where P is a 4×4 positive-definite matrix.

The controller can be designed as

$$u(t) = u_{\mathrm{eq}} + u_{\mathrm{n}} \tag{3.5}$$

$$u_{\mathrm{eq}} = -(B^{\mathrm{T}} PB)^{-1} B^{\mathrm{T}} PAx(t)$$

$$u_{\mathrm{n}} = -(B^{\mathrm{T}} PB)^{-1} (|B^{\mathrm{T}} PB| \delta_f + \varepsilon_0) \mathrm{sgn}(s)$$

Select the Lyapunov function as

$$V = \frac{1}{2} s^2 \tag{3.6}$$

$$\begin{aligned}
\dot{s} &= B^{\mathrm{T}} P\dot{x}(t) = B^{\mathrm{T}} P(Ax(t) + B(u + f(t))) \\
&= B^{\mathrm{T}} PAx(t) + B^{\mathrm{T}} PBu + B^{\mathrm{T}} PBf(t) \\
&= B^{\mathrm{T}} PAx(t) + B^{\mathrm{T}} PB(-(B^{\mathrm{T}} PB)^{-1} B^{\mathrm{T}} PAx(t) \\
&\quad -(B^{\mathrm{T}} PB)^{-1} (|B^{\mathrm{T}} PB| \delta_f + \varepsilon_0) \mathrm{sgn}(s)) + B^{\mathrm{T}} PBf(t) \\
&= -(|B^{\mathrm{T}} PB| \delta_f + \varepsilon_0) \mathrm{sgn}(s) + B^{\mathrm{T}} PBf(t)
\end{aligned}$$

$$\text{3 Advanced Sliding Mode Control}$$

Therefore, we have

$$\dot{V} = s\dot{s} = -(|\boldsymbol{B}^{\mathrm{T}}\boldsymbol{PB}|\delta_{\mathrm{f}} + \varepsilon_0)|s| + \boldsymbol{B}^{\mathrm{T}}\boldsymbol{PB}f(t) \leqslant -\varepsilon_0|s|$$

3.1.3 Sliding Mode Control Based on Auxiliary Feedback

In order to solve for symmetric positive-definite matrix $\boldsymbol{P}$, the controller is designed as[1,2]

$$u(t) = -\boldsymbol{K}\boldsymbol{x} + v(t) \tag{3.7}$$

where $v(t) = \boldsymbol{K}\boldsymbol{x} + u_{\mathrm{eq}} + u_{\mathrm{n}}$.

There exists $\boldsymbol{K}$ such that $\bar{\boldsymbol{A}} = \boldsymbol{A} - \boldsymbol{BK}$ is stable, therefore, we have

$$\dot{\boldsymbol{x}}(t) = \bar{\boldsymbol{A}}\boldsymbol{x}(t) + \boldsymbol{B}(v + f(t)) \tag{3.8}$$

where $\boldsymbol{K}$ is a 1×4 vector, $\boldsymbol{P}, \boldsymbol{A}$ and $\bar{\boldsymbol{A}}$ are 4×4 matrixes, and $\boldsymbol{B}$ is a 4×1 vector.

Select the Lyapunov function as

$$V = \boldsymbol{x}^{\mathrm{T}}\boldsymbol{P}\boldsymbol{x} \tag{3.9}$$

Therefore,

$$\dot{V} = 2\boldsymbol{x}^{\mathrm{T}}\boldsymbol{P}\dot{\boldsymbol{x}} = 2\boldsymbol{x}^{\mathrm{T}}\boldsymbol{P}(\bar{\boldsymbol{A}}\boldsymbol{x}(t) + \boldsymbol{B}(v + f(t)))$$
$$= 2\boldsymbol{x}^{\mathrm{T}}\boldsymbol{P}\bar{\boldsymbol{A}}\boldsymbol{x}(t) + 2\boldsymbol{x}^{\mathrm{T}}\boldsymbol{PB}(v + f(t))$$

When $t \geqslant t_0$, there exists $s = \boldsymbol{B}^{\mathrm{T}}\boldsymbol{P}\boldsymbol{x}(t) = 0$, i.e. $s^{\mathrm{T}} = \boldsymbol{x}^{\mathrm{T}}\boldsymbol{PB} = 0$, such that

$$\dot{V} = 2\boldsymbol{x}^{\mathrm{T}}\boldsymbol{P}\bar{\boldsymbol{A}}\boldsymbol{x} = \boldsymbol{x}^{\mathrm{T}}(\boldsymbol{P}\bar{\boldsymbol{A}} + \bar{\boldsymbol{A}}^{\mathrm{T}}\boldsymbol{P})\boldsymbol{x} = 2\boldsymbol{x}^{\mathrm{T}}\boldsymbol{M}\boldsymbol{x}$$

In order to satisfy $\dot{V} < 0$, $\boldsymbol{M} < 0$ is needed, i.e.

$$\boldsymbol{P}\bar{\boldsymbol{A}} + \bar{\boldsymbol{A}}^{\mathrm{T}}\boldsymbol{P} < 0$$

Since $\bar{\boldsymbol{A}}$ is Hurwitz, then $\boldsymbol{P}\bar{\boldsymbol{A}} + \bar{\boldsymbol{A}}^{\mathrm{T}}\boldsymbol{P} < 0$ can be guaranteed[3].

Multiplying $\boldsymbol{P}^{-1}$ in the above inequality, we have

$$\bar{\boldsymbol{A}}\boldsymbol{P}^{-1} + \boldsymbol{P}^{-1}\bar{\boldsymbol{A}}^{\mathrm{T}} < 0$$

Let $\boldsymbol{X} = \boldsymbol{P}^{-1}$, we get

$$\bar{\boldsymbol{A}}\boldsymbol{X} + \boldsymbol{X}\bar{\boldsymbol{A}}^{\mathrm{T}} < 0$$

$$(\boldsymbol{A} - \boldsymbol{BK})\boldsymbol{X} + \boldsymbol{X}(\boldsymbol{A} - \boldsymbol{BK})^{\mathrm{T}} < 0$$

Select $\boldsymbol{L} = \boldsymbol{KX}$, we have

$$\boldsymbol{A}\boldsymbol{X} - \boldsymbol{BL} + \boldsymbol{X}\boldsymbol{A}^{\mathrm{T}} - \boldsymbol{L}^{\mathrm{T}}\boldsymbol{B}^{\mathrm{T}} < 0 \tag{3.10}$$

In LMI, to guarantted $\boldsymbol{P}$ as symmetrical matrix, we design

$$\boldsymbol{P} = \boldsymbol{P}^{\mathrm{T}} \quad \text{or} \quad \boldsymbol{X} = \boldsymbol{X}^{\mathrm{T}} \tag{3.11}$$

83

3.1.4 Simulation Example

The parameters: $g = 9.8 \text{ m/s}^2$ (gravity acceleration), $M = 1.0 \text{ kg}$ (vehicle mass), $m = 0.1 \text{ kg}$ (pole mass), $L = 0.5 \text{ m}$ (half length of pole). Sampling period $T = 20 \text{ ms}$, initial states: $\theta(0) = -60°, \dot{\theta}(0) = 0,\ x(0) = 5.0, \dot{x}(0) = 0$, The desired states: $\theta(0) = 0,\ \dot{\theta}(0) = 0,\ x(0) = 0,\ \dot{x}(0) = 0$, and $f(t) = 0.3\sin t$.

Sliding mode controller is given in Eq. (3.5), and select $\delta_f = 0.30,\ \varepsilon_0 = 0.15$, the saturated function is adopted instead of switching function, and the boundary layer is selected as $\Delta = 0.05$. From Eqs. (3.10) and (3.11), we can get:

$$P = \begin{bmatrix} 7.4496 & 1.2493 & 1.0782 & 1.1384 \\ 1.2493 & 0.3952 & 0.2108 & 0.3252 \\ 1.0782 & 0.2108 & 0.3854 & 0.2280 \\ 1.1384 & 0.3252 & 0.2280 & 0.4286 \end{bmatrix}$$

The simulation results are shown in Fig. 3.1 – Fig. 3.3. Note that robust control can be realized by sliding mode controller for a single-stage inverted pendulum.

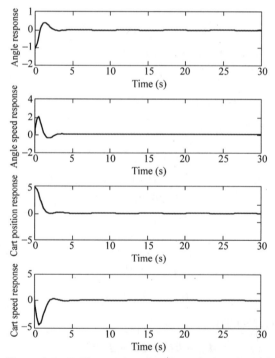

Figure 3.1 Rolling angle and rolling velocity of vehicle

3 Advanced Sliding Mode Control

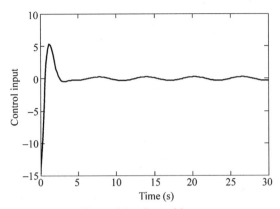

Figure 3.2 Control input

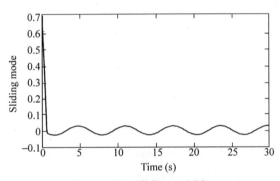

Figure 3.3 Sliding variable

Simulation programs:

(1) Program of LMI design: chap3_lmi.m

```
clear all;
close all;

g=9.8;M=1.0;m=0.1;L=0.5;

I=1/12*m*L^2;
l=1/2*L;
t1=m*(M+m)*g*l/[(M+m)*I+M*m*l^2];
t2=-m^2*g*l^2/[(m+M)*I+M*m*l^2];
t3=-m*l/[(M+m)*I+M*m*l^2];
t4=(I+m*l^2)/[(m+M)*I+M*m*l^2];

A=[0,1,0,0;
   t1,0,0,0;
   0,0,0,1;
   t2,0,0,0];
B=[0;t3;0;t4];
```

85

```
% LMI Var Description
setlmis([]);
X = lmivar(1, [4 1]);   % 1 -> symmetric block diagonal, then P is symmetric
L = lmivar(2, [1 4]);   % Define L is 1 row,4 column

% LMI
%First LMI
lmiterm([1 1 1 X], A, 1, 's');   % A*X+X'*A'<0
lmiterm([-1 1 1 L], B, 1, 's');  % 0<B*L+L'*B'

%Second LMI
lmiterm([-2 1 1 X], 1, 1);       % 0<X, then P is positive matrix

lmis=getlmis;

[tmin,xfeas] = feasp(lmis);
X = dec2mat(lmis,xfeas,X)
P=inv(X)

%Verify A_bar is Hurwitz
L = dec2mat(lmis,xfeas,L)
K=L*inv(X);
A_bar=A-B*K
eig(A_bar)

save Pfile A B P;
```

(2) Simulation program of continuous system

Simulink main program: chap3_1sim.mdl

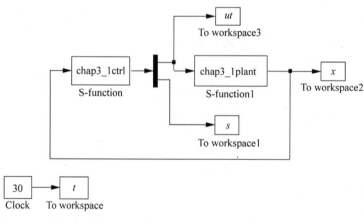

Program of controller: chap3_1ctrl.m

```
function [sys,x0,str,ts] = spacemodel(t,x,u,flag)
switch flag,
case 0,
    [sys,x0,str,ts]=mdlInitializeSizes;
```

3 Advanced Sliding Mode Control

```
case 3,
    sys=mdlOutputs(t,x,u);
case {2,4,9}
    sys=[];
otherwise
    error(['Unhandled flag = ',num2str(flag)]);
end
function [sys,x0,str,ts]=mdlInitializeSizes
sizes = simsizes;
sizes.NumContStates  = 0;
sizes.NumDiscStates  = 0;
sizes.NumOutputs     = 2;
sizes.NumInputs      = 4;
sizes.DirFeedthrough = 1;
sizes.NumSampleTimes = 1;
sys = simsizes(sizes);
x0  = [];
str = [];
ts  = [0 0];
function sys=mdlOutputs(t,x,u)
g=9.8;M=1.0;m=0.1;L=0.5;
I=1/12*m*L^2;
l=1/2*L;
t1=m*(M+m)*g*l/[(M+m)*I+M*m*l^2];
t2=-m^2*g*l^2/[(m+M)*I+M*m*l^2];
t3=-m*l/[(M+m)*I+M*m*l^2];
t4=(I+m*l^2)/[(m+M)*I+M*m*l^2];

A=[0,1,0,0;
   t1,0,0,0;
   0,0,0,1;
   t2,0,0,0];
B=[0;t3;0;t4];

% P is solved by LMI
P=[7.4496    1.2493    1.0782    1.1384;
   1.2493    0.3952    0.2108    0.3252;
   1.0782    0.2108    0.3854    0.2280;
   1.1384    0.3252    0.2280    0.4286];

deltaf=0.30;
epc0=0.5;

x=[u(1) u(2) u(3) u(4)]';

s=B'*P*x;
ueq=-inv(B'*P*B)*B'*P*A*x;

M=2;
if M==1
    un=-inv(B'*P*B)*(norm(B'*P*B)*deltaf+epc0)*sign(s);
```

```matlab
    elseif M==2                    %Saturated function
          delta=0.05;
          kk=1/delta;
          if abs(s)>delta
            sats=sign(s);
          else
            sats=kk*s;
          end
       un=-inv(B'*P*B)*(norm(B'*P*B)*deltaf+epc0)*sats;
end
ut=un+ueq;
sys(1)=ut;
sys(2)=s;
```

Program of the plant: chap3_1plant.m

```matlab
function [sys,x0,str,ts] = spacemodel(t,x,u,flag)
switch flag,
case 0,
    [sys,x0,str,ts]=mdlInitializeSizes;
case 1,
    sys=mdlDerivatives(t,x,u);
case 3,
    sys=mdlOutputs(t,x,u);
case {2,4,9}
    sys=[];
otherwise
    error(['Unhandled flag = ',num2str(flag)]);
end
function [sys,x0,str,ts]=mdlInitializeSizes
sizes = simsizes;
sizes.NumContStates  = 4;
sizes.NumDiscStates  = 0;
sizes.NumOutputs     = 4;
sizes.NumInputs      = 1;
sizes.DirFeedthrough = 0;
sizes.NumSampleTimes = 0;
sys = simsizes(sizes);
x0 =[-pi/3,0,5.0,0];
str = [];
ts = [];
function sys=mdlDerivatives(t,x,u)
g=9.8;M=1.0;m=0.1;L=0.5;

I=1/12*m*L^2;
l=1/2*L;
t1=m*(M+m)*g*l/[(M+m)*I+M*m*l^2];
t2=-m^2*g*l^2/[(m+M)*I+M*m*l^2];
t3=-m*l/[(M+m)*I+M*m*l^2];
t4=(I+m*l^2)/[(m+M)*I+M*m*l^2];

A=[0,1,0,0;
```

```
   t1,0,0,0;
   0,0,0,1;
   t2,0,0,0];
B=[0;t3;0;t4];

f=1*0.3*sin(t);
ut=u(1);
dx=A*x+B*(ut-f);

sys(1)=x(2);
sys(2)=dx(2);
sys(3)=x(4);
sys(4)=dx(4);
function sys=mdlOutputs(t,x,u)
sys(1)=x(1);
sys(2)=x(2);
sys(3)=x(3);
sys(4)=x(4);
```

Plot program: chap3_1plot.m

```
close all;

figure(1);
subplot(411);
plot(t,x(:,1),'r','linewidth',2);
xlabel('time(s)');ylabel('Angle response');
subplot(412);
plot(t,x(:,2),'r','linewidth',2);
xlabel('time(s)');ylabel('Angle speed response');
subplot(413);
plot(t,x(:,3),'r','linewidth',2);
xlabel('time(s)');ylabel('Cart position response');
subplot(414);
plot(t,x(:,4),'r','linewidth',2);
xlabel('time(s)');ylabel('Cart speed response');

figure(2);
plot(t,ut(:,1),'r','linewidth',2);
xlabel('time(s)');ylabel('Control input');

figure(3);
plot(t,s(:,1),'r','linewidth',2);
xlabel('time(s)');ylabel('Sliding mode');
```

(3) Simulation program of the discrete system Main program: chap3_2.m

```
%Single Link Inverted Pendulum Control: LMI
clear all;
close all;
global A B
load Pfile;
u_1=0;
```

```matlab
xk=[-pi/6,0,5.0,0];   %Initial state
ts=0.02;   %Sampling time
for k=1:1:1000
time(k)=k*ts;
Tspan=[0 ts];

para(1)=u_1;
para(2)=time(k);
[t,x]=ode45('chap3_2plant',Tspan,xk,[],para);
xk=x(length(x),:);

x1(k)=xk(1);
x2(k)=xk(2);
x3(k)=xk(3);
x4(k)=xk(4);
x=[x1(k) x2(k) x3(k) x4(k)]';

s(k)=B'*P*x;

deltaf=0.30;
epc0=0.5;

ueq(k)=-inv(B'*P*B)*B'*P*A*x;

M=2;
if M==1
   un(k)=-inv(B'*P*B)*(norm(B'*P*B)*deltaf+epc0)*sign(s(k));
elseif M==2                  %Saturated function
     delta=0.05;
     kk=1/delta;
     if abs(s(k))>delta
       sats=sign(s(k));
     else
       sats=kk*s(k);
     end
   un(k)=-inv(B'*P*B)*(norm(B'*P*B)*deltaf+epc0)*sats;
end
u(k)=ueq(k)+un(k);

u_1=u(k);
end
figure(1);
subplot(411);
plot(time,x1,'k','linewidth',2);       %Pendulum Angle
xlabel('time(s)');ylabel('Angle');
subplot(412);
plot(time,x2,'k','linewidth',2);       %Pendulum Angle Rate
xlabel('time(s)');ylabel('Angle rate');
subplot(413);
plot(time,x3,'k','linewidth',2);     %Car Position
xlabel('time(s)');ylabel('Cart position');
subplot(414);
```

3 Advanced Sliding Mode Control

```
plot(time,x4,'k','linewidth',2);      %Car Position Rate
xlabel('time(s)');ylabel('Cart rate');
figure(5);
plot(time,u,'k','linewidth',2);       %Force F change
xlabel('time(s)');ylabel('Control input');
```

Sub-program: chap3_2plant.m

```
function dx=dym(t,x,flag,para)
global A B
dx=zeros(4,1);

ut=para(1);
time=para(2);

%State equation for one link inverted pendulum
f=0.3*sin(time);
dx=A*x+B*(ut-f);
```

3.2 Backstepping Sliding Mode Control for a Inverted Pendulum

3.2.1 The Basic Theory

The basic idea of backstepping design is that a complex nonlinear system is decomposed into the subsystems, and the degree of each subsystem doesn't exceed that of the whole system. Accordingly, the Lyapunov function and medial-fictitious control are designed respectively, and the whole system is obtained through "backstepping". Thus the control rule is designed thoroughly. The backstepping method is called as back-deduce method, and the desired dynamic indexes are satisfied.

3.2.2 System Description

The backstepping method and the sliding mode control are integrated to designed a backstepping-sliding-mode controller which realizes the robust control for uncertain systems. Suppose the plant is a nonlinear system as under:

$$\left.\begin{array}{l} \dot{x}_1 = x_2 \\ \dot{x}_2 = f(x,t) + b(x,t)u + d(x,t) \end{array}\right\} \tag{3.12}$$

where $f(x,t)$ and $b(x,t)$ are the nonlinear functions, $d(x,t)$ is the sum of the unmatched uncertainties and the disturbances, and $|d(x,t)| \leqslant D, \ b(x,t) \neq 0$.

91

3.2.3 Controller Design

The steps of the basic backstepping-sliding-mode control cah be designed as follow.

Step 1

Let

$$e_1 = x_1 - r \qquad (3.13)$$

where r is the desired trajectory. Therefore, we have

$$\dot{e}_1 = \dot{x}_1 - \dot{r} = x_2 - \dot{r}$$

Select the Lyapunov function as

$$V_1 = \frac{1}{2} e_1^2 \qquad (3.14)$$

Therefore,

$$\dot{V}_1 = e_1 \dot{e}_1 = e_1 (x_2 - \dot{r})$$

In order to realize $\dot{V}_1 \leqslant 0$, we let $x_2 = s - c_1 e_1 + \dot{r}$, i.e.

$$s = x_2 + c_1 e_1 - \dot{r} = c_1 e_1 + \dot{e}_1, \quad c_1 > 0 \qquad (3.15)$$

where s is the sliding variable. Therefore, we have

$$\dot{V}_1 = e_1 s - c_1 e_1^2$$

If $s = 0$, then $\dot{V}_1 \leqslant 0$. Therefore, the next step is required.

Step 2

Select the Lyapunov be as

$$V_2 = V_1 + \frac{1}{2} s^2 \qquad (3.16)$$

Because $\dot{s} = \dot{x}_2 + c_1 \dot{e}_1 - \ddot{r} = f(x,t) + b(x,t)u + d(x,t) + c_1 \dot{e}_1 - \ddot{r}$, we have

$$\dot{V}_2 = \dot{V}_1 + s\dot{s} = e_1 s - c_1 e_1^2 + s(f(x,t) + b(x,t)u + d(x,t) + c_1 \dot{e}_1 - \ddot{r})$$

In order to realize $\dot{V}_2 \leqslant 0$, a controller is designed as

$$u = \frac{1}{b(x,t)}(-f(x,t) - c_2 s - e_1 - c_1 \dot{e}_1 + \ddot{r} - \eta \operatorname{sgn}(s)) \qquad (3.17)$$

where $c_2 > 0$, $\eta \geqslant D$. Therefore, we have

$$\dot{V}_2 = -c_1 e_1^2 - c_2 s^2 + sd(x,t) - \eta |s| \leqslant 0$$

Therefore, $e_1 \to 0$ and $e_2 \to 0$ as $t \to \infty$.

3.2.4 Simulation Example

Considering a one link inverted pendulum as follows:

$$\begin{cases} \dot{x}_1 = x_2 \\ \dot{x}_2 = \dfrac{g\sin x_1 - mlx_2^2 \cos x_1 \sin x_1 /(m_c + m)}{l(4/3 - m\cos^2 x_1 /(m_c + m))} + \dfrac{\cos x_1 /(m_c + m)}{l(4/3 - m\cos^2 x_1 /(m_c + m))} u \end{cases}$$

where x_1 and x_2 are the oscillation angle and the oscillation rate respectively. $g = 9.8$ m/s^2, m_c is the vehicle mass, $m_c = 1$ kg, m is the mass of pendulum bar, $m = 0.1$ kg, l is one half of pendulum length, $l = 0.5$ m, u is the control input.

The desired trajectory is $x_d(t) = 0.1\sin(\pi t)$, control rule is Eq. (3.17), and select $c_1 = 35$ and $c_2 = 15$. The initial state of the inverted pendulum is $[-\pi/60 \quad 0]$. Simulation results are shown in Fig. 3.4 and Fig. 3.5.

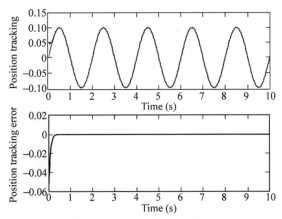

Figure 3.4 Position tracking

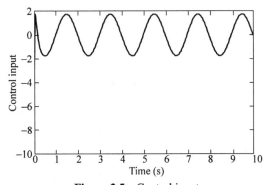

Figure 3.5 Control input

Simulation programs:

(1) Simulink main program: chap3_3sim.mdl

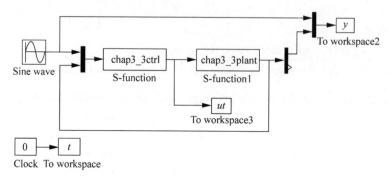

(2) S-function of controller: chap3_3ctrl.m

```
function [sys,x0,str,ts] = spacemodel(t,x,u,flag)

switch flag,
case 0,
    [sys,x0,str,ts]=mdlInitializeSizes;
case 3,
    sys=mdlOutputs(t,x,u);
case {2,4,9}
    sys=[];
otherwise
    error(['Unhandled flag = ',num2str(flag)]);
end

function [sys,x0,str,ts]=mdlInitializeSizes
global M V x0 fai

sizes = simsizes;
sizes.NumDiscStates  = 0;
sizes.NumOutputs     = 1;
sizes.NumInputs      = 3;
sizes.DirFeedthrough = 1;
sizes.NumSampleTimes = 1;
sys = simsizes(sizes);
x0=[];
str = [];
ts = [0 0];
function sys=mdlOutputs(t,x,u)
c1=35;
c2=15;

r=u(1);
dr=0.1*pi*cos(pi*t);
```

3 Advanced Sliding Mode Control

```
ddr=-0.1*pi^2*sin(pi*t);
x1=u(2);
x2=u(3);

g=9.8;mc=1.0;m=0.1;l=0.5;
S=l*(4/3-m*(cos(x1))^2/(mc+m));
fx=g*sin(x1)-m*l*x2^2*cos(x1)*sin(x1)/(mc+m);
fx=fx/S;
gx=cos(x1)/(mc+m);
gx=gx/S;

e1=x1-r;
de1=x2-dr;

s=x2+c1*e1-dr;
xite=0.010;
ut=(1/gx)*(-fx-c2*s-e1-c1*de1+ddr-xite*sign(s));

sys(1)=ut;
```

(3) The program of the plant: chap3_3plant.m

```
function [sys,x0,str,ts]=s_function(t,x,u,flag)
switch flag,
case 0,
    [sys,x0,str,ts]=mdlInitializeSizes;
case 1,
    sys=mdlDerivatives(t,x,u);
case 3,
    sys=mdlOutputs(t,x,u);
case {2, 4, 9 }
    sys = [];
otherwise
    error(['Unhandled flag = ',num2str(flag)]);
end
function [sys,x0,str,ts]=mdlInitializeSizes
sizes = simsizes;
sizes.NumContStates  = 2;
sizes.NumDiscStates  = 0;
sizes.NumOutputs     = 2;
sizes.NumInputs      = 1;
sizes.DirFeedthrough = 0;
sizes.NumSampleTimes = 0;
sys=simsizes(sizes);
x0=[pi/60 0];
str=[];
ts=[];
function sys=mdlDerivatives(t,x,u)
g=9.8;mc=1.0;m=0.1;l=0.5;
```

```
S=l*(4/3-m*(cos(x(1)))^2/(mc+m));
fx=g*sin(x(1))-m*l*x(2)^2*cos(x(1))*sin(x(1))/(mc+m);
fx=fx/S;
gx=cos(x(1))/(mc+m);
gx=gx/S;

sys(1)=x(2);
sys(2)=fx+gx*u;
function sys=mdlOutputs(t,x,u)
sys(1)=x(1);
sys(2)=x(2);
```

(4) Plot program: chap3_3plot.m

```
close all;

figure(1);
subplot(211);
plot(t,y(:,1),'r',t,y(:,2),'k:','linewidth',2);
xlabel('time(s)');ylabel('Position tracking');
subplot(212);
plot(t,y(:,1)-y(:,2),'k','linewidth',2);
xlabel('time(s)');ylabel('Position tracking error');

figure(2);
plot(t,ut(:,1),'k','linewidth',2);
xlabel('time(s)');ylabel('Control input');
```

References

[1] Gouaisbaut F, Dambrine M, Richard JP. Robust control of delay systems: a sliding mode control, design via LMI, Systems & Control Letters 46 (2002): 219 – 230

[2] Qu SC. Sliding mode control theory and application for uncertain system, Huazhong Normal University Press, 2008, 6 (In chinese)

[3] Khalil HK. Nonlinear Systems (third edition). Prentice Hall, 2002

4 Discrete Sliding Mode Control

Jinkun Liu

Beijing University of Aeronautics and Astronautics

P.R.China

E-mail: ljk@buaa.edu.cn

Xinhua Wang

National University of Singapore

Singapore

E-mail: wangxinhua04@gmail.com

Abstract This chapter introduces discrete sliding mode controllers, including a typical discrete sliding mode controller and a kind of discrete sliding mode controller based on disturbance observer.

Keywords discrete sliding mode control, disturbance observer, stability analysis

4.1 Discrete Sliding Mode Controller Design and Analysis

4.1.1 System Description

Consider the following uncertain system

$$x(k+1) = (A + \Delta A)x(k) + Bu(k) + f(k) \tag{4.1}$$

where x is system state, $A \in \mathbf{R}^{2 \times 2}$ and $\Delta A \in \mathbf{R}^{2 \times 2}$ are matrix, $B \in \mathbf{R}^{2 \times 1}$ is a vector, $u \in \mathbf{R}$ is control input, $f \in \mathbf{R}^{2 \times 1}$ is a vector, $B = [0 \ \ b]^{\mathrm{T}}$, $b > 0$.

The uncertain term ΔA and the perturbation term $f(k)$ satisfy the classical matching conditions, i.e.

$$\Delta A = B\tilde{A}, \quad f = B\tilde{f} \tag{4.2}$$

Then, the system (4.1) can be described as

$$x(k+1) = Ax(k) + B[u(k) + d(k)] \tag{4.3}$$

where $d(k) = \tilde{A}x(k) + \tilde{f}(k)$.

4.1.2 Controller Design and Analysis

The controller is designed as

$$u(k) = (C^{\mathrm{T}}B)^{-1}(C^{\mathrm{T}}x_{\mathrm{d}}(k+1) - C^{\mathrm{T}}Ax(k) + qs(k) - \eta\operatorname{sgn}(s(k))) \tag{4.4}$$

where η, q, c are positive constant values, c must be Hurwitz, $C = [c \ \ 1]^{\mathrm{T}}$, $0 < q < 1$, $|d| < D$, $C^{\mathrm{T}}BD < \eta$.

Stability analysis is given as follows: If the ideal position signal is $x_{\mathrm{d}}(k)$ then the tracking error is $e(k) = x(k) - x_{\mathrm{d}}(k)$, then

$$
\begin{aligned}
&s(k+1)\\
&= C^{\mathrm{T}}e(k+1)\\
&= C^{\mathrm{T}}x(k+1) - C^{\mathrm{T}}x_{\mathrm{d}}(k+1)\\
&= C^{\mathrm{T}}Ax(k) + C^{\mathrm{T}}Bu(k) + C^{\mathrm{T}}Bd(k) - C^{\mathrm{T}}x_{\mathrm{d}}(k+1)\\
&= C^{\mathrm{T}}Ax(k) + C^{\mathrm{T}}x_{\mathrm{d}}(k+1) - C^{\mathrm{T}}Ax(k) + qs(k) - \eta\operatorname{sgn}(s(k))\\
&\quad + C^{\mathrm{T}}Bd(k) - C^{\mathrm{T}}x_{\mathrm{d}}(k+1)\\
&= qs(k) - \eta\operatorname{sgn}(s(k)) + C^{\mathrm{T}}Bd(k)
\end{aligned}
\tag{4.5}
$$

Since $|C^{\mathrm{T}}Bd(k)| < C^{\mathrm{T}}BD < \eta$, then $-\eta < C^{\mathrm{T}}Bd(k) < \eta$, $-C^{\mathrm{T}}BD < C^{\mathrm{T}}Bd(k) < C^{\mathrm{T}}BD$, and then we have $\eta + C^{\mathrm{T}}Bd(k) > 0$, $-\eta + C^{\mathrm{T}}Bd(k) < 0$, $C^{\mathrm{T}}BD + C^{\mathrm{T}}Bd(k) > 0$ and $-C^{\mathrm{T}}BD + C^{\mathrm{T}}Bd(k) < 0$.

Four conditions are analyzed as follows:

(1) When $s(k) \geqslant C^{\mathrm{T}}BD + \eta$, we have

Consider $s(k) > 0$, $0 < q < 1$, $-\eta + C^{\mathrm{T}}Bd(k) < 0$, $C^{\mathrm{T}}BD + C^{\mathrm{T}}Bd(k) > 0$, then

$$s(k+1) - s(k) = (q-1)s(k) - \eta + C^{\mathrm{T}}Bd(k) < 0$$

$$
\begin{aligned}
s(k+1) + s(k) &= (q+1)s(k) - \eta + C^{\mathrm{T}}Bd(k) \geqslant (q+1)(C^{\mathrm{T}}BD + \eta) - \eta + C^{\mathrm{T}}Bd(k)\\
&= q(C^{\mathrm{T}}BD + \eta) + C^{\mathrm{T}}BD + C^{\mathrm{T}}Bd(k) > 0
\end{aligned}
$$

Then,

$$s(k+1)^2 < s(k)^2$$

(2) When $0 < s(k) < \boldsymbol{C}^{\mathrm{T}}\boldsymbol{B}D + \eta$, we have

$$s(k+1) = qs(k) - \eta + \boldsymbol{C}^{\mathrm{T}}\boldsymbol{B}d(k) < q(\boldsymbol{C}^{\mathrm{T}}\boldsymbol{B}D + \eta) - \eta + \boldsymbol{C}^{\mathrm{T}}\boldsymbol{B}d(k)$$
$$< q(\boldsymbol{C}^{\mathrm{T}}\boldsymbol{B}D + \eta) < \boldsymbol{C}^{\mathrm{T}}\boldsymbol{B}D + \eta$$

$$s(k+1) = qs(k) - \eta + \boldsymbol{C}^{\mathrm{T}}\boldsymbol{B}d(k) > -\eta + \boldsymbol{C}^{\mathrm{T}}\boldsymbol{B}d(k) > -\boldsymbol{C}^{\mathrm{T}}\boldsymbol{B}D - \eta$$

Then,

$$|s(k+1)| < \boldsymbol{C}^{\mathrm{T}}\boldsymbol{B}D + \eta$$

(3) When $-\boldsymbol{C}^{\mathrm{T}}\boldsymbol{B}D - \eta < s(k) < 0$, we have

$$s(k+1) = qs(k) + \eta + \boldsymbol{C}^{\mathrm{T}}\boldsymbol{B}d(k) > s(k) + \eta + \boldsymbol{C}^{\mathrm{T}}\boldsymbol{B}d(k)$$
$$> -\boldsymbol{C}^{\mathrm{T}}\boldsymbol{B}D - \eta + \eta + \boldsymbol{C}^{\mathrm{T}}\boldsymbol{B}d(k) > -\boldsymbol{C}^{\mathrm{T}}\boldsymbol{B}D - \eta$$

$$s(k+1) = qs(k) + \eta + \boldsymbol{C}^{\mathrm{T}}\boldsymbol{B}d(k) < \eta + \boldsymbol{C}^{\mathrm{T}}\boldsymbol{B}d(k) < \boldsymbol{C}^{\mathrm{T}}\boldsymbol{B}D + \eta$$

Then,

$$|s(k+1)| < \boldsymbol{C}^{\mathrm{T}}\boldsymbol{B}D + \eta$$

(4) When $s(k) \leqslant -\boldsymbol{C}^{\mathrm{T}}\boldsymbol{B}D - \eta < 0$, we have

$$s(k+1) - s(k) = (q-1)s(k) + \eta + \boldsymbol{C}^{\mathrm{T}}\boldsymbol{B}d(k) > 0$$

$$s(k+1) + s(k) = (q+1)s(k) + \eta + \boldsymbol{C}^{\mathrm{T}}\boldsymbol{B}d(k) < s(k) + \eta + \boldsymbol{C}^{\mathrm{T}}\boldsymbol{B}d(k)$$
$$\leqslant -\boldsymbol{C}^{\mathrm{T}}\boldsymbol{B}D - \eta + \eta + \boldsymbol{C}^{\mathrm{T}}\boldsymbol{B}d(k) = -\boldsymbol{C}^{\mathrm{T}}\boldsymbol{B}D + \boldsymbol{C}^{\mathrm{T}}\boldsymbol{B}d(k) < 0$$

Then,

$$s(k+1)^2 < s(k)^2$$

From the above analysis we conclude as follows:

$$\text{When } |s(k)| \geqslant \boldsymbol{C}^{\mathrm{T}}\boldsymbol{B}D + \eta, \ s(k+1)^2 < s(k)^2 \tag{4.6}$$

$$\text{When } |s(k)| < \boldsymbol{C}^{\mathrm{T}}\boldsymbol{B}D + \eta, \ |s(k+1)| < \boldsymbol{C}^{\mathrm{T}}\boldsymbol{B}D + \eta \tag{4.7}$$

From Eqs. (4.6) and (4.7), since $\eta > \boldsymbol{C}^{\mathrm{T}}\boldsymbol{B}D$, $s(k)$ converge to $\boldsymbol{C}^{\mathrm{T}}\boldsymbol{B}D + \eta$. Therefore, to increase convergence performance, a disturbance observer is required to be designed.

4.1.3 Simulation Example

Consider the plant

$$G(s) = \frac{133}{s^2 + 25s}$$

The sampling time is chosen as 0.001 s. Considering disturbance, the discrete system can be written as

$$x(k+1) = Ax(k) + B(u(k) + d(k))$$

where $A = \begin{bmatrix} 1 & 0.001 \\ 0 & 0.9753 \end{bmatrix}$, $B = \begin{bmatrix} 0.0001 \\ 0.1314 \end{bmatrix}$, and $d(k)$ is disturbance.

Using the control law Eq. (4.4), and assuming the disturbance as $d(k) = 1.5\sin t$, choosing the ideal position signal as $x_d(k) = \sin t$, and designing $C^T = [15\ 1]$, $q = 0.80$, $D = 1.5$. The initial state is $[0.15\ 0]$. The term $x_d(k+1)$ can be received by extrapolation method. The simulation results are shown in Fig. 4.1 – Fig. 4.3.

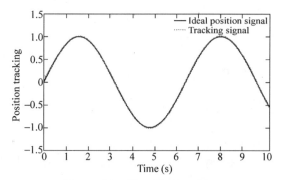

Figure 4.1 Sine signal tracking

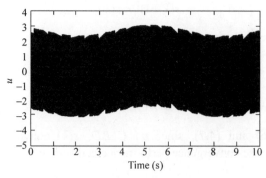

Figure 4.2 Control input

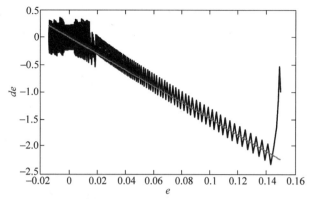

Figure 4.3 Phase trajectory

Simulation programs: chap4_1.m

```
%VSS controller based on decoupled disturbance compensator
clear all;
close all;

ts=0.001;
a=25;
b=133;
sys=tf(b,[1,a,0]);
dsys=c2d(sys,ts,'z');
[num,den]=tfdata(dsys,'v');

A=[0,1;0,-a];
B=[0;b];
C=[1,0];
D=0;
%Change transfer function to discrete position equation
[A1,B1,C1,D1]=c2dm(A,B,C,D,ts,'z');
A=A1;
b=B1;
c=15;
Ce=[c,1];
q=0.80;            %0<q<1

d_up=1.5;
eq=Ce*b*d_up+0.10;  %eq>abs(Ce*b*m/g);0<eq/fai<q<1

x_1=[0.15;0];
s_1=0;
u_1=0;
d_1=0;ed_1=0;
r_1=0;r_2=0;dr_1=0;

for k=1:1:10000
time(k)=k*ts;
```

```
d(k)=1.5*sin(k*ts);

x=A*x_1+b*(u_1+d(k));

r(k)=sin(k*ts);
%Using Waitui method
   dr(k)=(r(k)-r_1)/ts;
   dr_1=(r_1-r_2)/ts;
   r1(k)=2*r(k)-r_1;
   dr1(k)=2*dr(k)-dr_1;

   xd=[r(k);dr(k)];
   xd1=[r1(k);dr1(k)];

   e(k)=x(1)-r(k);
   de(k)=x(2)-dr(k);
   s(k)=c*e(k)+de(k);

   u(k)=inv(Ce*b)*(Ce*xd1-Ce*A*x+q*s(k)-eq*sign(s(k)));

   r_2=r_1;r_1=r(k);
   dr_1=dr(k);

   x_1=x;
   s_1=s(k);

   x1(k)=x(1);
   x2(k)=x(2);
   u_1=u(k);
end
figure(1);
plot(time,r,'k',time,x1,'r:','linewidth',2);
xlabel('time(s)');ylabel('Position tracking');
legend('Ideal position signal','tracking signal');
figure(2);
plot(time,u,'k','linewidth',2);
xlabel('time(s)');ylabel('u');
figure(3);
plot(e,de,'k',e,-Ce(1)*e,'r','linewidth',2);
xlabel('e');ylabel('de');
```

4.2 Discrete Sliding Mode Control Based on Disturbance Observer

4.2.1 System Description

Consider the uncertain discrete system as follow:

$$x(k+1) = Ax(k) + B(u(k) + d(k)) \tag{4.8}$$

4 Discrete Sliding Mode Control

where x is system state, $A \in \mathbf{R}^{2\times2}$ is a matrix, $B \in \mathbf{R}^{2\times1}$ is a vector, $u \in \mathbf{R}^{2\times1}$ is control input, $B = [0 \quad b]^{\mathrm{T}}, b > 0, d \in \mathbf{R}$ is the disturbance.

Let the desired input command be $x_{\mathrm{d}}(k)$, and the tracking error be $e(k) = x(k) - x_{\mathrm{d}}(k)$. The sliding variable is designed as

$$s(k) = Ce(k) \tag{4.9}$$

where $C = [c \quad 1], \ c > 0$.

4.2.2 Discrete Sliding Mode Control Based on Disturbance Observer

In this section, we introduce a typical sliding mode controller base on disturbance observer, which was proposed by Eun et al[1].

For Eq. (4.8), the sliding mode controller consists of the sliding mode control element and the disturbance compensation. The controller proposed by Eun et al. as[1]

$$u(k) = u_{\mathrm{s}}(k) + u_{\mathrm{c}}(k) \tag{4.10}$$

where

$$u_{\mathrm{s}}(k) = (C^{\mathrm{T}}B)^{-1}(C^{\mathrm{T}}x_{\mathrm{d}}(k+1) - C^{\mathrm{T}}Ax(k) + qs(k) - \eta\,\mathrm{sgn}(s(k)))$$

$$u_{\mathrm{c}}(k) = -\hat{d}(k)$$

The disturbance observer was proposed by Eun et al. as:

$$\hat{d}(k) = \hat{d}(k-1) + (C^{\mathrm{T}}B)^{-1}g(s(k) - qs(k-1) + \eta\,\mathrm{sgn}(s(k-1))) \tag{4.11}$$

where $\tilde{d}(k) = d(k) - \hat{d}(k)$, η, q, and g are positive constants.

From Eqs. (4.8) and (4.10), we have

$$\begin{aligned}
s(k+1) &= C^{\mathrm{T}}e(k+1) = C^{\mathrm{T}}x(k+1) - C^{\mathrm{T}}x_{\mathrm{d}}(k+1) \\
&= C^{\mathrm{T}}(Ax(k) + Bu(k) + Bd(k)) - C^{\mathrm{T}}x_{\mathrm{d}}(k+1) \\
&= C^{\mathrm{T}}Ax(k) + (C^{\mathrm{T}}x_{\mathrm{d}}(k+1) - C^{\mathrm{T}}Ax(k) + qs(k) \\
&\quad - \eta\,\mathrm{sgn}(s(k))) - C^{\mathrm{T}}B\hat{d}(k) + C^{\mathrm{T}}Bd(k) - C^{\mathrm{T}}x_{\mathrm{d}}(k+1) \\
&= qs(k) - \eta\,\mathrm{sgn}(s(k)) + C^{\mathrm{T}}B\tilde{d}(k)
\end{aligned} \tag{4.12}$$

From Eqs. (4.11) and (4.12), we can get

$$\begin{aligned}
\tilde{d}(k+1) &= d(k+1) - \hat{d}(k+1) \\
&= d(k+1) - \hat{d}(k) - (C^{\mathrm{T}}B)^{-1}g(s(k+1) - qs(k) + \eta\,\mathrm{sgn}(s(k))) \\
&= d(k+1) - d(k) + \tilde{d}(k) - (C^{\mathrm{T}}B)^{-1}g(C^{\mathrm{T}}B)\tilde{d}(k) \\
&= d(k+1) - d(k) + (1-g)\tilde{d}(k)
\end{aligned} \tag{4.13}$$

4.2.3 Convergent Analysis of Disturbance Observer

Theorem 1 proposed by Eun et al. as follows.

Theorem 1[1]: For the disturbance observer Eq. (4.11) there exists a positive constant m, if $|d(k+1)-d(k)|<m$ then k_0 exists, and when $k>k_0$ then $\tilde{d}(k)<m/g$ is satisfied where $0<g<1$.

Proof:

$\tilde{d}(k)$ can be decomposed as

$$\tilde{d}(k)=\tilde{d}_1(k)+\tilde{d}_2(k)$$

Let $\tilde{d}_1(0)=0$, we can get $\tilde{d}_2(0)=\tilde{d}(0)$, and because

$$\tilde{d}(k+1)=\tilde{d}_1(k+1)+\tilde{d}_2(k+1)$$

We let

$$\tilde{d}_1(k+1)=(1-g)\tilde{d}_1(k)+d(k+1)-d(k) \tag{4.14}$$

From Eq. (4.13), we have

$$\tilde{d}_2(k+1)=(1-g)\tilde{d}_2(k) \tag{4.15}$$

Inductive method is used to prove the theorem. Firstly, we prove $\tilde{d}_1(k)<m/g$.

(1) When $k=0$, we get: $\tilde{d}_1(0)=0<m/g$.

(2) Suppose $|\tilde{d}_1(k)|<m/g$, and from Eq. (4.14)and $0<g<1$, we can get when $k+1$,

$$|\tilde{d}_1(k+1)|\leqslant(1-g)|\tilde{d}_1(k)|+|d(k+1)-d(k)|<(1-g)\frac{m}{g}+m=\frac{m}{g}$$

is satisfied. From the above two equations, we have

$$|\tilde{d}_1(k)|<m/g, \quad k\geqslant0$$

From Eq. (4.15) and $0<1-g<1$, we get

$$\tilde{d}_2(k+1)=(1-g)\tilde{d}_2(k)\leqslant(1-g)|\tilde{d}_2(k)|<|\tilde{d}_2(k)|$$

Therefore, $\tilde{d}_2(k)$ is decreasing. And if there exists k_0', when $k>k_0'$, then $\tilde{d}_2(k)$ is arbitrary small.

From the analysis above, we find that there exists k_0, when $k>k_0$, such that

$$|\tilde{d}(k)|=|\tilde{d}_1(k)+\tilde{d}_2(k)|\leqslant|\tilde{d}_1(k)|+|\tilde{d}_2(k)|<\frac{m}{g}$$

4.2.4 Stability Analysis

Theorem 2 proposed by Eun et al. as follows.

Theorem 2[1]: For controller Eq. (4.10), the system is stable if the following conditions are satisfied:

(1) $0 < q < 1, \ 0 < g < 1$;

(2) There exists a positive constant m, $|d(k+1) - d(k)| < m$;

(3) $0 < C^T B \dfrac{m}{g} < \eta$.

Proof: Let $v(k) = C^T B \tilde{d}(k)$, we have

$$|v(k)| < C^T B \frac{m}{g} < \eta, \ \text{i.e.} -\eta < v(k) < \eta, \ -C^T B \frac{m}{g} < v(k) < C^T B \frac{m}{g}$$

Equation (4.12)can be written as

$$s(k+1) = qs(k) - \eta \, \mathrm{sgn}(s(k)) + v(k)$$

The following four cases are discussed:

(1) When $s(k) \geqslant C^T B \dfrac{m}{g} + \eta > 0$, we have

$$s(k+1) - s(k) = (q-1)s(k) - \eta + v(k) < 0$$

$$s(k+1) + s(k) = (q+1)s(k) - \eta + v(k) \geqslant (q+1)\left(C^T B \frac{m}{g} + \eta \right) - \eta + v(k)$$

$$= q\left(C^T B \frac{m}{g} + \eta \right) + C^T B \frac{m}{g} + v(k) > 0$$

Therefore,

$$s(k+1)^2 < s(k)^2$$

(2) When $s(k) \leqslant -C^T B \dfrac{m}{g} - \eta < 0$, we have

$$s(k+1) - s(k) = (q-1)s(k) + \eta + v(k) > 0$$

$$s(k+1) + s(k) = (q+1)s(k) + \eta + v(k) < s(k) + \eta + v(k)$$

$$\leqslant -C^T B \frac{m}{g} - \eta + \eta + v(k) = -C^T B \frac{m}{g} + v(k) < 0$$

Therefore,

$$s(k+1)^2 < s(k)^2$$

(3) When $0 < s(k) < C^T B \dfrac{m}{g} + \eta$, we have

$$s(k+1) = qs(k) - \eta + v(k) < q\left(C^T B \frac{m}{g} + \eta\right) - \eta + v(k)$$

$$< q\left(C^T B \frac{m}{g} + \eta\right) < C^T B \frac{m}{g} + \eta$$

$$s(k+1) = qs(k) - \eta + v(k) > -\eta + v(k) > -C^T B \frac{m}{g} - \eta$$

Therefore,

$$|s(k+1)| < C^T B \frac{m}{g} + \eta$$

(4) When $-C^T B \dfrac{m}{g} - \eta < s(k) < 0$, we have

$$s(k+1) = qs(k) + \eta + v(k) > s(k) + \eta + v(k)$$

$$> -C^T B \frac{m}{g} - \eta + \eta + v(k) > -C^T B \frac{m}{g} - \eta$$

$$s(k+1) = qs(k) + \eta + v(k) < \eta + v(k) < C^T B \frac{m}{g} + \eta$$

Therefore,

$$|s(k+1)| < C^T B \frac{m}{g} + \eta$$

From the above analysis the following conclusions can be obtained.

$$\text{When } |s(k)| \geqslant C^T B \frac{m}{g} + \eta, \quad s(k+1)^2 < s(k)^2 \tag{4.16}$$

$$\text{When } |s(k)| < C^T B \frac{m}{g} + \eta, \quad |s(k+1)| < C^T B \frac{m}{g} + \eta \tag{4.17}$$

The disturbance $d(t)$ is supposed to be continuous. If the sampling time is sufficiently small, then $|d(k+1) - d(k)| < m$ can be guaranteed and m is sufficiently small. If m and g are selected such that $\dfrac{m}{g} \ll 1$, and because $C^T B \dfrac{m}{g} < \eta$, η is selected sufficiently small and make $C^T B \dfrac{m}{g} + \eta \ll 1$. Therefore, the convergence of $s(k+1)$ can be realized.

4.2.5 Simulation Example

Consider the plant as follows:

$$G(s) = \dfrac{133}{s^2 + 25s}$$

The sampling time is 0.001 s. The discretization equation of the plant is after factoring disturbance is

$$x(k+1) = Ax(k) + B(u(k) + d(k))$$

where $A = \begin{bmatrix} 1 & 0.001 \\ 0 & 0.9753 \end{bmatrix}$, $B = \begin{bmatrix} 0.0001 \\ 0.1314 \end{bmatrix}$, $d(k)$ is disturbance, and $d(k) = 1.5\sin(2\pi t)$.

Let the desired command be $x_d(k) = \sin t$, and use the control law (4.10). Therefore, according to linear extrapolation method, we get $x_d(k+1) = 2x_d(k) - x_d(k-1)$. The controller parameters are $C^T = [15\ \ 1]$, $q = 0.80$, $g = 0.95$, $m = 0.01$, $\eta = C^T B \dfrac{m}{g} + 0.001$. The initial state vector is $[0.5\ \ 0]$. The simulation results are shown in Fig. 4.4 – Fig. 4.7.

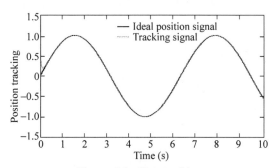

Figure 4.4 Sine tracking

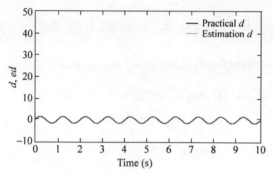

Figure 4.5 Observation of disturbance

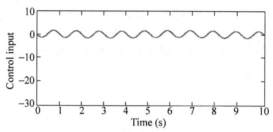

Figure 4.6 Control input

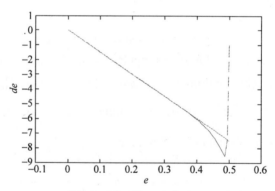

Figure 4.7 Phase trajectory

Simulation program:

chap4_2.m

```
%SMC controller based on decoupled disturbance compensator
clear all;
close all;

ts=0.001;
a=25;b=133;
sys=tf(b,[1,a,0]);
```

4 Discrete Sliding Mode Control

```
dsys=c2d(sys,ts,'z');
[num,den]=tfdata(dsys,'v');


A0=[0,1;0,-a];
B0=[0;b];
C0=[1,0];
D0=0;
%Change transfer function to discrete position xiteuation
[A1,B1,C1,D1]=c2dm(A0,B0,C0,D0,ts,'z');
A=A1;
B=B1;
c=15;
C=[c,1];
q=0.80;                %0<q<1
g=0.95;


m=0.010;               %m>abs(d(k+1)-d(k))

xite=C*B*m/g+0.0010;  %xite>abs(C*B*m/g);0<xite/fai<q<1

x_1=[0.5;0];
s_1=0;
u_1=0;
d_1=0;ed_1=0;
xd_1=0;xd_2=0;dxd_1=0;

for k=1:1:10000
time(k)=k*ts;

d(k)=1.5*sin(2*pi*k*ts);
d_1=d(k);

x=A*x_1+B*(u_1+d(k));

xd(k)=sin(k*ts);

    dxd(k)=(xd(k)-xd_1)/ts;
    dxd_1=(xd_1-xd_2)/ts;
    xd1(k)=2*xd(k)-xd_1; %Using Waitui method
    dxd1(k)=2*dxd(k)-dxd_1;
    Xd=[xd(k);dxd(k)];
    Xd1=[xd1(k);dxd1(k)];

    e(k)=x(1)-Xd(1);
    de(k)=x(2)-Xd(2);
    s(k)=C*(x-Xd);

    ed(k)=ed_1+inv(C*B)*g*(s(k)-q*s_1+xite*sign(s_1));

    u(k)=-ed(k)+inv(C*B)*(C*Xd1-C*A*x+q*s(k)-xite*sign(s(k)));
```

```
    xd_2=xd_1;xd_1=xd(k);
    dxd_1=dxd(k);

     ed_1=ed(k);
     x_1=x;
     s_1=s(k);

     x1(k)=x(1);
     x2(k)=x(2);
     u_1=u(k);
end
figure(1);
plot(time,xd,'k',time,x1,'r:','linewidth',2);
xlabel('time(s)');ylabel('Position tracking');
legend('Ideal position signal','tracking signal');
figure(2);
plot(time,d,'k',time,ed,'r:','linewidth',2);
xlabel('time(s)');ylabel('d,ed');
legend('Practical d','Estimation d');
figure(3);
plot(time,u,'r','linewidth',2);
xlabel('time(s)');ylabel('Control input');
figure(4);
plot(e,de,'b',e,-C(1)*e,'r');
xlabel('e');ylabel('de');
```

Reference

[1] Yongsoon Eun, Jung-Ho Kim, Kwangsoo Kim, Dong-ll Cho, Discrete-time variable structure controller with a decoupled disturbance compensator and its application to a CNC servomechanism, IEEE Transactions on Control Systems Technology, 1999, 7(4): 414 – 423

5 Dynamic Sliding Mode Control

Jinkun Liu
Beijing University of Aeronautics and Astronautics
P.R.China
E-mail: ljk@buaa.edu.cn

Xinhua Wang
National University of Singapore
Singapore
E-mail: wangxinhua04@gmail.com

Abstract This chapter introduces a kind of dynamic sliding mode controller design, stability analysis and simulation examples are given.

Keywords dynamic sliding mode control, stability analysis

5.1 Problem Statement

Dynamic sliding method is used to design a new switching function. Alternatively, it is used to construct a switching s in the normal sliding mode into a new switching function. The switching function is relative to the first-order or high-order derivative in the control input. Also, it can shift the discontinuous items into the first-order or high-order derivative in the control input[1]. Accordingly, a continuous dynamic sliding mode control rule is obtained and the chatting phenomenon can be reduced sufficiently.

5.2 Dynamic Sliding Mode Control Based on Dynamic Switching Functions

5.2.1 System Description

Consider a nonlinear system as under:

Advanced Sliding Mode Control for Mechanical Systems: Design, Analysis and MATLAB Simulation

$$\left.\begin{array}{l} \dot{x}_1 = x_2 \\ \dot{x}_2 = f(x) + g(x)u + d(t) \\ y = x_1 \end{array}\right\} \tag{5.1}$$

where $x = [x_1 \quad x_2]$, x_1 and x_2 are system states, y is output, $f(x)$ and $g(x)$ are the known smoothing functions, $d(t)$ is uncertain, and $|d(t)| \leqslant D_0$, $|\dot{d}(t)| \leqslant D$.

5.2.2 Design of Controller

Define the tracking error and the switching function as $e = y - y_d$ and $s = ce + \dot{e}$ respectively. Where $c > 0$ must be Hurwitz. Therefore,

$$\dot{s} = f(x) + g(x)u + d(t) - \ddot{y}_d + c\dot{e} \tag{5.2}$$

Construct a new dynamic switching function as

$$\sigma = \dot{s} + \lambda s \tag{5.3}$$

where $\lambda > 0$ must be Hurwitz.

When $\sigma = 0$, $\dot{s} + \lambda s = 0$ is a asymptotically stable, therefore, $e \to 0$ and $\dot{e} \to 0$. Stability analysis is given as follows: from Eq. (5.3), we have

$$\sigma = \dot{s} + \lambda s = f(x) + g(x)u + d(t) - \ddot{y}_d + c\dot{e} + \lambda s$$

Therefore,

$$\begin{aligned} \dot{\sigma} &= \dot{f}(x) + \dot{g}(x)u + g(x)\dot{u} + \dot{d}(t) - \dddot{y}_d + c\ddot{e} + \lambda \dot{s} \\ &= \dot{f}(x) + \dot{g}(x)u + g(x)\dot{u} + \dot{d}(t) - \dddot{y}_d + c(f(x) + g(x)u + d(t) - \ddot{y}_d) \\ &\quad + \lambda(f(x) + g(x)u + d(t) - \ddot{y}_d + c\dot{e}) \\ &= \dot{f}(x) - (c + \lambda)\dddot{y}_d - \dddot{y}_d + \dot{d}(t) + (c + \lambda)d(t) + (\dot{g}(x) + cg(x) + \lambda g(x))u \\ &\quad + (c + \lambda)f(x) + g(x)\dot{u} + \lambda c\dot{e} \end{aligned} \tag{5.4}$$

Select the dynamic controller as

$$\begin{aligned} \dot{u} = \frac{1}{g(x)}(&-\dot{f}(x) + (c + \lambda)\dddot{y}_d + \dddot{y}_d - (\dot{g}(x) + cg(x) \\ &+ \lambda g(x))u - (c + \lambda)f(x) - \lambda c\dot{e} - \eta \operatorname{sgn}(\sigma)) \end{aligned} \tag{5.5}$$

From Eqs. (5.5) and (5.4), we can get

$$\dot{\sigma} = \dot{d}(t) + (c + \lambda)d(t) - \eta \operatorname{sgn}(\sigma)$$

Let $\eta > D + (c + \lambda)D_0$, therefore,

$$\begin{aligned} \sigma\dot{\sigma} &= \sigma(\dot{d}(t) + (c + \lambda)d(t) - \eta \operatorname{sgn}(\sigma)) \\ &= \sigma(\dot{d}(t) + (c + \lambda)d(t)) - \eta|\sigma| \leqslant (D + (c + \lambda)D_0)\sigma - \eta|\sigma| < 0 \end{aligned}$$

5.2.3 Simulation Example

Consider the time-variant system below:

$$\dot{x}_1 = x_2$$
$$\dot{x}_2 = -25x_2 + 133u + 3\sin t$$

where $f(x) = -25x_2$, $g(x) = 133$, $d(t) = 3\sin t$.

Therefore, we have $D_0 = 3$, $D = 3$, $\dot{f}(x) = -25\dot{x}_2$, $\dot{g}(x) = 0$. Then $\eta > D + (c+\lambda)D_0 = 3 + (5+15) \times 3 = 63$.

Let the desired trajectory be $r = \sin t$, the tracking error is $e = x_1 - r$. Let $c = 5$, $\lambda = 15$, The initial state vector is $x(0) = [0.5 \quad 0]$. The controller is shown in Eq. (5.5), i.e.

$$\dot{u} = \frac{1}{g(x)}(-\dot{f}(x) + (c+\lambda)\ddot{y}_d + \dddot{y}_d - (c+\lambda)g(x)u - (c+\lambda)f(x) - \lambda c\dot{e} - \eta\,\text{sgn}(\sigma))$$

The simulation results are shown in Fig. 5.1 – Fig. 5.3.

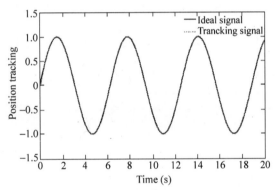

Figure 5.1 Position tracking

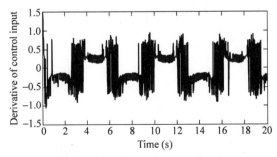

Figure 5.2 Dynamic controller $\dot{u}$

Advanced Sliding Mode Control for Mechanical Systems: Design, Analysis and MATLAB Simulation

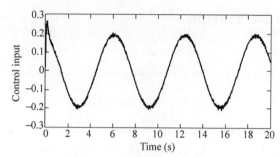

Figure 5.3 Actual controller u

Simulation programs:

(1) Main program: chap5_1sim.mdl

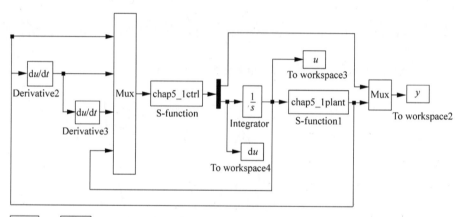

(2) S-function: chap5_1ctrl.m

```
function [sys,x0,str,ts] = spacemodel(t,x,u,flag)
switch flag,
case 0,
    [sys,x0,str,ts]=mdlInitializeSizes;
case 3,
    sys=mdlOutputs(t,x,u);
case {2,4,9}
    sys=[];
otherwise
    error(['Unhandled flag = ',num2str(flag)]);
end
function [sys,x0,str,ts]=mdlInitializeSizes
sizes = simsizes;
sizes.NumContStates  = 0;
sizes.NumDiscStates  = 0;
sizes.NumOutputs     = 2;
```

5 Dynamic Sliding Mode Control

```
sizes.NumInputs      = 4;
sizes.DirFeedthrough = 1;
sizes.NumSampleTimes = 0;
sys = simsizes(sizes);
x0  = [];
str = [];
ts  = [];
function sys=mdlOutputs(t,x,u)
x1=u(1);
dx1=u(2);
ddx1=u(3);
ut=u(4);

r=sin(t);
dr=cos(t);
ddr=-sin(t);
dddr=-cos(t);

e=x1-r;
de=dx1-dr;
dde=ddx1-ddr;

c=15;
s=c*e+de;

fx=-25*dx1;df=-25*ddx1;
gx=133;
nmn=15;

D0=3;D=3;
xite=D+(c+nmn)*D0+0.50;

ds=c*de+dde;
rou=ds+nmn*s;
du=1/gx*[-df+(c+nmn)*ddr+dddr-(c+nmn)*gx*ut-(c+nmn)*fx-nmn*c*de-xite*sign(
rou)];

sys(1)=r;
sys(2)=du;
```

(3) The program of the plant: chap5_1plant.m

```
function [sys,x0,str,ts]=s_function(t,x,u,flag)
switch flag,
case 0,
    [sys,x0,str,ts]=mdlInitializeSizes;
case 1,
    sys=mdlDerivatives(t,x,u);
case 3,
    sys=mdlOutputs(t,x,u);
case {2, 4, 9 }
    sys = [];
```

115

```
otherwise
    error(['Unhandled flag = ',num2str(flag)]);
end
function [sys,x0,str,ts]=mdlInitializeSizes
sizes = simsizes;
sizes.NumContStates  = 2;
sizes.NumDiscStates  = 0;
sizes.NumOutputs     = 1;
sizes.NumInputs      = 1;
sizes.DirFeedthrough = 0;
sizes.NumSampleTimes = 0;
sys=simsizes(sizes);
x0=[0,0];
str=[];
ts=[];
function sys=mdlDerivatives(t,x,u)
dt=3*sin(t);
sys(1)=x(2);
sys(2)=-25*x(2)+133*u+dt;
function sys=mdlOutputs(t,x,u)
sys(1)=x(1);
```

(4) Plot program: chap5_1plot.m

```
close all;

figure(1);
plot(t,y(:,1),'k',t,y(:,2),'r:','linewidth',2);
xlabel('time(s)');ylabel('Position tracking');
legend('ideal signal','tracking signal');

figure(2);
plot(t,du(:,1),'r','linewidth',2);
xlabel('time(s)');ylabel('Derivative of Control input');

figure(3);
plot(t,u,'r','linewidth',2);
xlabel('time(s)');ylabel('Control input');
```

Reference

[1] Ramirez HS, Santiago OL. Adaptive dynamical sliding mode control via backstepping, Proceedings of the 32th Conference on Decision and Control, San Antonia, Texas, December, 1992, 1422 – 1427

6 Adaptive Sliding Mode Control for Mechanical Systems

Jinkun Liu

Beijing University of Aeronautics and Astronautics

P.R.China

E-mail: ljk@buaa.edu.cn

Xinhua Wang

National University of Singapore

Singapore

E-mail: wangxinhua04@gmail.com

Abstract This chapter introduces a kind of adaptive sliding mode control for mechanical systems. stability analysis and simulation examples are given.

Keywords adaptive sliding mode control, mechanical systems, stability analysis

6.1 Adaptive Sliding Mode Control for Mechanical Systems

In this section, m is assumed unknown.

6.1.1 System Description

The uncertain mechanical system is described as

$$\frac{\mathrm{d}x_1}{\mathrm{d}t} = x_2 \tag{6.1}$$

$$m\frac{\mathrm{d}x_2}{\mathrm{d}t} = u(t) + \Delta \tag{6.2}$$

where x_1 and x_2 are the position and velocity respectively. m is the unknown moment inertia and a constant value. Δ is the uncertainty including matched and unmatched disturbances.

Let $\theta = m$, then, equation (6.2) can be written as

$$\theta \frac{dx_2}{dt} = u + \Delta \tag{6.3}$$

Assumption 1: The upper bound of the uncertain parameter θ is defined as:

$$\theta \in \Omega \overset{\text{def}}{=} \{\theta : 0 < \theta_{min} \leqslant \theta \leqslant \theta_{max}\} \tag{6.4}$$

Assumption 2: The uncertainty Δ is bounded, and

$$|\Delta| \leqslant D \tag{6.5}$$

6.1.2 Design of Adaptive Sliding Mode Controller

We select the sliding variable as

$$\left.\begin{array}{l} s = \dot{e} + ce = x_2 - q \\ q = \dot{x}_d - ce \end{array}\right\} \tag{6.6}$$

where $e = x_1 - x_d$ is the position tracking error and $c > 0$ must be Hurwitz. Therefore, we have $\dot{s} = \dot{x}_2 - \dot{q}$, the controller is selected as

$$u = u_a + u_{s1} + u_{s2} \tag{6.7}$$

where

$$u_a = \hat{\theta}\dot{q} \tag{6.8}$$

$$u_{s1} = -k_s s \tag{6.9}$$

$$u_{s2} = -\eta\,\mathrm{sgn}(s) \tag{6.10}$$

and $\hat{\theta}$ is estimation of θ, u_a is the adaptive compensation, u_{s1} is the feedback item, u_{s2} is the robustness item, and $k_s > 0$, $\eta > D$.

Therefore, controller Eq. (6.7) can be rewritten as

$$u = \hat{\theta}\dot{q} - k_s s - \eta\,\mathrm{sgn}(s)$$

Select the Lyapunov function as

$$V = \frac{1}{2}\theta s^2 + \frac{1}{2\gamma}\tilde{\theta}^2 \tag{6.11}$$

where $\tilde{\theta} = \hat{\theta} - \theta$, $\gamma > 0$.

Therefore, we get

6 Adaptive Sliding Mode Control for Mechanical Systems

$$\dot{V} = \theta s \dot{s} + \frac{1}{\gamma}\tilde{\theta}\dot{\tilde{\theta}} = s(\theta \dot{x}_2 - \theta \dot{q}) + \frac{1}{\gamma}\tilde{\theta}\dot{\tilde{\theta}}$$

Select the adaptive law as

$$\dot{\hat{\theta}} = -\gamma \dot{q}s \tag{6.12}$$

Therefore,

$$\dot{V} = s(u + \Delta - \theta \dot{q}) + \frac{1}{\gamma}\tilde{\theta}\dot{\tilde{\theta}}$$

$$= s(\hat{\theta}\dot{q} - k_s s - \eta\,\mathrm{sgn}(s) + \Delta - \theta\dot{q}) + \frac{1}{\gamma}\tilde{\theta}(-\gamma\dot{q}s)$$

$$= s(\tilde{\theta}\dot{q} - k_s s - \eta\,\mathrm{sgn}(s) + \Delta) - \tilde{\theta}(\dot{q}s)$$

$$= -k_s s^2 - \eta\,|s| + \Delta \cdot s < -k_s s^2 \leqslant 0$$

In order to avoid $\hat{\theta}$ which is too big to make $u(t)$ too big, we rewrite Eq. (6.12) by using the discontinuous projection mapping proposed in [1] as

$$\dot{\hat{\theta}} = \mathrm{Proj}_{\hat{\theta}}(-\gamma\dot{q}s) \tag{6.13}$$

$$\mathrm{Proj}_{\hat{\theta}}(\cdot) = \begin{cases} 0, & \text{if } \hat{\theta} = \theta_{max} \text{ and } \cdot > 0 \\ 0, & \text{if } \hat{\theta} = \theta_{min} \text{ and } \cdot < 0 \\ \cdot, & \text{otherwise} \end{cases}$$

6.1.3 Simulation Example

The plant is

$$\frac{\mathrm{d}x_1}{\mathrm{d}t} = x_2$$

$$m\frac{\mathrm{d}x_2}{\mathrm{d}t} = u(t) + \Delta$$

where $m = 1.0$, Δ is the friction model and denoted as $\Delta = 0.5\dot{\theta} + 1.5\mathrm{sign}(\dot{\theta})$.

The desired trajectory is selected as $\sin t$, and the range of the parameter θ is assumed as $\theta_{min} = 0.5$ and $\theta_{max} = 1.5$. Choosing $c = 15$, $k_s = 15$, $\gamma = 500$ and $\eta = D + 0.01 = 1.01$. The adaptive sliding mode controller (6.7) is adopted $(M=1)$. If the adaptive law is selected as Eq. (6.12) $(N=1)$, then the simulation results are shown in Fig. 6.1 – Fig. 6.3. If the adaptive law is selected as Eq. (6.13) $(N=2)$, then the simulation results are shown in Fig. 6.4 – Fig. 6.6. By adopting the improved adaptive law the range of θ can be limited and a too big $u(t)$ is avoided.

Advanced Sliding Mode Control for Mechanical Systems: Design, Analysis and MATLAB Simulation

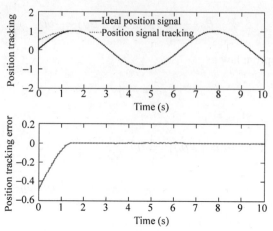

Figure 6.1 Position tracking based on adaptive law Eq. (6.12) (where $M=1, N=1$)

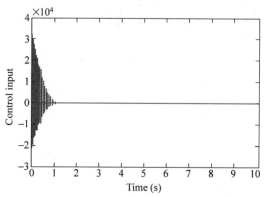

Figure 6.2 Control input based on adaptive law Eq. (6.12) (where $M=1, N=1$)

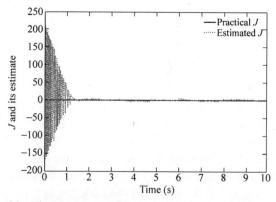

Figure 6.3 The parameter estimation based on adaptive law Eq. (6.12) (where $M=1, N=1$)

6 Adaptive Sliding Mode Control for Mechanical Systems

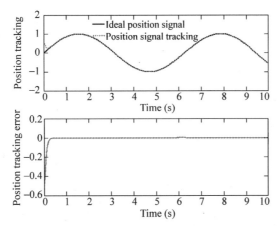

Figure 6.4 Position tracking based on adaptive law Eq. (6.13) (where $M=1, N=2$)

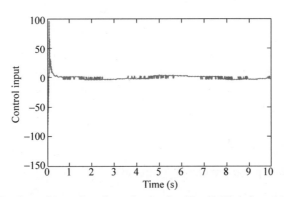

Figure 6.5 Control input based on adaptive law Eq. (6.13) (where $M=1, N=2$)

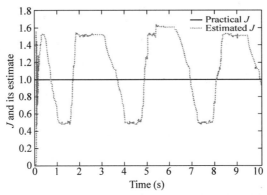

Figure 6.6 The parameter estimation based on adaptive law Eq. (6.13) (where $M=1, N=2$)

PD controller ($M=2$) is selected, and $k_p = 100$, $k_d = 50$. The simulation result is shown in Fig. 6.7. We can find that the flattop phenomenon happens and the high precise tracking performance can be obtained.

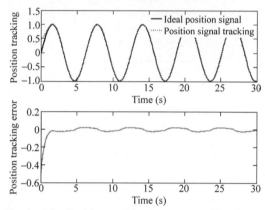

Figure 6.7 Position tracking by PD controller ($M=2$)

In the adaptive control simulation, the parameter estimation error isn't converged to zero for the latter case, the reason can be explained that the tracking error convergence can be achieved by many possible values of the estimated parameter $\hat{m}$, besides the true parameter m. Therefore, the parameter adaption law does not bother to find out the ture parameter m[5].

Simulation programs:

(1) Main Simulink program: chap6_1sim.mdl

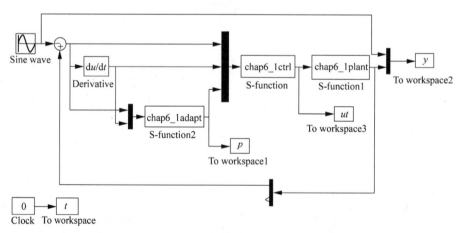

(2) Control law program: chap6_1ctrl.m

```
function [sys,x0,str,ts]=s_function(t,x,u,flag)
switch flag,
```

6 Adaptive Sliding Mode Control for Mechanical Systems

```
case 0,
    [sys,x0,str,ts]=mdlInitializeSizes;
case 3,
    sys=mdlOutputs(t,x,u);
case {1,2, 4, 9 }
    sys = [];
otherwise
    error(['Unhandled flag = ',num2str(flag)]);
end
function [sys,x0,str,ts]=mdlInitializeSizes
sizes = simsizes;
sizes.NumContStates  = 0;
sizes.NumDiscStates  = 0;
sizes.NumOutputs     = 1;
sizes.NumInputs      = 3;
sizes.DirFeedthrough = 1;
sizes.NumSampleTimes = 1;
sys=simsizes(sizes);
x0=[];
str=[];
ts=[0 0];
function sys=mdlOutputs(t,x,u)
e=u(1);
de=u(2);
dxd=cos(t);
ddxd=-sin(t);
thp=u(3);

c=15;
s=de+c*e;    %Sliding Mode
x2=dxd+de;
dq=ddxd-c*de;

ks=15;
xite=2.01;
ua=thp*dq;
us1=-ks*s;
us2=-xite*sign(s);

M=1;
if M==1  %DRC
    ut=ua+us1+us2;
elseif M==2  %PD
    kp=100;kd=50;
    ut=-kp*e-kd*de;
end

sys(1)=ut;
```

(3) Plant S-function：chap6_1plant.m

```
function [sys,x0,str,ts]=s_function(t,x,u,flag)
switch flag,
```

```
case 0,
    [sys,x0,str,ts]=mdlInitializeSizes;
case 1,
    sys=mdlDerivatives(t,x,u);
case 3,
    sys=mdlOutputs(t,x,u);
case {2, 4, 9 }
    sys = [];
otherwise
    error(['Unhandled flag = ',num2str(flag)]);
end
function [sys,x0,str,ts]=mdlInitializeSizes
sizes = simsizes;
sizes.NumContStates  = 2;
sizes.NumDiscStates  = 0;
sizes.NumOutputs     = 2;
sizes.NumInputs      = 1;
sizes.DirFeedthrough = 1;
sizes.NumSampleTimes = 0;
sys=simsizes(sizes);
x0=[0.5;0];
str=[];
ts=[];
function sys=mdlDerivatives(t,x,u)
m=1.0;
ut=u(1);

F=0.5*x(2)+1.5*sign(x(2));
sys(1)=x(2);
sys(2)=1/m*(ut-F);
function sys=mdlOutputs(t,x,u)
m=1.0;

sys(1)=x(1);
sys(2)=m;
```

(4) Adapt S-function of drc: chap6_1adapt.m

```
function [sys,x0,str,ts]=s_function(t,x,u,flag)
switch flag,
case 0,
    [sys,x0,str,ts]=mdlInitializeSizes;
case 1,
    sys=mdlDerivatives(t,x,u);
case 3,
    sys=mdlOutputs(t,x,u);
case {2, 4, 9 }
    sys = [];
otherwise
    error(['Unhandled flag = ',num2str(flag)]);
end
function [sys,x0,str,ts]=mdlInitializeSizes
sizes = simsizes;
```

6 Adaptive Sliding Mode Control for Mechanical Systems

```
sizes.NumContStates  = 1;
sizes.NumDiscStates  = 0;
sizes.NumOutputs     = 1;
sizes.NumInputs      = 2;
sizes.DirFeedthrough = 1;
sizes.NumSampleTimes = 0;
sys=simsizes(sizes);
x0=[0];
str=[];
ts=[];
function sys=mdlDerivatives(t,x,u)
e=u(1);
de=u(2);
dxd=cos(t);
ddxd=-sin(t);

x2=dxd+de;

c=15;
gama=500;

s=de+c*e;
thp=x(1);
dq=ddxd-c*de;

th_min=0.5;
th_max=1.5;

alaw=-gama*dq*s;   %Adaptive law

N=2;
if N==1        %Adaptive law
   sys(1)=alaw;
elseif N==2    %Adaptive law with Proj
   if thp>=th_max&alaw>0
       sys(1)=0;
   elseif thp<=th_min&alaw<0
       sys(1)=0;
   else
       sys(1)=alaw;
   end
end
function sys=mdlOutputs(t,x,u)
sys(1)=x(1);       %m estimate
```

(5) Plot program: chap6_1plot.m

```
close all;

figure(1);
subplot(211);
plot(t,y(:,1),'k',t,y(:,2),'r:','linewidth',2);
xlabel('time(s)');ylabel('Position tracking');
```

Advanced Sliding Mode Control for Mechanical Systems: Design, Analysis and MATLAB Simulation

```
legend('Ideal position signal','Position signal tracking');
subplot(212);
plot(t,y(:,1)-y(:,2),'r','linewidth',2);
xlabel('time(s)');ylabel('Position tracking error');

figure(2);
plot(t,ut(:,1),'r','linewidth',2);
xlabel('time(s)');ylabel('Control input');

figure(3);
plot(t,y(:,3),'k',t,p(:,1),'r:','linewidth',2);
xlabel('time(s)');ylabel('J and its estimate');
legend('Practical J','Estimated J');
```

6.2 Adaptive Sliding Mode Control of Inverted Pendulum

6.2.1 System Description

The kinetic equation of the inverted pendulum is given as follow:

$$\left.\begin{array}{l} \dot{x}_1 = x_2 \\ \dot{x}_2 = \dfrac{g \sin x_1 - m_p l x_2^2 \cos x_1 \sin x_1 /(m_c + m_p)}{l(4/3 - m_p \cos^2 x_1 /(m_c + m_p))} + \dfrac{\cos x_1 /(m_c + m_p)}{l(4/3 - m_p \cos^2 x_1 /(m_c + m_p))} u \end{array}\right\}$$

$$(6.14)$$

where x_1 and x_2 are the pendulum angle θ and pendulum speed $\dot{\theta}$ respectively, u is control input, m_c is the cart mass, m_p is the pendulum mass, and l is the half of pendulum length.

6.2.2 Control System Design

In order to realize the controller design for system (6.14) without modeling information, we arrange Eq. (6.14) by using the methods proposed by Ebrahim and Murphy[4] as follows:

$$l(4/3(m_c + m_p) - m_p \cos^2 x_1)\dot{x}_2 = g \sin x_1 (m_c + m_p) - m_p l x_2^2 \cos x_1 \sin x_1 + \cos x_1 u$$

and

$$l(4/3(m_c + m_p)\sec x_1 - m_p \cos x_1)\dot{x}_2 = g \tan x_1 (m_c + m_p) - m_p l x_2^2 \sin x_1 + u$$

6 Adaptive Sliding Mode Control for Mechanical Systems

Since $I = \dfrac{1}{3} m_{\mathrm{p}} l^2$, then $\dfrac{4}{3} l = \dfrac{I + m_{\mathrm{p}} l^2}{m_{\mathrm{p}} l}$ and

$$\left(\frac{I + m_{\mathrm{p}} l^2}{m_{\mathrm{p}} l} (m_{\mathrm{c}} + m_{\mathrm{p}}) \sec x_1 - m_{\mathrm{p}} l \cos x_1 \right) \dot{x}_2 = g \tan x_1 (m_{\mathrm{c}} + m_{\mathrm{p}}) - m_{\mathrm{p}} l x_2^2 \sin x_1 + u$$

$$(6.15)$$

In order to design controller without need model information, we choose[4]

$$\phi_1 = (m_{\mathrm{c}} + m_{\mathrm{p}}) \cdot \frac{(I + m_{\mathrm{p}} l^2)}{m_{\mathrm{p}} l}, \quad \phi_2 = (m_{\mathrm{c}} + m_{\mathrm{p}}) g, \quad \phi_3 = m_{\mathrm{p}} l$$

Considering outer disturbance, we transfer Eq. (6.15) to state equation as

$$\dot{x}_1 = x_2$$
$$g(x_1) \dot{x}_2 = u + \phi_2 \tan x_1 - \phi_3 x_2^2 \sin x_1 - dt$$

$$(6.16)$$

where $g(x_1) = \phi_1 \sec x_1 - \phi_3 \cos x_1$, dt is the outer disturbance.

Define θ_{d} as the ideal position signal and $e = x_1 - \theta_{\mathrm{d}}$ as the position tracking error. Then, the sliding function is $s = ce + \dot{e}$, $c > 0$.

The Lyapunov function is defined as

$$V = \frac{1}{2} g(x_1) s^2 + \frac{1}{2\gamma_1} (\phi_1 - \hat{\phi}_1)^2 + \frac{1}{2\gamma_2} (\phi_2 - \hat{\phi}_2)^2 + \frac{1}{2\gamma_3} (\phi_3 - \hat{\phi}_3)^2 \quad (6.17)$$

where $\gamma_i > 0$, $\hat{\phi}_i$ is estimation value of $\phi_i (i = 1, 2, 3)$.

Choose $V_1 = \dfrac{1}{2} g(x_1) s^2$, $V_2 = \dfrac{1}{2\gamma_1} (\phi_1 - \hat{\phi}_1)^2 + \dfrac{1}{2\gamma_2} (\phi_2 - \hat{\phi}_2)^2 + \dfrac{1}{2\gamma_3} (\phi_3 - \hat{\phi}_3)^2$, then

$$\dot{V}_1 = \frac{1}{2} \dot{g}(x_1) s^2 + g(x_1) s \dot{s}$$

$$\dot{V}_2 = -\frac{1}{\gamma_1} (\phi_1 - \hat{\phi}_1) \dot{\hat{\phi}}_1 - \frac{1}{\gamma_2} (\phi_2 - \hat{\phi}_2) \dot{\hat{\phi}}_2 - \frac{1}{\gamma_3} (\phi_3 - \hat{\phi}_3) \dot{\hat{\phi}}_3$$

where $\dot{g}(x_1) = \left(\phi_1 \sec x_1 \tan x_1 + \phi_3 \sin x_1 \right) x_2$,

$$g(x_1) s \dot{s} = g(x_1) s (c\dot{e} + \dot{x}_2 - \ddot{\theta}_{\mathrm{d}}) = s (g(x_1)(c\dot{e} - \ddot{\theta}_{\mathrm{d}})$$
$$+ (u + \phi_2 \tan x_1 - \phi_3 x_2^2 \sin x_1 - dt))$$

then

$$\dot{V}_1 = \frac{1}{2}(\phi_1 \sec x_1 \tan x_1 + \phi_3 \sin x_1)x_2 s^2 + s(g(x_1)(c\dot{e} - \ddot{\theta}_d)$$
$$+ (u + \phi_2 \tan x_1 - \phi_3 x_2^2 \sin x_1 - dt))$$
$$= \frac{1}{2}(\phi_1 \sec x_1 \tan x_1 + \phi_3 \sin x_1)x_2 s^2 + s((\phi_1 \sec x_1 - \phi_3 \cos x_1)(c\dot{e} - \ddot{\theta}_d)$$
$$+ (u + \phi_2 \tan x_1 - \phi_3 x_2^2 \sin x_1 - dt))$$
$$= \phi_1 \left(\frac{1}{2}x_2 s^2 \sec x_1 \tan x_1 + s \sec x_1 (c\dot{e} - \ddot{\theta}_d) \right) + \phi_2 (s \tan x_1)$$
$$+ \phi_3 \left(\frac{1}{2}x_2 s^2 \sin x_1 - sx_2^2 \sin x_1 - s \cos x_1 (c\dot{e} - \ddot{\theta}_d) \right) + s(u - dt)$$

The control law is defined as

$$u = -\eta \operatorname{sgn}(s) - \hat{\phi}_1 \left(\frac{1}{2}sx_2 \sec x_1 \tan x_1 + \sec x_1 (c\dot{e} - \ddot{\theta}_d) \right) - \hat{\phi}_2 \tan x_1$$
$$- \hat{\phi}_3 \left(\frac{1}{2}sx_2 \sin x_1 - x_2^2 \sin x_1 - \cos x_1 (c\dot{e} - \ddot{\theta}_d) \right) \tag{6.18}$$

where η is a constant and $\eta \geq \max |dt|$.

Substitute the control law Eq. (6.18) to $\dot{V}_1$, we have

$$\dot{V}_1 = -\eta |s| - sdt + (\phi_1 - \hat{\phi}_1) \left(\frac{1}{2}s^2 x_2 \sec x_1 \tan x_1 + s \sec x_1 (c\dot{e} - \ddot{\theta}_d) \right)$$
$$+ (\phi_2 - \hat{\phi}_2)(s \tan x_1) + (\phi_3 - \hat{\phi}_3) \left(\frac{1}{2}s^2 x_2 \sin x_1 - sx_2^2 \sin x_1 - s \cos x_1 (c\dot{e} - \ddot{\theta}_d) \right)$$

$$\dot{V} = \dot{V}_1 + \dot{V}_2 = -\eta |s| - sdt$$
$$+ (\phi_1 - \hat{\phi}_1) \left(\left(\frac{1}{2}s^2 x_2 \sec x_1 \tan x_1 + s \sec x_1 (c\dot{e} - \ddot{\theta}_d) \right) - \frac{1}{\gamma_1} \dot{\hat{\phi}}_1 \right)$$
$$+ (\phi_2 - \hat{\phi}_2) \left(s \tan x_1 - \frac{1}{\gamma_2} \dot{\hat{\phi}}_2 \right)$$
$$+ (\phi_3 - \hat{\phi}_3) \left(\left(\frac{1}{2}s^2 x_2 \sin x_1 - sx_2^2 \sin x_1 - s \cos x_1 (c\dot{e} - \ddot{\theta}_d) \right) - \frac{1}{\gamma_3} \dot{\hat{\phi}}_3 \right)$$

The adaptive law is designed as

128

$$\dot{\hat{\phi}}_1 = \gamma_1\left(\frac{1}{2}s^2 x_2 \sec x_1 \tan x_1 + s \sec x_1(c\dot{e} - \ddot{\theta}_d)\right)$$
$$\dot{\hat{\phi}}_2 = \gamma_2 s(\tan x_1) \qquad (6.19)$$
$$\dot{\hat{\phi}}_3 = \gamma_3\left(\frac{1}{2}s^2 x_2 \sin x_1 - sx_2^2 \sin x_1 - s\cos x_1(c\dot{e} - \ddot{\theta}_d)\right)$$

then

$$\dot{V} = -\eta|s| - sdt \leqslant 0$$

6.2.3 Simulation Example

Consider the dynamic Eq. (6.14), choose $g = 9.8 \text{ m/s}^2$, $m_c = 0.5 \text{ kg}$, $m_p = 0.5 \text{ kg}$, $l = 0.3 \text{ m}$, $dt = \sin t$. The desired trajectory is $\theta_d = 0.1 \sin t$.

Choose $c = 10$, and the initial states of the plant are $\theta(0) = 0.01$, $\omega(0) = 0$, the initial states of $\phi_i (i = 1, 2, 3)$ are $\phi_i(0) = 0$. Use the controller Eq. (6.18) and the adaptive law Eq. (6.19), and adapt saturation function instead of switch function in the controller, choose $c = 10$, $\Delta = 0.05$, $\gamma_1 = \gamma_2 = \gamma_3 = 150$. The simulation results are shown in Fig. 6.8–Fig. 6.10. It is seen that the tracking error converge to a very small value.

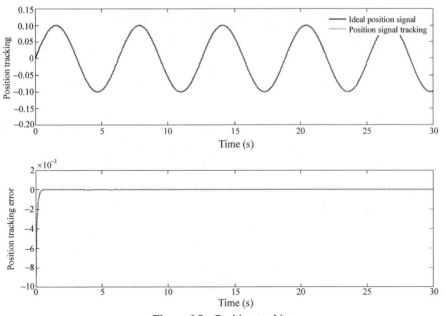

Figure 6.8 Position tracking

Advanced Sliding Mode Control for Mechanical Systems: Design, Analysis and MATLAB Simulation

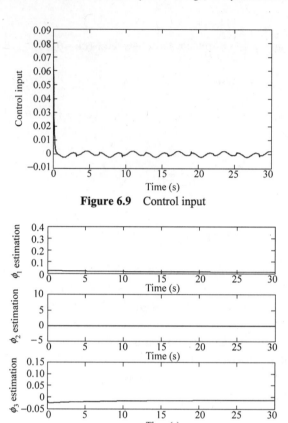

Figure 6.9 Control input

Figure 6.10 The parameters $\phi_i (i = 1, 2, 3)$ change

Simulation programs:

(1) Main Simulink program: chap6_2sim.mdl

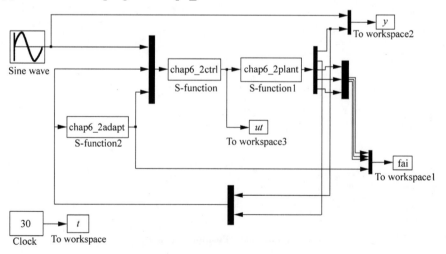

6 Adaptive Sliding Mode Control for Mechanical Systems

(2) Control law program: chap6_2ctrl.m

```
function [sys,x0,str,ts]=s_function(t,x,u,flag)
switch flag,
case 0,
    [sys,x0,str,ts]=mdlInitializeSizes;
case 3,
    sys=mdlOutputs(t,x,u);
case {1,2, 4, 9 }
    sys = [];
otherwise
    error(['Unhandled flag = ',num2str(flag)]);
end
function [sys,x0,str,ts]=mdlInitializeSizes
sizes = simsizes;
sizes.NumContStates  = 0;
sizes.NumDiscStates  = 0;
sizes.NumOutputs     = 1;
sizes.NumInputs      = 6;
sizes.DirFeedthrough = 1;
sizes.NumSampleTimes = 1;
sys=simsizes(sizes);
x0=[];
str=[];
ts=[0 0];
function sys=mdlOutputs(t,x,u)
thd=u(1);
dthd=0.1*cos(t);
ddthd=-0.1*sin(t);
x1=u(2);
x2=u(3);

fai1p=u(4);
fai2p=u(5);
fai3p=u(6);

e=x1-thd;
de=x2-dthd;
c=10;
s=c*e+de;

xite=1.0;

delta=0.05;
kk=1/delta;
if abs(s)>delta
    sats=sign(s);
else
    sats=kk*s;
```

```
end
    delta=0.05;
kk=1/delta;
if abs(s)>delta
   sats=sign(s);
else
    sats=kk*s;
end
%ut=-xite*sign(s)-fai1p*(0.5*s*x2*sec(x1)*tan(x1)+sec(x1)*(c*de-ddthd))
-fai2p*tan(x1)-fai3p*(0.5*s*x2*sin(x1)-x2^2*sin(x1)-cos(x1)*(c*de-ddthd));
ut=-xite*sats-fai1p*(0.5*s*x2*sec(x1)*tan(x1)+sec(x1)*(c*de-ddthd))-fai2p
*tan(x1)-fai3p*(0.5*s*x2*sin(x1)-x2^2*sin(x1)-cos(x1)*(c*de-ddthd));

sys(1)=ut;
```

(3) Plant S-function: chap6_2plant.m

```
function [sys,x0,str,ts]=s_function(t,x,u,flag)
switch flag,
case 0,
    [sys,x0,str,ts]=mdlInitializeSizes;
case 1,
    sys=mdlDerivatives(t,x,u);
case 3,
    sys=mdlOutputs(t,x,u);
case {2, 4, 9 }
    sys = [];
otherwise
    error(['Unhandled flag = ',num2str(flag)]);
end
function [sys,x0,str,ts]=mdlInitializeSizes
sizes = simsizes;
sizes.NumContStates  = 2;
sizes.NumDiscStates  = 0;
sizes.NumOutputs     = 5;
sizes.NumInputs      = 1;
sizes.DirFeedthrough = 1;
sizes.NumSampleTimes = 0;
sys=simsizes(sizes);
x0=[0.01;0];
str=[];
ts=[];
function sys=mdlDerivatives(t,x,u)
F=u(1);

mc=0.5;mp=0.5;
l=0.3;
I=0.006;
g=9.8;
```

6 Adaptive Sliding Mode Control for Mechanical Systems

```
fai1=(mc+mp)*(I+mp*l^2)/(mp*l);
fai2=(mc+mp)*g;
fai3=mp*l;


gx1=fai1*sec(x(1))-fai3*cos(x(1));


dt=1.0*sin(t);
sys(1)=x(2);
sys(2)=1/gx1*(u-dt+fai2*tan(x(1))-fai3*x(2)^2*sin(x(1)));
function sys=mdlOutputs(t,x,u)


mc=0.5;mp=0.5;
l=0.3;
I=1/3*mp*l^2;
g=9.8;


fai1=(mc+mp)*(I+mp*l^2)/(mp*l);
fai2=(mc+mp)*g;
fai3=mp*l;


sys(1)=x(1);
sys(2)=x(2);
sys(3)=fai1;
sys(4)=fai2;
sys(5)=fai3;
```

(4) Adaptive law S-function: chap6_2adapt.m

```
function [sys,x0,str,ts]=s_function(t,x,u,flag)
switch flag,
case 0,
    [sys,x0,str,ts]=mdlInitializeSizes;
case 1,
    sys=mdlDerivatives(t,x,u);
case 3,
    sys=mdlOutputs(t,x,u);
case {2, 4, 9 }
    sys = [];
otherwise
    error(['Unhandled flag = ',num2str(flag)]);
end
function [sys,x0,str,ts]=mdlInitializeSizes
sizes = simsizes;
sizes.NumContStates  = 3;
sizes.NumDiscStates  = 0;
sizes.NumOutputs     = 3;
sizes.NumInputs      = 2;
```

133

```matlab
sizes.DirFeedthrough = 1;
sizes.NumSampleTimes = 0;
sys=simsizes(sizes);
x0=[0 0 0];
str=[];
ts=[];
function sys=mdlDerivatives(t,x,u)
x1=u(1);
x2=u(2);

thd=0.1*sin(t);
dthd=0.1*cos(t);
ddthd=-0.1*sin(t);

e=x1-thd;
de=x2-dthd;
c=10;
s=c*e+de;

gama1=150;gama2=150;gama3=150;

sys(1)=gama1*(0.5*s^2*x2*sec(x1)*tan(x1)+s*sec(x1)*(c*de-ddthd));
sys(2)=gama2*s*tan(x1);
sys(3)=gama3*(0.5*s^2*x2*sin(x1)-s*x2^2*sin(x1)-s*cos(x1)*(c*de-ddthd));
function sys=mdlOutputs(t,x,u)
sys(1)=x(1);    %fai1
sys(2)=x(2);    %fai2
sys(3)=x(3);    %fai3
```

(5) Plot program: chap6_2plot.m

```matlab
close all;

figure(1);
subplot(211);
plot(t,y(:,1),'k',t,y(:,2),'r:','linewidth',2);
xlabel('time(s)');ylabel('Position tracking');
legend('Ideal position signal','Position signal tracking');
subplot(212);
plot(t,y(:,1)-y(:,2),'r','linewidth',2);
xlabel('time(s)');ylabel('Position tracking error');

figure(2);
plot(t,ut(:,1),'r','linewidth',2);
xlabel('time(s)');ylabel('Control input');

figure(3);
subplot(311);
```

6 Adaptive Sliding Mode Control for Mechanical Systems

```
plot(t,fai(:,1),'k',t,fai(:,4),'r','linewidth',2);
xlabel('time(s)');ylabel('fai1 estimation');
subplot(312);
plot(t,fai(:,2),'k',t,fai(:,5),'r','linewidth',2);
xlabel('time(s)');ylabel('fai2 estimation');
subplot(313);
plot(t,fai(:,3),'k',t,fai(:,6),'r','linewidth',2);
xlabel('time(s)');ylabel('fai3 estimation');
```

References

[1] Xu L, Yao B. Adaptive robust control of mechanical systems with non-linear dynamic friction compensation, International Journal of control, February 2008, 81(2): 167 – 176

[2] C.Canudas de Wit, Olsson H, Astrom KJ and Lischinsky P. A new model for control of systems with friction, IEEE Transaction on Automatic Control, 1995, 40: 419 – 425

[3] Tan Y and Kanellakopoulos I. Adaptive non-linear friction compensation with parametric uncertainties. Proc. of the American Control Conference, San Diego, 1999, 2511 – 2515

[4] Ebrahim A, Murphy GV. Adaptive backstepping controller design of an inverted pendulum, Proceedings of the Thirty-Seventh Southeastern Symposium on System Theory, 2005, 172 – 174

[5] Slotine JE, Li W. Applied Nonlinear Control. Prentice Hall, 1991

7 Terminal Sliding Mode Control

Jinkun Liu
Beijing University of Aeronautics and Astronautics
P.R.China
E-mail: ljk@buaa.edu.cn

Xinhua Wang
National University of Singapore
Singapore
E-mail: wangxinhua04@gmail.com

Abstract　This chapter introduces three kinds of terminal sliding mode controllers, including a typical terminal sliding mode controller, a nonsingular terminal sliding mode controller and a fast terminal sliding mode controller.

Keywords　typical terminal sliding mode controller, nonsingular terminal sliding mode controller, fast terminal sliding mode controller, stability analysis

7.1　Terminal Sliding Mode Control

Terminal sliding mode control adds nonlinear functions into the design of the sliding upper plane. Thus, a terminal sliding surface is constructed and the tracking errors on the sliding surface converge to zero in a finite time.

7.1.1　System Description

Consider the system as follows:

$$\left.\begin{aligned}\dot{x}_1 &= x_2 \\ \dot{x}_2 &= f(x) + g(x)u + d(t)\end{aligned}\right\} \tag{7.1}$$

where x_1 and x_2 are system states, $f(x)$ and $g(x)$ are the known nonlinear functions respectively, u is the control input, and $d(t)$ is the disturbance satisfied with

$$|d(t)| \leqslant D \tag{7.2}$$

7.1.2 Design of Terminal Sliding Mode Controller

In this section, we introduced a terminal sliding mode controller[1] proposed by Zhuang et al.

7.1.2.1 Design of Switch Plane

In order to make the states converge to the desired trajectories in a finite time the sliding variable proposed in[1] as:

$$\sigma = C(E - P) \tag{7.3}$$

where $C = [c \ \ 1]$, $c > 0$ must be Hurwitz, $E = [e \ \ \dot{e}]^T$, $P = [p(t) \ \ \dot{p}(t)]^T$, $e = x_1 - x_{1d}$ is the tracking error, and x_{1d} is the desired trajectory.

The design rule of $p(t)$ is: for $T > 0$, $p(t)$ has the upper boundless on $[0, T]$. In order to guarantee $\sigma(0) = 0$, let $E(0) = P(0)$, i.e. $p(0) = e(0)$, $\dot{p}(0) = \dot{e}(0)$; at the same time, we make $p(T) = 0$, $\dot{p}(T) = 0$ and $\ddot{p}(T) = 0$.

According to the above condition, Zhuang et al. designed $p(t)$ as

$$p(t) = \begin{cases} \sum_{k=0}^{2} \dfrac{1}{k!} e_i(0)^{(k)} t^k + \sum_{j=0}^{2} \left(\sum_{l=0}^{2} \dfrac{a_{jl}}{T^{j-l+3}} e_i(0)^{(l)} \right) \cdot t^{j+3}, & 0 \leqslant t \leqslant T \\ 0, & t > T \end{cases} \tag{7.4}$$

where a_{jl} is constant and can be obtained by solving the equations[1].

7.1.2.2 Design of Terminal Sliding Mode Controller

From Eq. (7.3), we get

$$\dot{\sigma} = C\dot{E} - C\dot{P} = C[\dot{e}, \ddot{e}]^T - C[\dot{p}, \ddot{p}]^T = c(\dot{e} - \dot{p}) + (\ddot{e} - \ddot{p})$$

i.e.

$$\dot{\sigma} = c(\dot{e} - \dot{p}) + f(x) + g(x)u + d(t) - \ddot{x}_d - \ddot{p}$$

Select the Lyapunov function as:

$$V = \frac{1}{2}\sigma^2 \tag{7.5}$$

The controller can be designed as:

$$u(t) = -\frac{1}{g(x)}(f(x) - \ddot{x}_d - \ddot{p} + c(\dot{e} - \dot{p}) + \eta \mathrm{sgn}(\sigma)) \tag{7.6}$$

where $\eta \geqslant D$. Therefore, we have

$$\dot{V} = \sigma\dot{\sigma} = \sigma(-\eta\mathrm{sgn}(\sigma) + d(t)) = -\eta|\sigma| + d(t)\sigma \leqslant 0$$

7 Terminal Sliding Mode Control

Remark1: From $p(0) = e(0)$, $\dot{p}(0) = \dot{e}(0)$ and Eq. (7.3), we have

$$\sigma(0) = CE(0) - W(0) = C(E(0) - P(0)) = 0$$

Therefore, in the initial state of the system on the sliding surface, the attaining phrase of the sliding mode control is removed and the global robustness of the closed-loop system is guaranteed.

Remark2: Because the global robustness can be guaranteed, i.e., $\sigma(t) = 0$, $E(t) = P(t)$. By selecting the sliding surface $P(T) = 0$, we can obtain $E(T) = 0$. Accordingly, the tracking error converges to zero in a finite time T.

Remark3: The switching function is substituted by the saturated function to reduce the chattering phenomenon.

7.1.3 The Solution of $p(t)$

For a second-order SISO system $i = 1$ and $j = 0,1,2$ the function $p(t)$ and its respective derivatives are as follows:

$$p(t) = e(0) + \dot{e}(0)t + \frac{1}{2}\ddot{e}(0)t^2 + \left(\frac{a_{00}}{T^3} e(0) + \frac{a_{01}}{T^2} \dot{e}(0) + \frac{a_{02}}{T} \ddot{e}(0) \right) t^3$$

$$+ \left(\frac{a_{10}}{T^4} e(0) + \frac{a_{11}}{T^3} \dot{e}(0) + \frac{a_{12}}{T^2} \ddot{e}(0) \right) t^4 + \left(\frac{a_{20}}{T^5} e(0) + \frac{a_{21}}{T^4} \dot{e}(0) + \frac{a_{22}}{T^3} \ddot{e}(0) \right) t^5$$

$$\dot{p}(t) = \dot{e}(0) + \ddot{e}(0)t + 3\left(\frac{a_{00}}{T^3} e(0) + \frac{a_{01}}{T^2} \dot{e}(0) + \frac{a_{02}}{T} \ddot{e}(0) \right) t^2$$

$$+ 4\left(\frac{a_{10}}{T^4} e(0) + \frac{a_{11}}{T^3} \dot{e}(0) + \frac{a_{12}}{T^2} \ddot{e}(0) \right) t^3 + 5\left(\frac{a_{20}}{T^5} e(0) + \frac{a_{21}}{T^4} \dot{e}(0) + \frac{a_{22}}{T^3} \ddot{e}(0) \right) t^4$$

$$\ddot{p}(t) = \ddot{e}(0) + 6\left(\frac{a_{00}}{T^3} e(0) + \frac{a_{01}}{T^2} \dot{e}(0) + \frac{a_{02}}{T} \ddot{e}(0) \right) t$$

$$+ 12\left(\frac{a_{10}}{T^4} e(0) + \frac{a_{11}}{T^3} \dot{e}(0) + \frac{a_{12}}{T^2} \ddot{e}(0) \right) t^2 + 20\left(\frac{a_{20}}{T^5} e(0) + \frac{a_{21}}{T^4} \dot{e}(0) + \frac{a_{22}}{T^3} \ddot{e}(0) \right) t^3$$

Because $p(T) = 0$, we have

$$p(T) = e(0) + \dot{e}(0)T + \frac{1}{2}\ddot{e}(0)T^2 + \left(\frac{a_{00}}{T^3} e(0) + \frac{a_{01}}{T^2} \dot{e}(0) + \frac{a_{02}}{T} \ddot{e}(0) \right) T^3$$

$$+ \left(\frac{a_{10}}{T^4} e(0) + \frac{a_{11}}{T^3} \dot{e}(0) + \frac{a_{12}}{T^2} \ddot{e}(0) \right) T^4 + \left(\frac{a_{20}}{T^5} e(0) + \frac{a_{21}}{T^4} \dot{e}(0) + \frac{a_{22}}{T^3} \ddot{e}(0) \right) T^5$$

$$= \left(1 + a_{00} + a_{10} + a_{20}\right)e(0) + \left(1 + a_{01} + a_{11} + a_{21}\right)\dot{e}(0)T$$
$$+ \left(\frac{1}{2} + a_{02} + a_{12} + a_{22}\right)\ddot{e}(0)T^2 = 0$$

Therefore, the conditions of $p(T) = 0$ are:

$$\left.\begin{array}{l} 1 + a_{00} + a_{10} + a_{20} = 0 \\ 1 + a_{01} + a_{11} + a_{21} = 0 \\ 0.5 + a_{02} + a_{12} + a_{22} = 0 \end{array}\right\} \tag{7.7}$$

At the same time, as $\dot{p}(T) = 0$, $\ddot{p}(T) = 0$, we have

$$\left.\begin{array}{l} 3a_{00} + 4a_{10} + 5a_{20} = 0 \\ 1 + 3a_{01} + 4a_{11} + 5a_{21} = 0 \\ 1 + 3a_{02} + 4a_{12} + 5a_{22} = 0 \end{array}\right\} \tag{7.8}$$

$$\left.\begin{array}{l} 6a_{00} + 12a_{10} + 20a_{20} = 0 \\ 6a_{01} + 12a_{11} + 20a_{21} = 0 \\ 1 + 6a_{02} + 12a_{12} + 20a_{22} = 0 \end{array}\right\} \tag{7.9}$$

From Eqs. (7.7) – (7.9), we can get:

$$\left\{\begin{array}{l} a_{00} + a_{10} + a_{20} = -1 \\ 3a_{00} + 4a_{10} + 5a_{20} = 0 \\ 6a_{00} + 12a_{10} + 20a_{20} = 0 \end{array}\right.$$

$$\left\{\begin{array}{l} a_{01} + a_{11} + a_{21} = -1 \\ 3a_{01} + 4a_{11} + 5a_{21} = -1 \\ 6a_{01} + 12a_{11} + 20a_{21} = 0 \end{array}\right.$$

$$\left\{\begin{array}{l} a_{02} + a_{12} + a_{22} = -0.5 \\ 3a_{02} + 4a_{12} + 5a_{22} = -1 \\ 6a_{02} + 12a_{12} + 20a_{22} = -1 \end{array}\right.$$

The above equations can be written as the following three forms respectively.

$$A_1 x_1 = B_1, \quad A_1 = \begin{bmatrix} 1 & 1 & 1 \\ 3 & 4 & 5 \\ 6 & 12 & 20 \end{bmatrix}, \quad B_1 = \begin{bmatrix} -1 \\ 0 \\ 0 \end{bmatrix}$$

7 Terminal Sliding Mode Control

$$A_2 x_2 = B_2, \quad A_2 = \begin{bmatrix} 1 & 1 & 1 \\ 3 & 4 & 5 \\ 6 & 12 & 20 \end{bmatrix}, \quad B_2 = \begin{bmatrix} -1 \\ -1 \\ 0 \end{bmatrix}$$

$$A_3 x_3 = B_3, \quad A_3 = \begin{bmatrix} 1 & 1 & 1 \\ 3 & 4 & 5 \\ 6 & 12 & 20 \end{bmatrix}, \quad B_3 = \begin{bmatrix} -0.5 \\ -1 \\ -1 \end{bmatrix}$$

Running the initializing sub-program chap7_1int.m, the solutions of the above equations are:

$$\begin{cases} a_{00} = -10 \\ a_{10} = 15 \\ a_{20} = -6 \end{cases} \quad \begin{cases} a_{01} = -6 \\ a_{11} = 8 \\ a_{21} = -3 \end{cases} \quad \begin{cases} a_{02} = -1.5 \\ a_{12} = 1.5 \\ a_{22} = -0.5 \end{cases}$$

Therefore, $p(t)$ can be written as:

$$p(t) = \begin{cases} e_0 + \dot{e}_0 t + \dfrac{1}{2}\ddot{e}_0 t^2 - \left(\dfrac{10}{T^3} e_0 + \dfrac{6}{T^2}\dot{e}_0 + \dfrac{3}{2T}\ddot{e}_0 \right) t^3 + \left(\dfrac{15}{T^4} e_0 + \dfrac{8}{T^3}\dot{e}_0 + \dfrac{3}{2T^2}\ddot{e}_0 \right) t^4 \\ \qquad - \left(\dfrac{6}{T^5} e_0 + \dfrac{3}{T^4}\dot{e}_0 + \dfrac{1}{2T^3}\ddot{e}_0 \right) t^5, \qquad 0 \leqslant t \leqslant T \\[2mm] 0, \hspace{7cm} t > T \end{cases}$$

$$(7.10)$$

From Eq. (7.10), we have $p(0) = e(0)$ and $\dot{p}(0) = \dot{e}(0)$.

7.1.4 Simulation Example: Terminal Sliding Mode Control for the Inverted Pendulum

The dynamic equation of the inverted pendulum is:

$$\begin{cases} \dot{x}_1 = x_2 \\ \dot{x}_2 = f(x) + g(x) \cdot u + d(t) \end{cases}$$

where $f(x) = \dfrac{g \sin x_1 - m l x_2^2 \cos x_1 \sin x_1 / (m_c + m)}{l(4/3 - m \cos^2 x_1 / (m_c + m))}$, $g(x) = \dfrac{\cos x_1 / (m_c + m)}{l(4/3 - m \cos^2 x_1 / (m_c + m))}$,

x_1 and x_2 are rolling angle and rolling rate respectively, $g = 9.8$ m/s^2, u is the control input.

141

The mass of vehicle is $m_c = 1$ kg, the mass of pendulum is $m = 0.1$ kg, half length of pendulum is $l = 0.5$ m, the disturbance is $d(t) = 3.0\sin(2\pi t)$. The desired trajectory is $x_d = \sin t$.

Select $C = (4\ 1)$, then, we have $\sigma = 4e + \dot{e} - 4p - \dot{p}$. Controller is shown in Eq. (7.6) and $p(t)$ is described in Eq. (7.10). In the simulation, the symbol function is adopted when $M=1$ and the saturated function is adopted when $M=2$. Let $\Delta = 0.05$, the system initial condition is $\begin{bmatrix} \dfrac{\pi}{60} & 0 \end{bmatrix}$, and $T = 1.0$. When $M=2$, simulation results are shown in Figs. 7.1 – 7.3. We can find that the tracking error keeps zero for $t \geq T$ and the chattering phenomenon can be reduced.

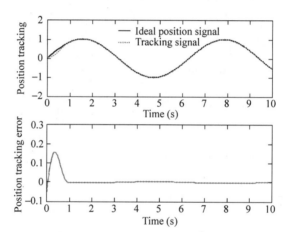

Figure 7.1 Position tracking ($T = 1.0$)

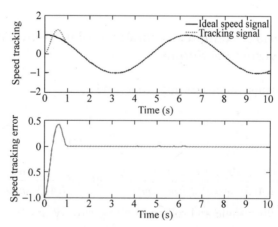

Figure 7.2 Velocity tracking ($T = 1.0$)

7 Terminal Sliding Mode Control

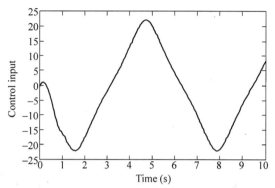

Figure 7.3 Control input ($T = 1.0$)

Simulation programs:

(1) Initialization program: chap7_1int.m

```
close all;
clear all;

A1=[1 1 1;3 4 5;6 12 20];
b1=[-1;0;0];
x1=A1\b1
A2=[1 1 1;3 4 5;6 12 20];
b2=[-1;-1;0];
x2=A2\b2
A3=[1 1 1;3 4 5;6 12 20];
b3=[-1/2;-1;-1];
x3=A3\b3
```

(2) Main program: chap7_1sim.mdl

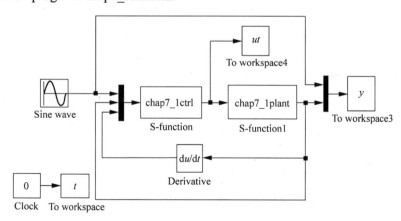

(3) S-function of controller: chap7_1ctrl.m

```
function [sys,x0,str,ts] = spacemodel(t,x,u,flag)
switch flag,
```

143

```
case 0,
    [sys,x0,str,ts]=mdlInitializeSizes;
case 3,
    sys=mdlOutputs(t,x,u);
case {2,4,9}
    sys=[];
otherwise
    error(['Unhandled flag = ',num2str(flag)]);
end
function [sys,x0,str,ts]=mdlInitializeSizes
sizes = simsizes;
sizes.NumContStates  = 0;
sizes.NumDiscStates  = 0;
sizes.NumOutputs     = 1;
sizes.NumInputs      = 5;
sizes.DirFeedthrough = 1;
sizes.NumSampleTimes = 1;
sys = simsizes(sizes);
x0  = [];
str = [];
ts  = [0 0];
function sys=mdlOutputs(t,x,u)
persistent e0 de0 dde0
T=1.0;

xd=u(1);dxd=cos(t);ddxd=-sin(t);
x1=u(2);x2=u(3);
dx1=u(4);dx2=u(5);

if t==0
   e0=x1;
   de0=x2-1;
   dde0=dx2;
end
e=x1-xd;
de=x2-dxd;

if t<=T
   A0=-10/T^3*e0-6/T^2*de0-1.5/T*dde0;
   A1=15/T^4*e0+8/T^3*de0+1.5/T^2*dde0;
   A2=-6/T^5*e0-3/T^4*de0-0.5/T^3*dde0;
   p=e0+de0*t+1/2*dde0*t^2+A0*t^3+A1*t^4+A2*t^5;
   dp=de0+dde0*t+A0*3*t^2+A1*4*t^3+A2*5*t^4;
   ddp=dde0+A0*3*2*t+A1*4*3*t^2+A2*5*4*t^3;
else
   p=0;dp=0;ddp=0;
end

c=15;
rou=(c*e+de)-(c*p+dp);
%%%%%%%%%%%%%%%%%%%%%%%%%%%%%%%%%%%%%%%%%
g=9.8;mc=1.0;m=0.1;l=0.5;
S=l*(4/3-m*(cos(x1))^2/(mc+m));
```

7 Terminal Sliding Mode Control

```
fx=g*sin(x1)-m*l*x2^2*cos(x1)*sin(x1)/(mc+m);
fx=fx/S;
gx=cos(x1)/(mc+m);
gx=gx/S;
%%%%%%%%%%%%%%%%%%%%%%%%%%%%%%%%%%%%%%%%%%
delta=0.05;
if abs(rou)>delta
    sat=sign(rou);
else
    sat=1/delta*rou;
end

xite=3.1;
M=2;
if M==1
    ut=-1/gx*(fx-ddxd-ddp+c*(de-dp)+xite*sign(rou));
elseif M==2
    ut=-1/gx*(fx-ddxd-ddp+c*(de-dp)+xite*sat);
end
sys(1)=ut;
```

(4) S-function of the plant: chap7_1plant.m

```
function [sys,x0,str,ts]=s_function(t,x,u,flag)
switch flag,
case 0,
    [sys,x0,str,ts]=mdlInitializeSizes;
case 1,
    sys=mdlDerivatives(t,x,u);
case 3,
    sys=mdlOutputs(t,x,u);
case {2, 4, 9 }
    sys = [];
otherwise
    error(['Unhandled flag = ',num2str(flag)]);
end
function [sys,x0,str,ts]=mdlInitializeSizes
sizes = simsizes;
sizes.NumContStates  = 2;
sizes.NumDiscStates  = 0;
sizes.NumOutputs     = 2;
sizes.NumInputs      = 1;
sizes.DirFeedthrough = 0;
sizes.NumSampleTimes = 0;
sys=simsizes(sizes);
x0=[pi/60 0];
str=[];
ts=[];
function sys=mdlDerivatives(t,x,u)
g=9.8;mc=1.0;m=0.1;l=0.5;
S=l*(4/3-m*(cos(x(1)))^2/(mc+m));
fx=g*sin(x(1))-m*l*x(2)^2*cos(x(1))*sin(x(1))/(mc+m);
fx=fx/S;
gx=cos(x(1))/(mc+m);
```

145

Advanced Sliding Mode Control for Mechanical Systems: Design, Analysis and MATLAB Simulation

```
gx=gx/S;
%%%%%%%%%
dt=3*sin(t);
%%%%%%%%%

sys(1)=x(2);
sys(2)=fx+gx*u+dt;
function sys=mdlOutputs(t,x,u)
sys(1)=x(1);
sys(2)=x(2);
```

(5) Plot program: chap7_1plot.m

```
close all;

figure(1);
subplot(211);
plot(t,y(:,1),'k',t,y(:,2),'r:','linewidth',2);
xlabel('time(s)');ylabel('Position tracking');
legend('Ideal position signal','tracking signal');
subplot(212);
plot(t,y(:,2)-y(:,1),'r','linewidth',2);
xlabel('time(s)');ylabel('Position tracking error');

figure(2);
subplot(211);
plot(t,cos(t),'k',t,y(:,3),'r:','linewidth',2);
xlabel('time(s)');ylabel('Speed tracking');
legend('Ideal speed signal','tracking signal');
subplot(212);
plot(t,y(:,3)-cos(t),'r','linewidth',2);
xlabel('time(s)');ylabel('Speed tracking error');

figure(3);
plot(t,ut,'r','linewidth',2);
xlabel('time(s)');ylabel('control input');
```

7.2 Nonsingular Terminal Sliding Mode Control

7.2.1 System Description

Consider the second-order uncertain nonlinear system as under:

$$\left.\begin{array}{l} \dot{x}_1 = x_2 \\ \dot{x}_2 = f(x) + g(x)u + d(x,t) \end{array}\right\} \tag{7.11}$$

where $x = [x_1 \ x_2]^{\mathrm{T}}$, x_1 and x_2 are system states, $g(x) \neq 0$, $d(x,t)$ is the uncertainty or disturbance, $|d(x,t)| \leqslant L$.

146

7.2.2 Normal Terminal Sliding Mode Control

7.2.2.1 Design of Controller

The sliding variable is selected as:

$$s = x_2 + \beta x_1^{q/p} \tag{7.12}$$

where $\beta > 0, p, q (p > q)$ are positive odd numbers.

The controller is designed as:

$$u = -g^{-1}(x)\left(f(x) + \beta \frac{q}{p} x_1^{q/p-1} x_2 + (L + \eta)\operatorname{sgn}(s) \right) \tag{7.13}$$

where $\eta > 0$.

Analysis of stability:

$$\dot{s} = \dot{x}_2 + \beta \frac{q}{p} x_1^{\frac{q}{p}-1} \dot{x}_1 = f(x) + g(x)u + d(x,t) + \beta \frac{q}{p} x_1^{\frac{q}{p}-1} \dot{x}_1$$

$$= f(x) + d(x,t) - f(x) - \beta \frac{q}{p} x_1^{\frac{q}{p}-1} x_2 - (l_g + \eta)\operatorname{sgn}(s) + \beta \frac{q}{p} x_1^{\frac{q}{p}-1} \dot{x}_1$$

$$= d(x,t) - (l_g + \eta)\operatorname{sgn}(s)$$

$$s\dot{s} = sd(x,t) - (L + \eta)|s| \leqslant -\eta|s|$$

From Eq. (7.12) we have $\dfrac{q}{p} - 1 < 0$. When $x_1 = 0$ and $x_2 \neq 0$ a singular problem exists for the normal terminal controller.

7.2.2.2 Finite-Time Analysis

Suppose the attaining time is t_r from $s(0) \neq 0$ to $s = 0$. When $t = t_r$, we have $s(t_r) = 0$.

When $s \geqslant 0$, from $s\dot{s} \leqslant -\eta|s|$, we can get

$$\dot{s} \leqslant -\eta$$

$$\int_{s=s(0)}^{s=s(t_r)} ds \leqslant \int_{t=0}^{t=t_r} -\eta dt$$

i.e.,

$$s(t_r) - s(0) \leqslant -\eta t_r$$

$$t_r \leqslant \frac{s(0)}{\eta}$$

At the same time, when $s \leqslant 0$, $t_r \leqslant -\dfrac{s(0)}{\eta}$, i.e.,

$$t_r \leqslant \frac{|s(0)|}{\eta} \tag{7.14}$$

Suppose the attaining time is t_s from $x_1(t_r) \neq 0$ to $x_1(t_s + t_r) = 0$. In this phase, $s = 0$, i.e.,

$$x_2 + \beta x_1^{q/p} = 0$$

$$\dot{x}_1 = -\beta x_1^{\frac{q}{p}}$$

Integrating the above differential equation, we have

$$\int_{x_1(t_r)}^{0} x_1^{-\frac{q}{p}} dx_1 = \int_{t_r}^{t_r + t_s} -\beta dt$$

$$-\frac{p}{p-q} x_1^{1-\frac{q}{p}}(t_r) = -\beta t_s$$

$$t_s = \frac{p}{\beta(p-q)} |x_1(t_r)|^{1-\frac{q}{p}} \tag{7.15}$$

7.2.3 Nonsingular Terminal Sliding Mode Control

A nonsingular terminal sliding mode control method is proposed by Feng et al.[2] to deal with the singular problem of normal terminal sliding mode control.

The nonsingular sliding variable is designed by Feng et al. as:

$$s = x_1 + \frac{1}{\beta} x_2^{p/q} \tag{7.16}$$

where $\beta > 0, p, q(p > q)$ are positive odd numbers[2].

The nonsingular sliding mode controller is designed by Feng et al. as:

$$u = -g^{-1}(x)\left(f(x) + \beta \frac{q}{p} x_2^{2-p/q} + (L + \eta)\mathrm{sgn}(s) \right) \tag{7.17}$$

where $1 < p/q < 2$, $\eta > 0$.
Analysis of stability

148

$$\dot{s} = \dot{x}_1 + \frac{1}{\beta}\frac{p}{q}x_2^{\frac{p}{q}-1}\dot{x}_2 = x_2 + \frac{1}{\beta}\frac{p}{q}x_2^{\frac{p}{q}-1}(f(x)+d(x,t)+g(x)u)$$

$$= x_2 + \frac{1}{\beta}\frac{p}{q}x_2^{\frac{p}{q}-1}\left(f(x)+d(x,t)-f(x)-\beta\frac{q}{p}x_2^{2-p/q}-(L+\eta)\operatorname{sgn}(s)\right)$$

$$= \frac{1}{\beta}\frac{p}{q}x_2^{\frac{p}{q}-1}(d(x,t)-(L+\eta)\operatorname{sgn}(s))$$

$$s\dot{s} = \frac{1}{\beta}\frac{p}{q}x_2^{\frac{p}{q}-1}(sd(x,t)-(L+\eta)|s|)$$

Because $1 < \dfrac{p}{q} < 2$, we have $0 < \dfrac{p}{q}-1 < 1$. Moreover, $\beta > 0, p, q(p > q)$ are positive odd numbers, therefore,

$$x_2^{\frac{p}{q}-1} > 0 \text{ (when } x_2 \neq 0\text{)}$$

$$s\dot{s} \leqslant \frac{1}{\beta}\frac{p}{q}x_2^{\frac{p}{q}-1}(-\eta|s|) = -\frac{1}{\beta}\frac{p}{q}x_2^{\frac{p}{q}-1}\eta|s| = -\eta'|s|$$

where $\eta' = \dfrac{1}{\beta}\dfrac{p}{q}x_2^{\frac{p}{q}-1}\eta > 0$ (when $x_2 \neq 0$).

We find that the Lyapunov condition is satisfied when $x_2 \neq 0$.
From Eqs. (7.17) and (7.11), we have

$$\dot{x}_2 = -\beta\frac{q}{p}x_2^{2-p/q} + d(x,t) - (L+\eta)\operatorname{sgn}(s)$$

When $x_2 = 0$, we get

$$\dot{x}_2 = d(x,t) - (L+\eta)\operatorname{sgn}(s)$$

When $s > 0$, $\dot{x}_2 \leqslant -\eta$; when $s < 0$, $\dot{x}_2 \geqslant -\eta$; when $x_2 = 0$, $s = 0$ can be obtained in a finite time.

7.2.4 Simulation Example

The kinetic equation of the single-stage inverted pendulum is:

$$\begin{cases} \dot{x}_1 = x_2 \\ \dot{x}_2 = f(x) + g(x)u + d(t) \end{cases}$$

where

$$f(x) = \frac{g\sin x_1 - mlx_2^2 \cos x_1 \sin x_1 / (m_c + m)}{l(4/3 - m\cos^2 x_1 / (m_c + m))}$$

$$g(x) = \frac{\cos x_1 / (m_c + m)}{l(4/3 - m\cos^2 x_1 / (m_c + m))}$$

x_1 and x_2 are the roll angle and roll rate respectively, $g = 9.8 \text{ m/s}^2$, u is the control input. $m_c = 1$ kg is the mass of the vehicle, $m = 0.1$ kg is the mass of the roll pole, $l = 0.5$ m is the haft length of the roll pole, and $d(t) = 3.0 \sin(2\pi t)$ is selected as the disturbance.

Let $q = 3, p = 5$, The sliding variables of NTSM and TSM are designed as:

$$s_{TSM} = x_2 + x_1^{3/5} \text{ and}$$

$$s_{NTSM} = x_1 + x_2^{5/3}.$$

The initial state vector is (0.1 0) and the parameters of the controller are $L = 5$, $\beta = 1.0$, $\eta = 0.20$. The controllers of TSM and NTSM in the programs are denoted as $M = 1$ and $M = 2$ respectively. The simulation results are shown in Figs. 7.4–7.9. The chattering phenomenon can be reduced effectively if sgn(s) is used in the controllers instead of the saturated functions.

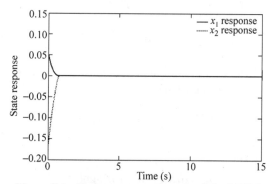

Figure 7.4 State response trajectories ($M = 1$:TSM)

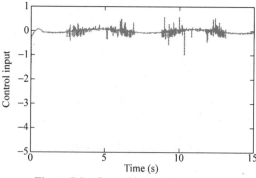

Figure 7.5 Control input ($M = 1$:TSM)

7 Terminal Sliding Mode Control

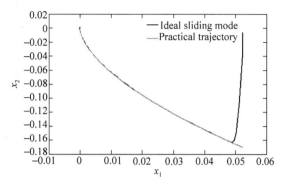

Figure 7.6 Phase trajectory ($M = 1$:TSM)

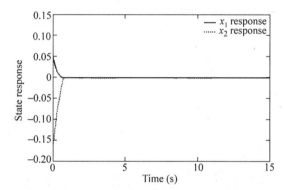

Figure 7.7 State response trajectories ($M = 2$:NTSM)

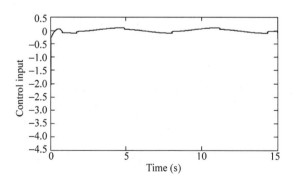

Figure 7.8 Control input ($M = 2$:NTSM)

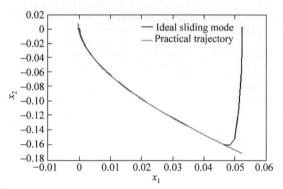

Figure 7.9 Phase trajectories ($M=2$:NTSM)

Simulation programs:

(1) Main program: chap7_2sim.mdl

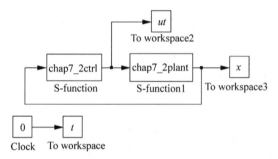

(2) S-function of control input: chap7_2ctrl.m

```
function [sys,x0,str,ts]=s_function(t,x,u,flag)
switch flag,
case 0,
    [sys,x0,str,ts]=mdlInitializeSizes;
case 3,
    sys=mdlOutputs(t,x,u);
case {2, 4, 9 }
    sys = [];
otherwise
    error(['Unhandled flag = ',num2str(flag)]);
end
function [sys,x0,str,ts]=mdlInitializeSizes
sizes = simsizes;
sizes.NumContStates  = 0;
sizes.NumDiscStates  = 0;
sizes.NumOutputs     = 1;
sizes.NumInputs      = 2;
sizes.DirFeedthrough = 1;
```

7 Terminal Sliding Mode Control

```
sizes.NumSampleTimes = 0;
sys=simsizes(sizes);
x0=[];
str=[];
ts=[];
function sys=mdlOutputs(t,x,u)
x1=u(1);x2=u(2);

g=9.8;mc=1.0;m=0.1;l=0.5;
S=l*(4/3-m*(cos(x1))^2/(mc+m));
fx=g*sin(x1)-m*l*x2^2*cos(x1)*sin(x1)/(mc+m);
fx=fx/S;
gx=cos(x1)/(mc+m);
gx=gx/S;

L=5;
beta=1.0;
xite=0.3;

q=3;p=5;

M=1;
if M==1        %TSM
   T1=abs(x1)^(q/p)*sign(x1);
   T2=abs(x1)^(q/p-1)*sign(x1);

   s=x2+beta*T1;
   delta=0.015;
   kk=1/delta;
    if abs(s)>delta
        sats=sign(s);
     else
        sats=kk*s;
     end
%  ut=-inv(gx)*(fx+beta*q/p*T2*x2+(L+xite)*sign(s));
   ut=-inv(gx)*(fx+beta*q/p*T2*x2+(L+xite)*sats);    %With saturation
elseif M==2   %NTSM
   T1=abs(x2)^(p/q)*sign(x2);
   T2=abs(x2)^(2-p/q)*sign(x2);
   s=x1+1/beta*T1;
   delta=0.015;
   kk=1/delta;
    if abs(s)>delta
        sats=sign(s);
     else
        sats=kk*s;
     end
%  ut=-inv(gx)*(fx+beta*q/p*T2+(L+xite)*sign(s));
   ut=-inv(gx)*(fx+beta*q/p*T2+(L+xite)*sats);   %With saturation
```

```
end
sys(1)=ut;
```

(3) S-function of the plant: chap7_2plant.m

```
function [sys,x0,str,ts]=s_function(t,x,u,flag)
switch flag,
case 0,
    [sys,x0,str,ts]=mdlInitializeSizes;
case 1,
    sys=mdlDerivatives(t,x,u);
case 3,
    sys=mdlOutputs(t,x,u);
case {2, 4, 9 }
    sys = [];
otherwise
    error(['Unhandled flag = ',num2str(flag)]);
end
function [sys,x0,str,ts]=mdlInitializeSizes
sizes = simsizes;
sizes.NumContStates  = 2;
sizes.NumDiscStates  = 0;
sizes.NumOutputs     = 2;
sizes.NumInputs      = 1;
sizes.DirFeedthrough = 0;
sizes.NumSampleTimes = 0;
sys=simsizes(sizes);
x0=[pi/60 0];
str=[];
ts=[];
function sys=mdlDerivatives(t,x,u)
g=9.8;mc=1.0;m=0.1;l=0.5;
S=l*(4/3-m*(cos(x(1)))^2/(mc+m));
fx=g*sin(x(1))-m*l*x(2)^2*cos(x(1))*sin(x(1))/(mc+m);
fx=fx/S;
gx=cos(x(1))/(mc+m);
gx=gx/S;
%%%%%%%%%
dt=0.1*sin(t);
%%%%%%%%%

sys(1)=x(2);
sys(2)=fx+gx*u+dt;
function sys=mdlOutputs(t,x,u)
sys(1)=x(1);
sys(2)=x(2);
```

(4) Plot program: chap7_2plot.m

```
close all;

figure(1);
```

7 Terminal Sliding Mode Control

```
plot(t,x(:,1),'k',t,x(:,2),'k:','linewidth',2);
xlabel('time(s)');ylabel('State response');
legend('x1 response','x2 response');

figure(2);
plot(t,ut(:,1),'r','linewidth',2);
xlabel('time(s)');ylabel('Control input');

figure(3);
M=1;
q=3;p=5;
if M==1      %TSM
plot(x(:,1),x(:,2),'k',x(:,1),-(abs(x(:,1))).^(q/p).*sign(x(:,1)),'r','lin
ewidth',2);
  legend('ideal sliding mode','practical trajectory');
  elseif M==2 %NTSM
plot(x(:,1),x(:,2),'k',x(:,1),(abs(-x(:,1))).^(q/p).*sign(-x(:,1)),'r','li
newidth',2);
  legend('ideal sliding mode','practical trajectory');
  end
xlabel('x1');ylabel('x2');
```

7.3 Fast Terminal Sliding Mode Control

Fast Terminal sliding mode control can make the system states converge to zero in a finite time. Asymptotical convergence of states under the normal sliding mode is overcome. The convergent characteristic of fast terminal sliding mode control is superior to that of the normal sliding mode control. Moreover, there is no switch function in terminal sliding mode control, therefore, the chattering phenomenon is evitable.

7.3.1 Design of Fast Terminal Sliding Mode Controller

7.3.1.1 Traditional Terminal Sliding Surface

A kind of fast terminal sliding surface was proposed by park et al. as follows:

$$s = \dot{x} + \beta x^{q/p} = 0 \tag{7.18}$$

where $x \in \mathbf{R}$ is the state, $\beta > 0, p, q(p > q)$ are positive odd numbers[3].
From Eq. (7.18), we have

$$\frac{\mathrm{d}x}{\mathrm{d}t} = -\beta x^{q/p}$$

155

i.e.,

$$dt = -\frac{1}{\beta}x^{-q/p}dx$$

Therefore,

$$\int_0^t dt = \int_{x_0}^0 -\frac{1}{\beta}x^{-q/p}dx$$

The time interval that the initial state $x(0) \neq 0$ takes to attain equilibrium $x = 0$ along the sliding surface Eq. (7.18) is:

$$t_s = \frac{p}{\beta(p-q)}|x(0)|^{(p-q)/p} \tag{7.19}$$

The equilibrium $x = 0$ is called as the terminal attractor. The convergent velocity increases as the nonlinear part $\beta x^{q/p}$ is introduced. However, the convergent time of the terminal sliding mode control may not be optimal. This is because the convergent velocity of nonlinear sliding surface Eq. (7.19) is slower than that of the linear one $(p = q)$ when the state approaches equilibrium. Therefore, a new global fast terminal sliding surface was presented in[3].

7.3.1.2 Global Fast Terminal Sliding Surface

Considering the linear and the terminal sliding surfaces a new global fast terminal sliding surface proposed by Park et al. as follows:

$$s = \dot{x} + \alpha x + \beta x^{q/p} = 0 \tag{7.20}$$

where $x \in \mathbf{R}$ is state, $\alpha, \beta > 0$, p and $q(p > q)$ are positive odd numbers[3].

The time interval that the initial state $x(0) \neq 0$ attains at $x = 0$ is:

$$t_s = \frac{p}{\alpha(p-q)}\ln\frac{\alpha x(0)^{(p-q)/p} + \beta}{\beta} \tag{7.21}$$

By designing α, β, p, q we can make the system state attain equilibrium in a finite time t_s. From Eq. (7.20), we have

$$\dot{x} = -\alpha x - \beta x^{q/p} \tag{7.22}$$

When the state x is far away from the origin, then, the convergent time is decided by the fast terminal attractor $\dot{x} = -\beta x^{q/p}$; when the state x approaches the origin $x = 0$, then, the convergent time is decided by the equation $\dot{x} = -\alpha x$. Exponentially, x converges to zero. Therefore, the terminal attractor is introduced in the sliding surface Eq. (7.20) and makes the state converge to zero in a finite time. Moreover, the speed of the linear sliding surface is guaranteed. Accordingly, the state can converge to equilibrium speedily and precisely. We call the sliding surface Eq. (7.20) as the global fast sliding surface.

7.3.2 Design of Global Fast Sliding Mode Controller

Consider a SISO second-order nonlinear system as follows:

$$\left.\begin{array}{l} \dot{x}_1 = x_2 \\ \dot{x}_2 = f(x) + g(x)u + d(t) \end{array}\right\} \tag{7.23}$$

where $x = [x_1 \quad x_2]$, x_1 and x_2 are system states, $f(x), g(x)$ are smooth functions, $g(x) \neq 0$, $d(t)$ denotes the uncertainties and $|d(t)| \leqslant L$ denotes the disturbances.

The fast sliding surface is selected as[3]:

$$s_1 = \dot{s}_0 + \alpha_0 s_0 + \beta_0 s_0^{q_0/p_0} \tag{7.24}$$

where $\alpha_0, \beta_0 > 0$, and $q_0, p_0 (q_0 < p_0)$ are positive odd numbers, $s_0 = x_1$.

The global fast sliding mode controller is designed as:

$$u(t) = -\frac{1}{g(x)}\left(f(x) + \alpha_0 \dot{s}_0 + \beta_0 \frac{\mathrm{d}}{\mathrm{d}t} s_0^{q_0/p_0} + \phi s_1 + \gamma s_1^{q/p} \right) \tag{7.25}$$

where $\gamma > 0$.

The Lyapunov function is selected as

$$V = \frac{1}{2}s_1^2$$

Because

$$\dot{s}_1 = \ddot{s}_0 + \alpha_0 \dot{s}_0 + \beta_0 \frac{\mathrm{d}}{\mathrm{d}t} s_0^{q_0/p_0} = f(x) + g(x)u + d(t) + \alpha_0 \dot{s}_0 + \beta_0 \frac{\mathrm{d}}{\mathrm{d}t} s_0^{q_0/p_0}$$

Equation (7.25) is introduced into the above equation, then, we have:

$$\dot{s}_1 = -\phi s_1 - \gamma s_1^{q/p} + d(t)$$

Therefore,

$$\dot{V} = s_1 \dot{s}_1 = -\phi s_1^2 - \gamma s_1^{(q+p)/p} + s_1 d(t) \tag{7.26}$$

We know that $(p+q)$ is an even number because $-\gamma s_1^{(q+p)/p} + s_1 d(t) \leqslant 0$ satisfied, i.e., $\gamma \geqslant \left|\frac{1}{s_1^{q/p}}\right| |d(t)|$ or $\gamma \geqslant \left|\frac{1}{s_1^{q/p}}\right| L$, therefore, we have $\dot{V} \leqslant 0$.

7.3.3 Design of Position Tracking Controller

Let the desired position command be x_d, and $s_0 = x_1 - x_d$, therefore, $\ddot{s}_0 = \ddot{x}_1 - \ddot{x}_d$. The position tracking controller is designed as:

$$u(t) = -\frac{1}{g(x)}\left(f(x) - \ddot{x}_d + \alpha_0 \dot{s}_0 + \beta_0 \frac{d}{dt} s_0^{q_0/p_0} + \phi s_1 + \gamma s_1^{q/p} \right) \qquad (7.27)$$

Because

$$\dot{s}_1 = \ddot{s}_0 + \alpha_0 \dot{s}_0 + \beta_0 \frac{d}{dt} s_0^{q_0/p_0} = f(x) + g(x)u + d(t) - \ddot{x}_d + \alpha_0 \dot{s}_0 + \beta_0 \frac{d}{dt} s_0^{q_0/p_0}$$

we have

$$\dot{s}_1 = -\phi s_1 - \gamma s_1^{q/p} + d(t)$$

The stability analysis is the same as that of Eq. (7.26).

7.3.4 Simulation Example

The kinetic equation of the single-stage inverted pendulum is:

$$\begin{cases} \dot{x}_1 = x_2 \\ \dot{x}_2 = f(x) + g(x) \cdot u + d(t) \end{cases}$$

where

$$f(x) = \frac{g \sin x_1 - mlx_2^2 \cos x_1 \sin x_1 /(m_c + m)}{l(4/3 - m\cos^2 x_1 /(m_c + m))}$$

$$g(x) = \frac{\cos x_1 /(m_c + m)}{l(4/3 - m\cos^2 x_1 /(m_c + m))}$$

x_1 and x_2 are the roll angular and roll rate respectively, $g = 9.8 \text{ m}/\text{s}^2$, u is the control input. $m_c = 1 \text{ kg}$ is the mass of the vehicle, $m = 0.1 \text{ kg}$ is the mass of the pendulum, $l = 0.5 \text{ m}$ is half of the pendulum, and $d(t) = 0.3 \sin t$ is the disturbance.

The desired position command is $x_d = 0.1\sin t$. The controller is given in Eq. (7.27), $L = 0.3$, the parameters of controller are $\alpha_0 = 2, \beta_0 = 1, \ p_0 = 9, \ q_0 = 5$, $\phi = 0.10, \ p = 3, q = 1, \ \gamma = \dfrac{L}{|s_1^{q/p}|} + \eta, \ \eta = 0.10$. The simulation results are shown in Figs. 7.10 and 7.11.

7 Terminal Sliding Mode Control

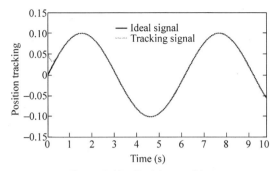

Figure 7.10 Position tracking

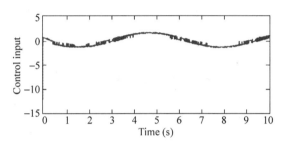

Figure 7.11 Control input

Simulation programs:

(1) Simulink main program: chap7_3sim.mdl

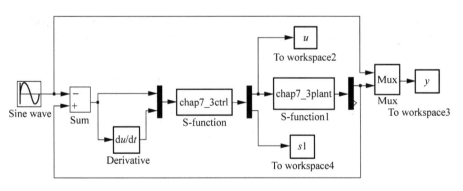

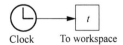

(2) S-function of controller: chap7_3ctrl.m

```
function [sys,x0,str,ts]=s_function(t,x,u,flag)
switch flag,
case 0,
```

159

```matlab
    [sys,x0,str,ts]=mdlInitializeSizes;
case 3,
    sys=mdlOutputs(t,x,u);
case {2, 4, 9 }
    sys = [];
otherwise
    error(['Unhandled flag = ',num2str(flag)]);
end
function [sys,x0,str,ts]=mdlInitializeSizes
sizes = simsizes;
sizes.NumContStates  = 0;
sizes.NumDiscStates  = 0;
sizes.NumOutputs     = 1;
sizes.NumInputs      = 2;
sizes.DirFeedthrough = 1;
sizes.NumSampleTimes = 0;
sys=simsizes(sizes);
x0=[];
str=[];
ts=[];
function sys=mdlOutputs(t,x,u)
x1=u(1);x2=u(2);

g=9.8;mc=1.0;m=0.1;l=0.5;
S=l*(4/3-m*(cos(x1))^2/(mc+m));
fx=g*sin(x1)-m*l*x2^2*cos(x1)*sin(x1)/(mc+m);
fx=fx/S;
gx=cos(x1)/(mc+m);
gx=gx/S;

L=5;
beta=1.0;
xite=0.3;

q=3;p=5;

M=1;
if M==1       %TSM
   T1=abs(x1)^(q/p)*sign(x1);
   T2=abs(x1)^(q/p-1)*sign(x1);

   s=x2+beta*T1;
   delta=0.015;
   kk=1/delta;
    if abs(s)>delta
        sats=sign(s);
    else
         sats=kk*s;
    end
%  ut=-inv(gx)*(fx+beta*q/p*T2*x2+(L+xite)*sign(s));
```

```
    ut=-inv(gx)*(fx+beta*q/p*T2*x2+(L+xite)*sats);   %With saturation
elseif M==2  %NTSM
   T1=abs(x2)^(p/q)*sign(x2);
   T2=abs(x2)^(2-p/q)*sign(x2);
   s=x1+1/beta*T1;
   delta=0.015;
   kk=1/delta;
    if abs(s)>delta
        sats=sign(s);
    else
         sats=kk*s;
    end
%  ut=-inv(gx)*(fx+beta*q/p*T2+(L+xite)*sign(s));
   ut=-inv(gx)*(fx+beta*q/p*T2+(L+xite)*sats);  %With saturation
end
sys(1)=ut;
```

(3) S-function of the plant: chap7_3plant.m

```
function [sys,x0,str,ts]=s_function(t,x,u,flag)
switch flag,
case 0,
    [sys,x0,str,ts]=mdlInitializeSizes;
case 1,
    sys=mdlDerivatives(t,x,u);
case 3,
    sys=mdlOutputs(t,x,u);
case {2, 4, 9 }
    sys = [];
otherwise
    error(['Unhandled flag = ',num2str(flag)]);
end
function [sys,x0,str,ts]=mdlInitializeSizes
sizes = simsizes;
sizes.NumContStates  = 2;
sizes.NumDiscStates  = 0;
sizes.NumOutputs     = 2;
sizes.NumInputs      = 1;
sizes.DirFeedthrough = 0;
sizes.NumSampleTimes = 0;
sys=simsizes(sizes);
x0=[pi/60 0];
str=[];
ts=[];
function sys=mdlDerivatives(t,x,u)
g=9.8;mc=1.0;m=0.1;l=0.5;
S=l*(4/3-m*(cos(x(1)))^2/(mc+m));
fx=g*sin(x(1))-m*l*x(2)^2*cos(x(1))*sin(x(1))/(mc+m);
fx=fx/S;
gx=cos(x(1))/(mc+m);
```

```
gx=gx/S;
%%%%%%%%
dt=0.1*sin(t);
%%%%%%%%

sys(1)=x(2);
sys(2)=fx+gx*u+dt;
function sys=mdlOutputs(t,x,u)
sys(1)=x(1);
sys(2)=x(2);
```

(4) Plot program: chap7_3plot.m

```
close all;

figure(1);
plot(t,x(:,1),'k',t,x(:,2),'k:','linewidth',2);
xlabel('time(s)');ylabel('State response');
legend('x1 response','x2 response');

figure(2);
plot(t,ut(:,1),'r','linewidth',2);
xlabel('time(s)');ylabel('Control input');

figure(3);
M=1;
q=3;p=5;
if M==1     %TSM
plot(x(:,1),x(:,2),'k',x(:,1),-(abs(x(:,1))).^(q/p).*sign(x(:,1)),'r','lin
ewidth',2);
 legend('ideal sliding mode','practical trajectory');
 elseif M==2  %NTSM
plot(x(:,1),x(:,2),'k',x(:,1),(abs(-x(:,1))).^(q/p).*sign(-x(:,1)),'r','li
newidth',2);
 legend('ideal sliding mode','practical trajectory');
 end
 xlabel('x1');ylabel('x2');
```

References

[1] Zhuang KY, Zhang KQ, Su HY, and Chu J. Terminal sliding mode control for high-order nonlinear dynamic systems. Journal of Zhejiang University, 2002,36(5):482−485

[2] Feng Y, Yu XH, Man ZH. Non-singular terminal sliding mode control of rigid manipulators, Automatica, 2002, 38: 2159−2167

[3] Park KB, Tsuiji T. Terminal sliding mode control of second-order nonlinear uncertain systems, International Journal of Robust and Nonlinear Control, 1999, 9 (11): 769−780

8 Sliding Mode Control Based on Observer

Jinkun Liu
Beijing University of Aeronautics and Astronautics
P.R.China
E-mail: ljk@buaa.edu.cn

Xinhua Wang
National University of Singapore
Singapore
E-mail: wangxinhua04@gmail.com

Abstract   This chapter introduces the sliding mode control based on several observers. Five kinds of observers are used, including high gain observer, extended state observer, integral-chain differentiator, disturbance observer and delayed output observer.

Keywords   sliding mode control, high gain observer, extended state observer, integral-chain differentiator, disturbance observer, delayed output observer

8.1   High-Gain Observer

8.1.1   High-Gain Observer Description

The high-gain observer is designed as

$$\left.\begin{aligned}
\dot{\hat{x}}_1 &= \hat{x}_2 - \frac{a_n}{\varepsilon}(\hat{x}_1 - v(t)) \\
\dot{\hat{x}}_2 &= \hat{x}_3 - \frac{a_{n-1}}{\varepsilon^2}(\hat{x}_1 - v(t)) \\
&\vdots \\
\dot{\hat{x}}_{n-1} &= \hat{x}_n - \frac{a_2}{\varepsilon^{n-1}}(\hat{x}_1 - v(t)) \\
\dot{\hat{x}}_n &= -\frac{a_1}{\varepsilon^n}(\hat{x}_1 - v(t))
\end{aligned}\right\} \tag{8.1}$$

where $[x_1 \; x_2 \; \cdots \; x_n]$ is the system state vector, $[\hat{x}_1 \; \hat{x}_2 \; \cdots \; \hat{x}_n]$ is the estimated system state vector, $v(t)$ is the measurement signal, $a_i(i=1,2,\cdots,n)$ is selected such that $s^n + a_n s^{n-1} + \cdots + a_2 s + a_1 = 0$ is a Hurwitz polynomial. By high-gain observer, the system states can be observed, i.e., Eq. (8.1) is satisfied with the following condition[1,2]:

$$\lim_{\varepsilon \to 0} x_i = v^{(i-1)}(t), \quad i=1,2,\cdots,n \tag{8.2}$$

8.1.2 Stability Analysis for Second-Order System

Consider the second-order system, x_1 is the measurement signal. The high-gain observer is designed as:

$$\left.\begin{aligned}\dot{\hat{x}}_1 &= \hat{x}_2 - \frac{a_2}{\varepsilon}(\hat{x}_1 - x_1) \\ \dot{\hat{x}}_2 &= -\frac{a_1}{\varepsilon^2}(\hat{x}_1 - x_1)\end{aligned}\right\} \tag{8.3}$$

where α_1 and α_2 are constants and make the real parts of the eigenvalues of the following equation negative:

$$s^2 + \alpha_1 s + \alpha_2 = 0 \tag{8.4}$$

The observing error is defined as:

$$\eta = [\eta_1 \quad \eta_2]^{\mathrm{T}}$$

where $\eta_1 = \dfrac{x_1 - \hat{x}_1}{\varepsilon^2}$, $\eta_2 = \dfrac{x_2 - \hat{x}_2}{\varepsilon}$.

Because

$$\varepsilon \dot{\eta}_1 = \frac{\dot{x}_1 - \dot{\hat{x}}_1}{\varepsilon} = \frac{1}{\varepsilon}\left(x_2 - \left(\hat{x}_2 - \frac{a_2}{\varepsilon}(\hat{x}_1 - x_1)\right)\right)$$

$$= \frac{1}{\varepsilon}\left(x_2 - \hat{x}_2 - \frac{\alpha_2}{\varepsilon}(x_1 - \hat{x}_1)\right) = -\frac{\alpha_2}{\varepsilon^2}(x_1 - \hat{x}_1) + \frac{1}{\varepsilon}(x_2 - \hat{x}_2) = -\alpha_2 \eta_1 + \eta_2$$

$$\varepsilon \dot{\eta}_2 = \varepsilon \frac{\dot{x}_2 - \dot{\hat{x}}_2}{\varepsilon} = \left(bu - \left(bu + \frac{\alpha_2}{\varepsilon^2}(x_1 - \hat{x}_1)\right)\right) = -\frac{\alpha_2}{\varepsilon^2}(x_1 - \hat{x}_1) = -\alpha_2 \eta_1$$

We can obtain the observing error equation as follow:

$$\varepsilon \dot{\eta} = \bar{A}\eta \tag{8.5}$$

8 Sliding Mode Control Based on Observer

where $\bar{A} = \begin{bmatrix} -\alpha_1 & 1 \\ -\alpha_2 & 0 \end{bmatrix}$, $\bar{B} = \begin{bmatrix} 0 \\ 1 \end{bmatrix}$.

The characteristic equation of matrix $\bar{A}$ is:

$$|\lambda I - \bar{A}| = \begin{vmatrix} \lambda + \alpha_1 & -1 \\ \alpha_2 & \lambda \end{vmatrix} = 0$$

Therefore,

$$(\lambda + \alpha_1)\lambda + \alpha_2 = 0$$

i.e.,

$$\lambda^2 + \alpha_1\lambda + \alpha_2 = 0 \tag{8.6}$$

The design of $\alpha_i (i = 1, 2)$: For equation $\lambda^2 + \alpha_1\lambda + \alpha_2 = 0$, in order to make the eigenvalues negative, $\lambda_1 = -1$ and $\lambda_2 = -2$ are selected, i.e. $(\lambda + 1)(\lambda + 2) = 0$, therefore, $\lambda^2 + 3\lambda + 2 = 0$. Finally we get $\alpha_1 = 3$, $\alpha_2 = 2$.

Because the negative real parts of equation roots are required in the design of observer, matrix $\bar{A}$ is Hurwitz. Based on stability theory, for the arbitrary given positive-definite matrix $Q \in \mathbf{R}^3$, the following Lyapunov equation

$$\bar{A}^\mathrm{T} P + P\bar{A} + Q = 0 \tag{8.7}$$

has a positive-definite symmetrical solution P.

For the observing error system (8.5), the following Lyapunov function is designed

$$V_\mathrm{o} = \varepsilon\eta^\mathrm{T} P\eta \tag{8.8}$$

Therefore,

$$\dot{V}_\mathrm{o} = \varepsilon\dot{\eta}^\mathrm{T} P\eta + \varepsilon\eta^\mathrm{T} P\dot{\eta} = (\bar{A}\eta)^\mathrm{T} P\eta + \eta^\mathrm{T} P(\bar{A}\eta)$$
$$= \eta^\mathrm{T} \bar{A}^\mathrm{T} P\eta + \eta^\mathrm{T} P\bar{A}\eta = \eta^\mathrm{T} (\bar{A}^\mathrm{T} P + P\bar{A})\eta \leqslant -\eta^\mathrm{T} Q\eta$$

Therefore, we get

$$\dot{V}_\mathrm{o} \leqslant -\lambda_{\min}(Q) \| \eta \|^2$$

where $\lambda_{\min}(Q)$ is the minimum eigenvalue of matrix Q.

Therefore, the convergence condition of $\dot{V}_\mathrm{o} \leqslant 0$ is

$$\| \eta \| \leqslant \frac{2\varepsilon L \| P\bar{B} \|}{\lambda_{\min}(Q)} \tag{8.9}$$

From the analysis above, we can find that the convergent velocity of the observing error η is related with parameter ε. In fact, when parameter ε is very small, from the singular perturbation, the error dynamic Eq. (8.5) is a rapid-variant sub-system. Moreover, the smaller ε is, the more rapid the convergent

165

velocity of η is. $\|\eta\|$ is $O(\varepsilon)$, and with ε decreasing, the observing error converges to zero.

8.1.3 Simulation Example

Consider the second-order system as follow:

$$\dot{x}_1 = x_2$$
$$\dot{x}_2 = -25x_2 + 133u - d(t)$$

where $d(t) = \text{sgn}(x_2)$, x_1 is the measurement signal.

Use the designed observer Eq. (8.3), and we choose $\alpha_1 = 6$, $\alpha_2 = 9$, $\varepsilon = 0.01$. The observed values of x_1 and x_2 are shown in Fig. 8.1.

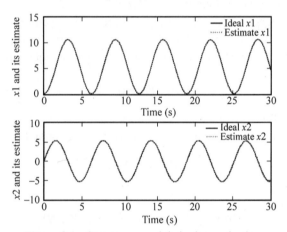

Figure 8.1 States x_1, x_2 and their observed values

Simulation programs:

(1) Main Simulink: chap8_1sim.mdl

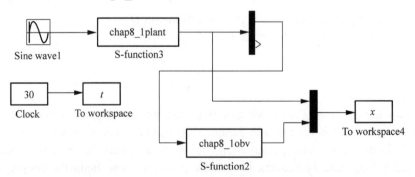

8 Sliding Mode Control Based on Observer

(2) High gain observer: chap8_1obv.m

```
function [sys,x0,str,ts]=s_function(t,x,u,flag)
switch flag,
case 0,
    [sys,x0,str,ts]=mdlInitializeSizes;
case 1,
    sys=mdlDerivatives(t,x,u);
case 3,
    sys=mdlOutputs(t,x,u);
case {2, 4, 9 }
    sys = [];
otherwise
    error(['Unhandled flag = ',num2str(flag)]);
end
function [sys,x0,str,ts]=mdlInitializeSizes
sizes = simsizes;
sizes.NumContStates  = 2;
sizes.NumDiscStates  = 0;
sizes.NumOutputs     = 2;
sizes.NumInputs      = 1;
sizes.DirFeedthrough = 1;
sizes.NumSampleTimes = 0;
sys=simsizes(sizes);
x0=[0 0];
str=[];
ts=[];
function sys=mdlDerivatives(t,x,u)
v=u(1);

alfa2=6;alfa1=9;
epc=0.01;

e=x(1)-v;

sys(1)=x(2)-alfa2/epc*e;
sys(2)=-alfa1/(epc^2)*e;
function sys=mdlOutputs(t,x,u)
sys(1)=x(1);
sys(2)=x(2);
```

(3) Plant program: chap8_1plant.m

```
function [sys,x0,str,ts]=s_function(t,x,u,flag)
switch flag,
case 0,
    [sys,x0,str,ts]=mdlInitializeSizes;
case 1,
    sys=mdlDerivatives(t,x,u);
case 3,
    sys=mdlOutputs(t,x,u);
case {2, 4, 9 }
    sys = [];
otherwise
    error(['Unhandled flag = ',num2str(flag)]);
```

```
end
function [sys,x0,str,ts]=mdlInitializeSizes
sizes = simsizes;
sizes.NumContStates  = 2;
sizes.NumDiscStates  = 0;
sizes.NumOutputs     = 2;
sizes.NumInputs      = 1;
sizes.DirFeedthrough = 0;
sizes.NumSampleTimes = 0;
sys=simsizes(sizes);
x0=[0.05;0];
str=[];
ts=[];
function sys=mdlDerivatives(t,x,u)
a=25;
b=133;
ut=u(1);

dt=1*sign(x(2));
f=-a*x(2)-dt;

sys(1)=x(2);
sys(2)=f+b*ut;
function sys=mdlOutputs(t,x,u)
sys(1)=x(1);
sys(2)=x(2);
```

(4) Plot program: chap8_1plot.m

```
close all;

figure(1);
subplot(211);
plot(t,x(:,1),'k',t,x(:,3),'r:','linewidth',2);
xlabel('time(s)');ylabel('x1 and its estimate');
legend('ideal x1','estimate x1');

subplot(212);
plot(t,x(:,2),'k',t,x(:,4),'r:','linewidth',2);
xlabel('time(s)');ylabel('x2 and its estimate');
legend('ideal x2','estimate x2');
```

8.2　Sliding Mode Control Based on High Gain Observer

8.2.1　System Description

Consider the plant as

$$\ddot{\theta} = bu(t) + f(t) \tag{8.10}$$

where θ and $\dot{\theta}$ are position signal and speed signal respectively, $u(t)$ is control

8 Sliding Mode Control Based on Observer

input, $\dot{\theta}$ is unknown, and $f(t)$ is uncertain and bounded, $|f(t)| \leqslant l_f$, l_f is a positive constant.

Let $x_1 = \theta, x_2 = \dot{\theta}$, then we have

$$\left.\begin{array}{l} \dot{x}_1 = x_2 \\ \dot{x}_2 = f(t) + bu(t) \end{array}\right\} \tag{8.11}$$

The designed extended observer is

$$\left.\begin{array}{l} \dot{\hat{x}}_1 = \hat{x}_2 - \dfrac{k_1}{\varepsilon}(\hat{x}_1 - \theta) \\ \dot{\hat{x}}_2 = -\dfrac{k_2}{\varepsilon^2}(\hat{x}_1 - \theta) \end{array}\right\} \tag{8.12}$$

Therefore, we have

$$\lim_{\varepsilon \to 0} \hat{x}_1 = x_1, \quad \lim_{\varepsilon \to 0} \hat{x}_2 = x_2$$

8.2.2 Controller Design

Let r denote the desired trajectory and $e_1 = x_1 - r, e_2 = x_2 - \dot{r}$. Therefore, the error system is

$$\left.\begin{array}{l} \dot{e}_1 = e_2 \\ \dot{e}_2 = f(t) - \ddot{r} + bu(t) \end{array}\right\} \tag{8.13}$$

Denote the sliding mode variable as $s = e_2 + ce_1$, where $c > 0$ is a positive constant. Moreover, denote the observing sliding mode variable as $\hat{s} = \hat{e}_2 + c\hat{e}_1$, where $\hat{e}_1 = \hat{x}_1 - r, \hat{e}_2 = \hat{x}_2 - \dot{r}$. Therefore, we have

$$\dot{s} = \dot{e}_2 + c\dot{e}_1 = f(t) - \ddot{r} + bu(t) + ce_2$$

Let the Lyapunov function be

$$V = \frac{1}{2}s^2$$

Therefore, we have

$$\dot{V} = s\dot{s} = s(f(t) - \ddot{r} + bu(t) + ce_2)$$

Select the controller as

$$u = \frac{1}{b}(\ddot{r} - c\hat{e}_2 - l\operatorname{sgn}(\hat{s})) \tag{8.14}$$

where $l > l_f > 0$.
Then

$$\dot{V} = s\left(f(t) - \ddot{r} + b\frac{1}{b}(\ddot{r} - c\hat{e}_2 - l\operatorname{sgn}(\hat{s})) + ce_2 \right)$$

$$\begin{aligned}
&= s(-l\,\mathrm{sgn}(\hat{s}) + f(t) + c(e_2 - \hat{e}_2)) \\
&= -(\hat{s} + s - \hat{s})l\,\mathrm{sgn}(\hat{s}) + (\hat{s} + s - \hat{s})f(t) + (\hat{s} + s - \hat{s})c(e_2 - \hat{e}_2) \\
&\leqslant -\hat{s}l\,\mathrm{sgn}(\hat{s}) + l\,|s - \hat{s}| + (|f(t)| + c\,|e_2 - \hat{e}_2|)|\hat{s}| + |s - \hat{s}|(|f(t)| + c\,|e_2 - \hat{e}_2|) \\
&= -l\,|\hat{s}| + l\,|s - \hat{s}| + (|f(t)| + c\,|x_2 - \hat{x}_2|)|\hat{s}| + |s - \hat{s}|(|f(t)| + c\,|x_2 - \hat{x}_2|) \\
&\leqslant -l\,|\hat{s}| + (l_f + c\,|x_2 - \hat{x}_2|)|\hat{s}| + |s - \hat{s}|(l + l_f + c\,|x_2 - \hat{x}_2|)
\end{aligned}$$

Because of the convergence of the extended observer we have

$$|x_2 - \hat{x}_2| \text{ and } |s - \hat{s}|$$

are bounded and sufficiently small, therefore, $|s - \hat{s}|(l + l_f + c\,|x_2 - \hat{x}_2|)$ is sufficiently small, then We have that $\dot{V} < 0$.

8.2.3 Simulation Example

Consider a servo system as follows

$$J\ddot{\theta} = u(t) - d(t)$$

where J represents equivalent inertia, u represents control input signal, $d(t)$ represents total uncertainties, which include equivalent friction force and disturbance, and θ represents angle.

In this simulation, we choose $d(t) = 5\sin t$. For the plant equation, we assume $J = 10 \mathrm{N} \cdot \mathrm{ms}^2/\mathrm{rad}$.

We assume the ideal signal is $\theta_d = \sin t$. Use the designed control law Eq. (8.14) with the proposed observer Eq. (8.12), and we choose $c = 50$, $k_1 = 3$, $k_2 = 2$, $\varepsilon = 0.01$, $l = 1.5$. The observed values of position signal, speed signal are shown in Fig. 8.2, the position tracking, speed tracking are shown in Fig. 8.3. From the results, we can see that good position tracking performance, speed signal can be estimated.

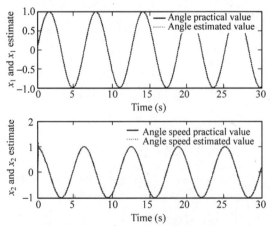

Figure 8.2 θ, $\dot{\theta}$ and their observed values

8 Sliding Mode Control Based on Observer

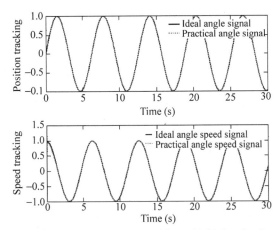

Figure 8.3 Position and speed tracking with high gain observer

Matlab programs:

(1) Main Simulink: chap8_2sim.mdl

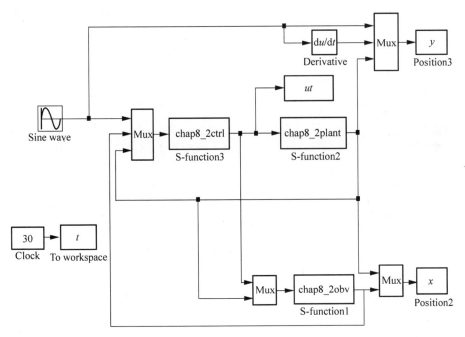

(2) Sliding mode control: chap8_2ctrl.m

```
function [sys,x0,str,ts]=s_function(t,x,u,flag)
switch flag,
case 0,
    [sys,x0,str,ts]=mdlInitializeSizes;
case 3,
```

```
    sys=mdlOutputs(t,x,u);
case {1,2, 4, 9 }
    sys = [];
otherwise
    error(['Unhandled flag = ',num2str(flag)]);
end
function [sys,x0,str,ts]=mdlInitializeSizes
sizes = simsizes;
sizes.NumContStates  = 0;
sizes.NumDiscStates  = 0;
sizes.NumOutputs     = 1;
sizes.NumInputs      = 5;
sizes.DirFeedthrough = 1;
sizes.NumSampleTimes = 0;
sys=simsizes(sizes);
x0=[];
str=[];
ts=[];
function sys=mdlOutputs(t,x,u)
r=u(1);
x1p=u(2);x2p=u(3);
x1=u(4);x2=u(5);

dr=cos(t);
ddr=-sin(t);

J=10;b=1/J;

c=50;
e1p=x1p-r;
e2p=x2p-dr;
sp=e2p+c*e1p;

delta=0.15;
kk=1/delta;
if sp>delta
    sat_sp=1;
elseif abs(sp)<=delta
    sat_sp=kk*sp;
elseif sp<-delta
    sat_sp=-1;
end

M=2;
l=1.50;    %l>=5/10;
if M==1
    ut=1/b*(ddr-c*e2p-l*sign(sp));
elseif M==2
    ut=1/b*(ddr-c*e2p-l*sat_sp);
```

```
end
sys(1)=ut;
```

(3) Plant program: chap8_2plant.m

```
function [sys,x0,str,ts]=s_function(t,x,u,flag)
switch flag,
case 0,
    [sys,x0,str,ts]=mdlInitializeSizes;
case 1,
    sys=mdlDerivatives(t,x,u);
case 3,
    sys=mdlOutputs(t,x,u);
case {2, 4, 9 }
    sys = [];
otherwise
    error(['Unhandled flag = ',num2str(flag)]);
end
function [sys,x0,str,ts]=mdlInitializeSizes
sizes = simsizes;
sizes.NumContStates  = 2;
sizes.NumDiscStates  = 0;
sizes.NumOutputs     = 2;
sizes.NumInputs      = 1;
sizes.DirFeedthrough = 0;
sizes.NumSampleTimes = 0;
sys=simsizes(sizes);
x0=[0.1;0];
str=[];
ts=[];
function sys=mdlDerivatives(t,x,u)
J=10;
ut=u(1);
d=5.0*sin(t);
sys(1)=x(2);
sys(2)=1/J*(ut-d);
function sys=mdlOutputs(t,x,u)
sys(1)=x(1);
sys(2)=x(2);
```

(4) Plot program: chap8_2plot.m

```
close all;

figure(1);
subplot(211);
plot(t,y(:,1),'k',t,y(:,3),'r:','linewidth',2);
xlabel('time(s)');ylabel('Position tracking');
legend('ideal angle signal','practical angle signal');
subplot(212);
plot(t,y(:,2),'k',t,y(:,4),'r:','linewidth',2);
```

```
xlabel('time(s)');ylabel('speed tracking');
legend('ideal angle speed signal','practical angle speed signal');

figure(2);
plot(t,ut(:,1),'k','linewidth',2);
xlabel('time(s)');ylabel('control input');
```

(5) Observer Plot program:chap8_2obv_plot

```
close all;
figure(1);
subplot(211);
plot(t,x(:,1),'k',t,x(:,3),'r:','linewidth',2);
xlabel('time(s)');ylabel('x1 and x1 estimate');
legend('angle practical value','angle estimated value');
subplot(212);
plot(t,x(:,2),'k',t,x(:,4),'r:','linewidth',2);
xlabel('time(s)');ylabel('x2 and x2 estimate');
legend('angle speed practical value','angle speed estimated value');
```

8.3 Extended State Observer Design

8.3.1 System Description

A classical servo system can be described as follows:

$$J\ddot{\theta} = u(t) - d(t) \tag{8.15}$$

where J is the moment of inertia, u is control input, θ represents practical position, $J > 0$, $d(t)$ represents disturbance.

The Eq. (8.15) can also be expressed as

$$\ddot{\theta} = bu(t) + f(t) \tag{8.16}$$

where $b = \dfrac{1}{J}$, $f(t) = -\dfrac{1}{J}d(t)$, the derivative of $f(\cdot)$ exits and is limited.

Equation (8.16) can be expressed as

$$\dot{x} = Ax + B(bu + f(t)) \tag{8.17}$$

$$y = Cx \tag{8.18}$$

where $x = \begin{bmatrix} x_1 \\ x_2 \end{bmatrix} = \begin{bmatrix} \theta \\ \dot{\theta} \end{bmatrix}$, $A = \begin{bmatrix} 0 & 1 \\ 0 & 0 \end{bmatrix}$, $B = \begin{bmatrix} 0 \\ 1 \end{bmatrix}$, $C = \begin{bmatrix} 1 & 0 \end{bmatrix}$, $|\dot{f}(\cdot)| \leqslant L$.

8.3.2 Extended State Observer Design

Refer to [3], the extended state observer is designed as follows:

$$\dot{\hat{x}}_1 = \hat{x}_2 + \frac{\alpha_1}{\varepsilon}(y - \hat{x}_1) \tag{8.19}$$

$$\dot{\hat{x}}_2 = bu + \hat{\sigma} + \frac{\alpha_2}{\varepsilon^2}(y - \hat{x}_1) \tag{8.20}$$

$$\dot{\hat{\sigma}} = \frac{\alpha_3}{\varepsilon^3}(y - \hat{x}_1) \tag{8.21}$$

The goals of the observer are that

$$\hat{x}_1(t) \to x_1(t), \hat{x}_2(t) \to x_2(t), \hat{x}_3(t) \to f(\theta, \dot{\theta}, t) \quad \text{as} \quad t \to \infty.$$

where $\hat{x}_1, \hat{x}_2$ and $\hat{\sigma}$ are states of the observer, $\varepsilon > 0$, α_1, α_2 and α_3 are positive constants, polynomial $s^3 + \alpha_1 s^2 + \alpha_2 s + \alpha_3$ is Hurwitz.

Refer to [4], we define observer error as

$$\boldsymbol{\eta} = \begin{bmatrix} \eta_1 & \eta_2 & \eta_3 \end{bmatrix}^{\mathrm{T}}$$

where

$$\eta_1 = \frac{x_1 - \hat{x}_1}{\varepsilon^2}, \quad \eta_2 = \frac{x_2 - \hat{x}_2}{\varepsilon}, \quad \eta_3 = f - \hat{\sigma}$$

Since

$$\varepsilon \dot{\eta}_1 = \frac{\dot{x}_1 - \dot{\hat{x}}_1}{\varepsilon} = \frac{1}{\varepsilon}\left(x_2 - \left(\hat{x}_2 + \frac{\alpha_1}{\varepsilon}(y - \hat{x}_1)\right)\right)$$

$$= \frac{1}{\varepsilon}\left(x_2 - \hat{x}_2 - \frac{\alpha_1}{\varepsilon}(y - \hat{x}_1)\right) = -\frac{\alpha_1}{\varepsilon^2}(x_1 - \hat{x}_1) + \frac{1}{\varepsilon}(x_2 - \hat{x}_2) = -\alpha_1 \eta_1 + \eta_2$$

$$\varepsilon \dot{\eta}_2 = \varepsilon \frac{\dot{x}_2 - \dot{\hat{x}}_2}{\varepsilon} = \left(bu + f(\cdot) - \left(bu + \hat{\sigma} + \frac{\alpha_2}{\varepsilon^2}(y - \hat{x}_1)\right)\right)$$

$$= \left(f(\cdot) - \hat{\sigma} - \frac{\alpha_2}{\varepsilon^2}(y - \hat{x}_1)\right) = -\frac{\alpha_2}{\varepsilon^2}(x_1 - \hat{x}_1) + (f - \hat{\sigma}) = -\alpha_2 \eta_1 + \eta_3$$

$$\varepsilon \dot{\eta}_3 = \varepsilon(\dot{f} - \dot{\hat{\sigma}}) = \varepsilon\left(\dot{f} - \frac{\alpha_3}{\varepsilon^3}(y - \hat{x}_1)\right) = \varepsilon \dot{f} - \frac{\alpha_3}{\varepsilon^2}(y - \hat{x}_1) = -\alpha_3 \eta_1 + \varepsilon \dot{f}$$

From above, we can get the observation error system as

$$\varepsilon\dot{\eta} = \bar{A}\eta + \varepsilon\bar{B}\dot{f} \tag{8.22}$$

where

$$\bar{A} = \begin{bmatrix} -\alpha_1 & 1 & 0 \\ -\alpha_2 & 0 & 1 \\ -\alpha_3 & 0 & 0 \end{bmatrix}, \quad \bar{B} = \begin{bmatrix} 0 \\ 0 \\ 1 \end{bmatrix}$$

The characteristic equation of matrix $\bar{A}$ is

$$|\lambda I - \bar{A}| = \begin{vmatrix} \lambda + \alpha_1 & -1 & 0 \\ \alpha_2 & \lambda & -1 \\ \alpha_3 & 0 & \lambda \end{vmatrix} = 0$$

then

$$(\lambda + \alpha_1)\lambda^2 + \alpha_2\lambda + \alpha_3 = 0$$

and

$$\lambda^3 + \alpha_1\lambda^2 + \alpha_2\lambda + \alpha_3 = 0 \tag{8.23}$$

If $\alpha_i (i = 1, 2, 3)$ is properly chosen so that $\bar{A}$ is Hurwitz, then for any given symmetric positive definite matrix Q, there exists a unique symmetric positive definite matrix P satisfying the Lyapunov equation as follows:

$$\bar{A}^T P + P\bar{A} + Q = 0 \tag{8.24}$$

We define the Lyapunov function as follows:

$$V_o = \varepsilon\eta^T P\eta \tag{8.25}$$

then

$$\begin{aligned}
\dot{V}_o &= \varepsilon\dot{\eta}^T P\eta + \varepsilon\eta^T P\dot{\eta} \\
&= (\bar{A}\eta + \varepsilon\bar{B}\dot{f})^T P\eta + \eta^T P(\bar{A}\eta + \varepsilon\bar{B}\dot{f}) \\
&= \eta^T \bar{A}^T P\eta + \varepsilon(\bar{B}\dot{f})^T P\eta + \eta^T P\bar{A}\eta + \varepsilon\eta^T P\bar{B}\dot{f} \\
&= \eta^T (\bar{A}^T P + P\bar{A})\eta + 2\varepsilon\eta^T P\bar{B}\dot{f} \\
&\leqslant -\eta^T Q\eta + 2\varepsilon \| P\bar{B} \| \cdot \| \eta \| \cdot | \dot{f} |
\end{aligned}$$

8 Sliding Mode Control Based on Observer

and

$$\dot{V}_0 \leqslant -\lambda_{\min}(\boldsymbol{Q}) \| \boldsymbol{\eta} \|^2 + 2\varepsilon L \| \boldsymbol{P\bar{B}} \| \| \boldsymbol{\eta} \| \tag{8.26}$$

where $\lambda_{\min}(\boldsymbol{Q})$ is the minimum eigenvalue of $\boldsymbol{Q}$.

From $\dot{V}_0 \leqslant 0$, we get observer error convergence conclusion as

$$\| \boldsymbol{\eta} \| \leqslant \frac{2\varepsilon L \| \boldsymbol{P\bar{B}} \|}{\lambda_{\min}(\boldsymbol{Q})} \tag{8.27}$$

From Eq. (8.27), we can see the convergence of observer error $\boldsymbol{\eta}$ is related to ε. If ε is designed as very positive small, $\| \boldsymbol{\eta} \|$ is $O(\varepsilon)$.

Remark:

(1) If the initial value of the extended observer and the initial value of the plant is different, for very small ε, peaking phenomenon will appear, which can affect convergence of the extended observer greatly. To alleviate peaking phenomenon, we design ε as [5]

$$\frac{1}{\varepsilon} = R = \begin{cases} 100t^3, & 0 \leqslant t \leqslant 1 \\ 100, & t > 1 \end{cases} \tag{8.28}$$

or

$$\frac{1}{\varepsilon} = R = \begin{cases} \mu \dfrac{1 - e^{-\lambda_1 t}}{1 + e^{-\lambda_2 t}}, & 0 \leqslant t \leqslant t_{\max} \\ \mu, & t > t_{\max} \end{cases} \tag{8.29}$$

where μ, λ_1 and λ_2 are positive value.

For example, choose $\lambda_1 = \lambda_2 = 50$, $\mu = 100$, run simulink program chap8_3sim.mdl, the change of R and ε are shown in Fig. 8.4.

(2) If the practical measurement signal is mixed with noise, for very small ε, big observer error can be caused. To alleviate the effect of noisy signal, a switched-gain can be used in the observer[6].

(3) Design of $\alpha_i (i = 1, 2, 3)$. For $\lambda^3 + \alpha_1\lambda^2 + \alpha_2\lambda + \alpha_3 = 0$, we choose $(\lambda + 1)(\lambda + 2)(\lambda + 3) = 0$, then $\lambda^3 + 6\lambda^2 + 11\lambda + 6 = 0$, we can get $\alpha_1 = 6$, $\alpha_2 = 11$, $\alpha_3 = 6$.

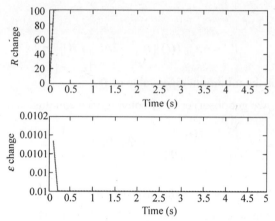

Figure 8.4 The change of R and ε

8.3.3 Simulation Example

Consider a servo system as follows:

$$J\ddot{\theta} = u(t) - d(t)$$

where J represents equivalent inertia, u represents control input signal, $d(t)$ represents total uncertainties, which include equivalent friction force and disturbance, θ represents angle.

In this simulation, we choose $d(t) = 3\sin t$ and $J = 10$. We assume the input signal is $u(t) = 0.1\sin t$.

In the extended observer Eqs. (8.19) – (8.21), we choose $\alpha_1 = 6$, $\alpha_2 = 11$, $\alpha_3 = 6$. The conventional gain is chosen as $\varepsilon = 0.01$, to alleviate peaking phenomenon, we design ε with Eq. (8.28) or Eq. (8.29), the observed value of position signal, speed signal, and control input are shown in Fig. 8.5 – Fig. 8.7.

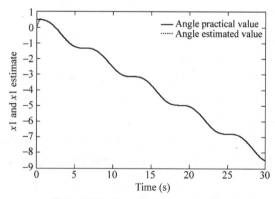

Figure 8.5 θ and its observed value

8 Sliding Mode Control Based on Observer

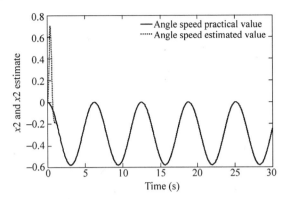

Figure 8.6 $\dot{\theta}$ and its observed value

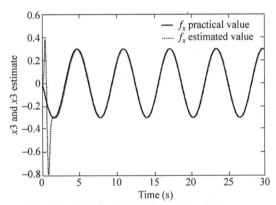

Figure 8.7 Total uncertainty and its observed value

Simulation programs of peak supression function:

(1) Simulink program: chap8_3sim.mdl

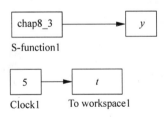

(2) S-function of peak program: chap8_3.m

```
function [sys,x0,str,ts]=s_function(t,x,u,flag)
switch flag,
case 0,
    [sys,x0,str,ts]=mdlInitializeSizes;
case 3,
    sys=mdlOutputs(t,x,u);
```

```
case {1, 2, 4, 9 }
    sys = [];
otherwise
    error(['Unhandled flag = ',num2str(flag)]);
end
function [sys,x0,str,ts]=mdlInitializeSizes
sizes = simsizes;
sizes.NumDiscStates  = 0;
sizes.NumOutputs     = 2;
sizes.NumInputs      = 0;
sizes.DirFeedthrough = 1;
sizes.NumSampleTimes = 1;
sys = simsizes(sizes);
x0  = [];
str = [];
ts  = [0 0];
function sys=mdlOutputs(t,x,u)
Lambda=50;
R=100*(1-exp(-Lambda*t))/(1+exp(-Lambda*t));
Epsilon=1/R;
sys(1)=R;
sys(2)=Epsilon;
```

(3) plot program: chap8_3plot.m

```
close all;

figure(1);
subplot(211);
plot(t,y(:,1),'r','linewidth',2);
xlabel('time(s)');ylabel('R change');
subplot(212);
plot(t,y(:,2),'r','linewidth',2);
xlabel('time(s)');ylabel('Epsilon change');
```

Simulation programs of ESO:

(1) Main Simulink: chap8_4sim.mdl

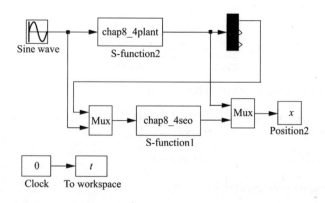

(2) Extended observer: chap8_4eso.m

```
function [sys,x0,str,ts]=s_function(t,x,u,flag)
switch flag,
case 0,
    [sys,x0,str,ts]=mdlInitializeSizes;
case 1,
    sys=mdlDerivatives(t,x,u);
case 3,
    sys=mdlOutputs(t,x,u);
case {2, 4, 9 }
    sys = [];
otherwise
    error(['Unhandled flag = ',num2str(flag)]);
end
function [sys,x0,str,ts]=mdlInitializeSizes
sizes = simsizes;
sizes.NumContStates  = 3;
sizes.NumDiscStates  = 0;
sizes.NumOutputs     = 3;
sizes.NumInputs      = 2;
sizes.DirFeedthrough = 1;
sizes.NumSampleTimes = 0;
sys=simsizes(sizes);
x0=[0 0 0];
str=[];
ts=[];
function sys=mdlDerivatives(t,x,u)
y=u(1);
ut=u(2);

J=10;
b=1/J;

alfa1=6;alfa2=11;alfa3=6;

M=1;
if M==1
    epc=0.01;
elseif M==2
    if t<=1;
        R=100*t^3;
    elseif t>1;
        R=100;
    end
    epc=1/R;
elseif M==3
    nmn=0.1;
    R=100*(1-exp(-nmn*t))/(1+exp(-nmn*t));
```

```matlab
    epc=1/R;
end

e=y-x(1);
sys(1)=x(2)+alfa1/epc*e;
sys(2)=b*ut+x(3)+alfa2/epc^2*e;
sys(3)=alfa3/epc^3*e;
function sys=mdlOutputs(t,x,u)
sys(1)=x(1);
sys(2)=x(2);
sys(3)=x(3);
```

(3) Plant program: chap8_4plant.m

```matlab
function [sys,x0,str,ts]=s_function(t,x,u,flag)
switch flag,
case 0,
    [sys,x0,str,ts]=mdlInitializeSizes;
case 1,
    sys=mdlDerivatives(t,x,u);
case 3,
    sys=mdlOutputs(t,x,u);
case {2, 4, 9 }
    sys = [];
otherwise
    error(['Unhandled flag = ',num2str(flag)]);
end
function [sys,x0,str,ts]=mdlInitializeSizes
sizes = simsizes;
sizes.NumContStates  = 2;
sizes.NumDiscStates  = 0;
sizes.NumOutputs     = 3;
sizes.NumInputs      = 1;
sizes.DirFeedthrough = 0;
sizes.NumSampleTimes = 0;
sys=simsizes(sizes);
x0=[0.5;0];
str=[];
ts=[];
function sys=mdlDerivatives(t,x,u)
J=10;
ut=u(1);

d=3.0*sin(t);
sys(1)=x(2);
sys(2)=1/J*(ut-d);
function sys=mdlOutputs(t,x,u)
J=10;
d=3.0*sin(t);
```

8 Sliding Mode Control Based on Observer

```
f=-d/J;
sys(1)=x(1);
sys(2)=x(2);
sys(3)=f;
```

(4) Plot program: chap8_4plot.m

```
close all;

figure(1);
plot(t,x(:,1),'k',t,x(:,4),'k:','linewidth',2);
xlabel('time(s)');ylabel('x1 and x1 estimate');
legend('angle practical value','angle estimated value');

figure(2);
plot(t,x(:,2),'k',t,x(:,5),'k:','linewidth',2);
xlabel('time(s)');ylabel('x2 and x2 estimate');
legend('angle speed practical value','angle speed estimated value');

figure(3);
plot(t,x(:,3),'k',t,x(:,6),'k:','linewidth',2);
xlabel('time(s)');ylabel('x3 and x3 estimate');
legend('fx practical value','fx estimated value');
```

8.4 Sliding Mode Control Based on Extended State Observer

8.4.1 System Description

Consider a second order system as

$$\ddot{\theta} = bu(t) + f(t) \tag{8.30}$$

Let $x_1 = \theta, x_2 = \dot{\theta},$ then we have

$$\left. \begin{aligned} \dot{x}_1 &= x_2 \\ \dot{x}_2 &= f(t) + bu(t) \end{aligned} \right\} \tag{8.31}$$

Let $x_3 = f(t), \rho(t) = \dot{f}(t),$ therefore, the original system can be transferred into

$$\left. \begin{aligned} \dot{x}_1 &= x_2 \\ \dot{x}_2 &= x_3 + bu(t) \\ \dot{x}_3 &= \rho(t) \end{aligned} \right\} \tag{8.32}$$

183

Advanced Sliding Mode Control for Mechanical Systems: Design, Analysis and MATLAB Simulation

The designed extended observer is

$$\begin{aligned}
\dot{\hat{x}}_1 &= \hat{x}_2 - \frac{k_1}{\varepsilon}(\hat{x}_1 - \theta) \\
\dot{\hat{x}}_2 &= \hat{x}_3 - \frac{k_2}{\varepsilon^2}(\hat{x}_1 - \theta) + bu(t) \\
\dot{\hat{x}}_3 &= -\frac{k_3}{\varepsilon^3}(\hat{x}_1 - \theta)
\end{aligned} \right\} \qquad (8.33)$$

we have

$$\lim_{\varepsilon \to 0} \hat{x}_1 = x_1, \quad \lim_{\varepsilon \to 0} \hat{x}_2 = x_2, \quad \lim_{\varepsilon \to 0} \hat{x}_3 = f(t)$$

8.4.2 Sliding Mode Controller Design

Denote the desired trajectory as r, and $e_1 = x_1 - r, e_2 = x_2 - \dot{r}$. Therefore, the error system is

$$\left. \begin{aligned}
\dot{e}_1 &= e_2 \\
\dot{e}_2 &= f(t) - \ddot{r} + bu(t)
\end{aligned} \right\} \qquad (8.34)$$

Select sliding mode variable be $s = e_2 + ce_1$, where $c > 0$ is a positive constant. Moreover, the observing sliding mode variable be $\hat{s} = \hat{e}_2 + c\hat{e}_1$, where $\hat{e}_1 = \hat{x}_1 - r, \hat{e}_2 = \hat{x}_2 - \dot{r}$. Therefore, we have

$$\dot{s} = \dot{e}_2 + c\dot{e}_1 = f(t) - \ddot{r} + bu(t) + ce_2$$

Let the Lyapunov function be

$$V = \frac{1}{2}s^2$$

we have

$$\dot{V} = s\dot{s} = s(f(t) - \ddot{r} + bu(t) + ce_2)$$

Select the controller as

$$u = \frac{1}{b}(-\hat{x}_3 + \ddot{r} - c\hat{e}_2 - l\,\mathrm{sgn}(\hat{s})) \qquad (8.35)$$

where $l > 0$.

184

then

$$\dot{V} = s\left(f(t) - \ddot{r} + b\frac{1}{b}(-\hat{x}_3 + \ddot{r} - c\hat{e}_2 - l\,\mathrm{sgn}(\hat{s})) + ce_2 \right)$$

$$= s(-l\,\mathrm{sgn}(\hat{s}) + f(t) - \hat{x}_3 + c(e_2 - \hat{e}_2))$$

$$= -(\hat{s} + s - \hat{s})l\,\mathrm{sgn}(\hat{s}) + (\hat{s} + s - \hat{s})(f(t) - \hat{x}_3) + (\hat{s} + s - \hat{s})c(e_2 - \hat{e}_2)$$

$$\leqslant -\hat{s}l\,\mathrm{sgn}(\hat{s}) + l\,|\,s - \hat{s}\,| + (|\,f(t) - \hat{x}_3\,| + c\,|\,e_2 - \hat{e}_2\,|)\,|\,\hat{s}\,| + |\,s - \hat{s}\,|\,(|\,f(t)$$
$$- \hat{x}_3\,| + c\,|\,e_2 - \hat{e}_2\,|)$$

$$= -l\,|\,\hat{s}\,| + l\,|\,s - \hat{s}\,| + (|\,f(t) - \hat{x}_3\,| + c\,|\,x_2 - \hat{x}_2\,|)\,|\,\hat{s}\,| + |\,s - \hat{s}\,|\,(|\,f(t)$$
$$- \hat{x}_3\,| + c\,|\,x_2 - \hat{x}_2\,|)$$

Because of the convergence of the extended observer,

$$l\,|\,s - \hat{s}\,| + (|\,f(t) - \hat{x}_3\,| + c\,|\,x_2 - \hat{x}_2\,|)\,|\,\hat{s}\,| + |\,s - \hat{s}\,|\,(|\,f(t) - \hat{x}_3\,| + c\,|\,x_2 - \hat{x}_2\,|)$$

is bounded and sufficiently small, and then we have $\dot{V} < 0$.

8.4.3 Simulation Example

Consider a servo system as follows:

$$J\ddot{\theta} = u(t) - d(t)$$

where J represents equivalent inertia, u represents control input signal, $d(t)$ represents total uncertainties, which include equivalent friction force and disturbance, θ represents angle.

In this simulation, we choose $d(t) = 3\sin t$. For the plant equation, we assume $J = 10$. The plant can be described as

$$\ddot{\theta} = bu(t) + f(t)$$

where $b = 0.10$, $f(t) = 0.3\sin t$.

We assume the ideal signal is $\theta_d = 0.1\sin t$. Use the designed control law Eq. (8.35) with the proposed observer Eq. (8.33), and we choose $c = 10$, $\alpha_1 = 6$, $\alpha_2 = 11$, $\alpha_3 = 6$, $\varepsilon = 0.01$, $l = 0.50$. The observed value of position signal, speed signal, and total uncertainties are shown in Fig. 8.8 and Fig. 8.9, the position tracking, speed tracking and control input are shown in Fig. 8.10 and Fig. 8.11. From the results, we can see that good position tracking performance and high robustness can be achieved, friction and disturbance can be estimated and compensated in the controller, chattering phenomenon can be alleviated effectively.

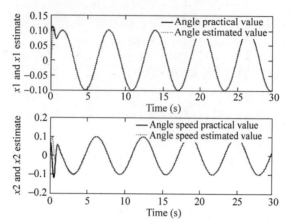

Figure 8.8 Position, speed value and their observed values

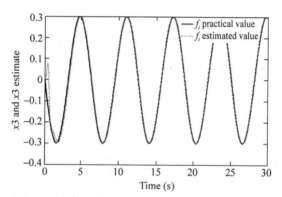

Figure 8.9 Total uncertainty and its observed value

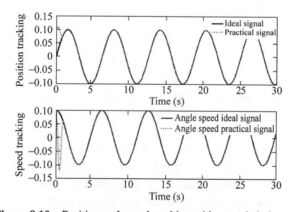

Figure 8.10 Position and speed tracking with extended observer

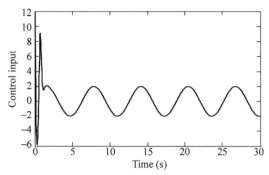

Figure 8.11 Control input with extended observer

Simulation programs:

(1) Main Simulink: chap8_5sim.mdl

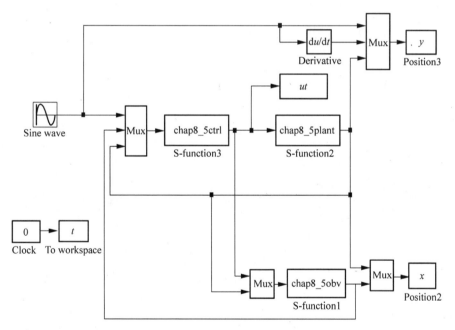

(2) Extended observer: chap8_5eso.m

```
function [sys,x0,str,ts]=s_function(t,x,u,flag)
switch flag,
case 0,
    [sys,x0,str,ts]=mdlInitializeSizes;
case 1,
    sys=mdlDerivatives(t,x,u);
case 3,
    sys=mdlOutputs(t,x,u);
case {2, 4, 9 }
```

```matlab
    sys = [];
otherwise
    error(['Unhandled flag = ',num2str(flag)]);
end
function [sys,x0,str,ts]=mdlInitializeSizes
sizes = simsizes;
sizes.NumContStates  = 3;
sizes.NumDiscStates  = 0;
sizes.NumOutputs     = 3;
sizes.NumInputs      = 4;
sizes.DirFeedthrough = 1;
sizes.NumSampleTimes = 0;
sys=simsizes(sizes);
x0=[0 0 0];
str=[];
ts=[];
function sys=mdlDerivatives(t,x,u)
ut=u(1);
y=u(2);
b=0.1;
alfa1=6;alfa2=11;alfa3=6;
M=3;
if M==1
    epc=0.01;
elseif M==2
    if t<=1;
        R=100*t^3;
    elseif t>1;
        R=100;
    end
    epc=1/R;
elseif M==3
    nmn=0.1;
    R=100*(1-exp(-nmn*t))/(1+exp(-nmn*t));
    epc=1/R;    -
end

e=y-x(1);
sys(1)=x(2)+alfa1/epc*e;
sys(2)=b*ut+x(3)+alfa2/epc^2*e;
sys(3)=alfa3/epc^3*e;
function sys=mdlOutputs(t,x,u)
sys(1)=x(1);
sys(2)=x(2);
sys(3)=x(3);
```

(3) Controller program: chap8_5ctrl.m

```matlab
function [sys,x0,str,ts]=s_function(t,x,u,flag)
switch flag,
```

8 Sliding Mode Control Based on Observer

```matlab
case 0,
    [sys,x0,str,ts]=mdlInitializeSizes;
case 3,
    sys=mdlOutputs(t,x,u);
case {1,2, 4, 9 }
    sys = [];
otherwise
    error(['Unhandled flag = ',num2str(flag)]);
end
function [sys,x0,str,ts]=mdlInitializeSizes
sizes = simsizes;
sizes.NumContStates  = 0;
sizes.NumDiscStates  = 0;
sizes.NumOutputs     = 1;
sizes.NumInputs      = 7;
sizes.DirFeedthrough = 1;
sizes.NumSampleTimes = 0;
sys=simsizes(sizes);
x0=[];
str=[];
ts=[];
function sys=mdlOutputs(t,x,u)
r=u(1);
x1p=u(2);x2p=u(3);x3p=u(4);
x1=u(5);x2=u(6);
dr=0.1*cos(t);
ddr=-0.1*sin(t);

b=0.1;c=10;l=0.5;
e1p=x1p-r;
e2p=x2p-dr;
sp=e2p+c*e1p;
ut=1/b*(-x3p+ddr-c*e2p-l*sign(sp)); %With Extended Observer
delta=0.15;
kk=1/delta;
if sp>delta
    sat_sp=1;
elseif abs(sp)<=delta
    sat_sp=kk*sp;
elseif sp<-delta
    sat_sp=-1;
end
ut=1/b*(-x3p+ddr-c*e2p-l*sat_sp); %With Extended Observer
sys(1)=ut;
```

(4) Plant program: chap8_5plant.m

```matlab
function [sys,x0,str,ts]=s_function(t,x,u,flag)
switch flag,
case 0,
```

```matlab
    [sys,x0,str,ts]=mdlInitializeSizes;
case 1,
    sys=mdlDerivatives(t,x,u);
case 3,
    sys=mdlOutputs(t,x,u);
case {2, 4, 9 }
    sys = [];
otherwise
    error(['Unhandled flag = ',num2str(flag)]);
end
function [sys,x0,str,ts]=mdlInitializeSizes
sizes = simsizes;
sizes.NumContStates  = 2;
sizes.NumDiscStates  = 0;
sizes.NumOutputs     = 3;
sizes.NumInputs      = 1;
sizes.DirFeedthrough = 0;
sizes.NumSampleTimes = 0;
sys=simsizes(sizes);
x0=[0.1;0];
str=[];
ts=[];
function sys=mdlDerivatives(t,x,u)
b=0.10;
f=0.3*sin(t);
ut=u(1);
sys(1)=x(2);
sys(2)=b*ut+f;
function sys=mdlOutputs(t,x,u)
b=0.10;
f=0.3*sin(t);
sys(1)=x(1);
sys(2)=x(2);
sys(3)=f;
```

(5) Plot program: chap8_5plot.m

```matlab
close all;

figure(1);
plot(t,y(:,1),'k',t,y(:,3),'r:','linewidth',2);
xlabel('time(s)');ylabel('Position tracking');
legend('ideal signal','practical signal');

figure(2);
plot(t,y(:,2),'k',t,y(:,4),'r:','linewidth',2);
xlabel('time(s)');ylabel('speed tracking');
legend('angle speed ideal signal','angle speed practical signal');

figure(3);
plot(t,ut(:,1),'k','linewidth',2);
xlabel('time(s)');ylabel('control input');
```

(6) Plot program of ESO: chap8_5eso_plot.m

```
close all;

figure(1);
plot(t,x(:,1),'k',t,x(:,4),'r:','linewidth',2);
xlabel('time(s)');ylabel('x1 and x1 estimate');
legend('angle practical value','angle estimated value');

figure(2);
plot(t,x(:,2),'k',t,x(:,5),'r:','linewidth',2);
xlabel('time(s)');ylabel('x2 and x2 estimate');
legend('angle speed practical value','angle speed estimated value');

figure(3);
plot(t,x(:,3),'k',t,x(:,6),'r:','linewidth',2);
xlabel('time(s)');ylabel('x3 and x3 estimate');
legend('ft practical value','ft estimated value');
```

8.5 Universal Approximation Using High-Order Integral-Chain Differentiator

8.5.1 System Description

Consider n-order nonlinear system as follow:

$$\left.\begin{aligned}
\dot{x}_1 &= x_2 \\
\dot{x}_2 &= x_3 \\
&\vdots \\
\dot{x}_{n-1} &= x_n \\
\dot{x}_n &= f(x) + g(x)u \\
y &= x_1
\end{aligned}\right\} \tag{8.36}$$

where $x = [x_1 \quad x_2 \quad \cdots \quad x_n]^T$ is the state vector, f and g are all nonlinear functions, $u \in \mathbf{R}$ and $y \in \mathbf{R}$ are the input control and output respectively. Function $g(x)$ is bounded.

8.5.2 Integral-Chain Differentiator

For the system (8.36), we suppose that $f(x)$ is uncertain and $x_2, x_3, \cdots, x_n$ are unknown. We give the following estimation theorem.

Theorem 1: For the system (8.36), we design the following integral-chain differentiator[5]:

$$\left.\begin{array}{l} \dot{\hat{x}}_1 = \hat{x}_2 \\[4pt] \dot{\hat{x}}_2 = \hat{x}_3 \\[4pt] \quad\vdots \\[4pt] \dot{\hat{x}}_{n-1} = \hat{x}_n \\[4pt] \dot{\hat{x}}_n = \hat{x}_{n+1} \\[4pt] \dot{\hat{x}}_{n+1} = -\dfrac{a_1}{\varepsilon^{n+1}}(\hat{x}_1 - x_1) - \dfrac{a_2}{\varepsilon^n}\hat{x}_2 - \cdots - \dfrac{a_n}{\varepsilon^2}\hat{x}_n - \dfrac{a_{n+1}}{\varepsilon}\hat{x}_{n+1} \end{array}\right\} \tag{8.37}$$

to approximate $f(x)$ and estimate $x_2, x_3, \cdots, x_n$ from the output $y = x_1$ and input u of the system (8.36). Where $\varepsilon > 0$ perturbation parameter which is sufficiently small. $s^{n+1} + a_{n+1}s^n + \cdots + a_2 s + a_1 = 0$ is Hurwitz. Therefore, we have that

$$\lim_{\varepsilon \to 0} \hat{x}_i = x_i, \quad i = 1, 2, \cdots, n \tag{8.38}$$

and

$$\lim_{\varepsilon \to 0} \hat{x}_{n+1} = f(x) + g(x)u \quad \text{or} \quad f(t) = \lim_{\varepsilon \to 0}(\hat{x}_{n+1} - g(\hat{x})u) \tag{8.39}$$

where

$$\hat{x} = [\hat{x}_1 \quad \hat{x}_2 \quad \cdots \quad \hat{x}_n]^{\mathrm{T}}$$

Proof: The Laplace transformation of the integral-chain differentiator (8.37) is

$$\hat{X}_{i-k}(s) = \frac{\hat{X}_i(s)}{s^k}, \quad k = 0, 1, \cdots, i-1; \quad i = 1, 2, \cdots, n+1 \tag{8.40}$$

$$s\hat{X}_{n+1}(s) + \frac{a_{n+1}}{\varepsilon}\hat{X}_{n+1}(s) + \frac{a_n}{\varepsilon^2}\hat{X}_n(s) + \cdots + \frac{a_2}{\varepsilon^n}\hat{X}_2(s) + \frac{a_1}{\varepsilon^{n+1}}\hat{X}_1(s) = \frac{a_1}{\varepsilon^{n+1}}X_1(s)$$

$$\tag{8.41}$$

where $\hat{X}_i(s)$ is the Laplace transformation of $\hat{x}_i(t)$, $i = 1, 2, \cdots, n+1$.

From Eqs. (8.39) and (8.40), we have

$$\left(\varepsilon^{n+1}s^{n-i+2} + \varepsilon^n a_{n+1}s^{n-i+1} + \varepsilon^{n-1}a_n s^{n-i} + \cdots \right.$$

$$\left. + \varepsilon^i a_{i+1}s + \varepsilon^{i-1}a_i + \frac{\varepsilon^{i-2}a_{i-1}}{s} + \cdots + \frac{\varepsilon a_2}{s^{i-2}} + \frac{a_1}{s^{i-1}} \right)\hat{X}_i(s) = a_1 X_1(s)$$

$$i = 1, 2, \cdots, n \tag{8.42}$$

Therefore, we get

$$\lim_{\varepsilon \to 0}\frac{\hat{X}_i(s)}{X_1(s)} = s^{i-1}, \quad i=1,2,\cdots,n+1 \tag{8.43}$$

Accordingly, we get Eq. (8.38). Moreover, from Eq. (8.37), we have

$$\lim_{\varepsilon \to 0}\hat{x}_{n+1} = \dot{x}_n$$

From $\dot{x}_n = f(x)+g(x)u$ in Eq. (8.36), we can get Eq. (8.39).
This concludes the proof.
Remark: From Eq. (8.41), we get

$$\frac{\hat{X}_1(s)}{X_1(s)} = \frac{\dfrac{a_1}{\varepsilon^{n+1}}}{s^{n+1}+\dfrac{a_{n+1}}{\varepsilon}s^n+\dfrac{a_n}{\varepsilon^2}s^n+\cdots+\dfrac{a_2}{\varepsilon^n}s+\dfrac{a_1}{\varepsilon^{n+1}}}$$

We know that if the selection of $a_1,a_2,\cdots,a_{n+1}$ is suitable, the filtering ability can be obtained.

8.5.3 Simulation Example

Consider the following inverted pendulum:

$$\begin{cases}\dot{x}_1 = x_2 \\ \dot{x}_2 = \dfrac{g\sin x_1 - mlx_2^2\cos x_1 \sin x_1/(m_c+m)}{l(4/3-m\cos^2 x_1/(m_c+m))}+\dfrac{\cos x_1/(m_c+m)}{l(4/3-m\cos^2 x_1/(m_c+m))}u\end{cases}$$

where x_1 and x_2 are the swing angle and swing rate respectively. $g=9.8$ m/s^2, $m_c=1$ kg is the vehicle mass, $m=0.1$ kg is the mass of pendulum. $l=0.5$ m is one half of the pendulum length, and u is the control input.

From Eq. (8.37), the integral-chain differentiator is designed as

$$\dot{\hat{x}}_1 = \hat{x}_2$$
$$\dot{\hat{x}}_2 = \hat{x}_3$$
$$\dot{\hat{x}}_3 = -\frac{a_1}{\varepsilon^3}(\hat{x}_1-x_1)-\frac{a_2}{\varepsilon^2}\hat{x}_2-\frac{a_3}{\varepsilon}\hat{x}_3$$

where $\varepsilon=0.01$, $a_1=a_2=a_3=10$. The input signal is $u(t)=0.1\sin t$, the initial state is $[\pi/60 \quad 0]$. The curves of position tracking, velocity estimation and uncertainty approximation using integral-chain differentiator are in Fig. 8.12 – Fig. 8.14.

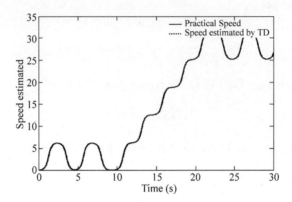

Figure 8.12 Position estimated by TD

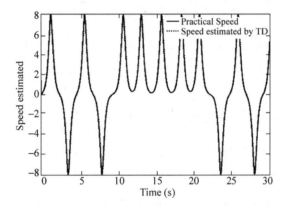

Figure 8.13 Speed estimated by TD

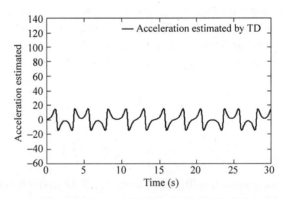

Figure 8.14 Acceleration estimated by TD

Simulation programs:

(1) Main Simulink program: chap8_6sim.mdl

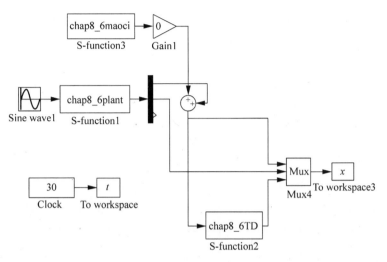

(2) TD differentiator program: chap8_6TD.m

```
function [sys,x0,str,ts] = Differentiator(t,x,u,flag)
switch flag,
case 0,
    [sys,x0,str,ts]=mdlInitializeSizes;
case 1,
    sys=mdlDerivatives(t,x,u);
case 3,
    sys=mdlOutputs(t,x,u);
case {2, 4, 9 }
    sys = [];
otherwise
    error(['Unhandled flag = ',num2str(flag)]);
end
function [sys,x0,str,ts]=mdlInitializeSizes
sizes = simsizes;
sizes.NumContStates  = 3;
sizes.NumDiscStates  = 0;
sizes.NumOutputs     = 3;
sizes.NumInputs      = 1;
sizes.DirFeedthrough = 1;
sizes.NumSampleTimes = 1;
sys = simsizes(sizes);
x0  = [0 0 0];
str = [];
ts  = [0 0];
function sys=mdlDerivatives(t,x,u)
vt=u(1);
```

195

```matlab
epc=0.01;

alfa1=1;
alfa2=3;
alfa3=3;

e=x(1)-vt;

sys(1)=x(2);
sys(2)=x(3);
sys(3)=-alfa1/epc^3*e-alfa2/epc^2*x(2)-alfa3/epc*x(3);
function sys=mdlOutputs(t,x,u)
sys = x;
```

(3) Plant program: chap8_6plant.m

```matlab
function [sys,x0,str,ts]=s_function(t,x,u,flag)
switch flag,
case 0,
    [sys,x0,str,ts]=mdlInitializeSizes;
case 1,
    sys=mdlDerivatives(t,x,u);
case 3,
    sys=mdlOutputs(t,x,u);
case {2, 4, 9 }
    sys = [];
otherwise
    error(['Unhandled flag = ',num2str(flag)]);
end
function [sys,x0,str,ts]=mdlInitializeSizes
sizes = simsizes;
sizes.NumContStates  = 2;
sizes.NumDiscStates  = 0;
sizes.NumOutputs     = 3;
sizes.NumInputs      = 1;
sizes.DirFeedthrough = 0;
sizes.NumSampleTimes = 0;
sys=simsizes(sizes);
x0=[pi/60 0];
str=[];
ts=[];
function sys=mdlDerivatives(t,x,u)
g=9.8;mc=1.0;m=0.1;l=0.5;
S=l*(4/3-m*(cos(x(1)))^2/(mc+m));
fx=g*sin(x(1))-m*l*x(2)^2*cos(x(1))*sin(x(1))/(mc+m);
fx=fx/S;
gx=cos(x(1))/(mc+m);
gx=gx/S;

sys(1)=x(2);
```

8 Sliding Mode Control Based on Observer

```
sys(2)=fx+gx*u;
function sys=mdlOutputs(t,x,u)
g=9.8;mc=1.0;m=0.1;l=0.5;
S=l*(4/3-m*(cos(x(1)))^2/(mc+m));
fx=g*sin(x(1))-m*l*x(2)^2*cos(x(1))*sin(x(1))/(mc+m);
fx=fx/S;

sys(1)=x(1);
sys(2)=x(2);
sys(3)=fx;
```

(4) Plot program: chap8_6plot.m

```
close all;

figure(1);
plot(t,x(:,1),'k',t,x(:,3),'k:','linewidth',2);
xlabel('time(s)');ylabel('Position estimated');
legend('Practical Position','Position estimated by TD');

figure(2);
plot(t,x(:,2),'k',t,x(:,4),'k:','linewidth',2);
xlabel('time(s)');ylabel('Speed estimated');
legend('Practical Speed','Speed estimated by TD');

figure(3);
plot(t,x(:,5),'k','linewidth',2);
xlabel('time(s)');ylabel('Acceleration estimated');
legend('Acceleration estimated by TD');
```

8.6 Sliding Mode Control Based on Integral-Chain Differentiator

8.6.1 Integral-Chain Differentiator Approximation

The desired trajectory is y_{d} which is derivable up to order n, therefore, the tracking error system from Eq. (8.36) is

$$
\left.\begin{aligned}
\dot{e}_1 &= e_2 \\
\dot{e}_2 &= e_3 \\
&\vdots \\
\dot{e}_{n-1} &= e_n \\
\dot{e}_n &= f(x) + g(x)u - y_{\mathrm{d}}^{(n)}
\end{aligned}\right\}
\tag{8.44}
$$

where $e_i = x_i - y_{\mathrm{d}}^{(i-1)}$, $i = 1, 2, \cdots, n$.

Let

$$\hat{e} = [\hat{e}_1 \quad \hat{e}_2 \quad \cdots \quad \hat{e}_n]^T = [\hat{x}_1 - y_d \quad \hat{x}_2 - y_d^{(1)} \quad \cdots \quad \hat{x}_n - y_d^{(n-1)}]^T$$

We select a bounded controller u, i.e.,

$$|u| \leqslant l_u$$

Let

$$\hat{f}(x) = \hat{x}_{n+1} - g(\hat{x})u \tag{8.45}$$

and $\hat{e}_i = \hat{x}_i - y_d^{(i-1)}$, $i = 1, 2, \cdots, n$.

From Eq. (8.36), we have

$$f(x) = \dot{x}_n - g(x)u$$

Therefore, we have

$$f(x) - \hat{f}(x) = \dot{x}_n - \hat{x}_{n+1} + (g(\hat{x}) - g(x))u$$

Therefore,

$$|f(x) - \hat{f}(x)| \leqslant |\dot{x}_n - \hat{x}_{n+1}| + |g(\hat{x}) - g(x)||u|$$

For bounded u, we suppose exist constant l_g such that

$$|g(\hat{x}) - g(x)| \leqslant l_g \|\hat{x} - x\| \tag{8.46}$$

Therefore, we get

$$|f(x) - \hat{f}(x)| \leqslant |\dot{x}_n - \hat{x}_{n+1}| + l_u l_g \|\hat{x} - x\| \tag{8.47}$$

For system (8.36), we will design a controller based on integral-chain differentiator to track desired trajectory, and given the following Theorem. Firstly, we can suppose $|-\hat{x}_{n+1} + y_d^{(n)} - c_{n-1}\hat{e}_n - \cdots - c_1\hat{e}_2|$ is bounded[7], i.e.

$$|-\hat{f}(x) + y_d^{(n)} + C^T\hat{e}| \leqslant l_1 \tag{8.48}$$

where $C = [-c_{n-1} \quad -c_{n-2} \quad \cdots \quad -c_1]^T$, $\hat{e} = [\hat{e}_n \quad \hat{e}_{n-1} \quad \cdots \quad \hat{e}_2]^T$ and

$$l_{inf} \leqslant |g(x)| \leqslant l_{sup} \tag{8.49}$$

8.6.2 Design of Sliding Mode Controller

The sliding variable:

$$s = \left(\frac{d}{dt} + c\right)^{n-1} e_1 = e_n + c_{n-1}e_{n-1} + \cdots + c_1e_1$$

8 Sliding Mode Control Based on Observer

The observing sliding variable:

$$\hat{s} = \left(\frac{d}{dt} + c\right)^{n-1} \hat{e}_1 = \hat{e}_n + c_{n-1}\hat{e}_{n-1} + \cdots + c_1\hat{e}_1$$

Theorem 2: For system (8.36) with unknown $f(x)$ and $x_2, x_3, \cdots, x_n$, we select the controller as follows:

$$u = \frac{1}{g(\hat{x})}(-\hat{f}(x) + y_d^{(n)} - c_{n-1}\hat{e}_n - \cdots - c_1\hat{e}_2 - l\text{sgn}(\hat{s})) \tag{8.50}$$

with the high-order integral-chain differentiator (8.37), we have a conclusion that

$$x_i \to y_d^{(i-1)}, \quad i = 1, 2, \cdots, n$$

as $t \to \infty$.

where

$$\left(\frac{d}{dt} + \lambda\right)^n e_1 = e_1^{(n)} + k_n e_1^{(n-1)} + \cdots + k_1 e_1$$

Proof:

Select the Lyapunov function as

$$V = \frac{1}{2}s^2$$

Therefore, we have

$$\begin{aligned}
\dot{V} &= s(\dot{e}_n + c_{n-1}e_n + \cdots + c_1 e_2) \\
&= s(f(x) + g(x)u - y_d^{(n)} + c_{n-1}e_n + \cdots + c_1 e_2) \\
&= s\left(f(x) + g(x)\frac{1}{g(\hat{x})}(-\hat{f}(x) + y_d^{(n)} - c_{n-1}\hat{e}_n - \cdots - c_1\hat{e}_2 - l\text{sgn}(\hat{s})) \right. \\
&\quad \left. -y_d^{(n)} + c_{n-1}e_n + \cdots + c_1 e_2 \right) \\
&= s\left(f(x) + \frac{g(\hat{x}) + g(x) - g(\hat{x})}{g(\hat{x})}(-\hat{f}(x) + y_d^{(n)} - c_{n-1}\hat{e}_n - \cdots - c_1\hat{e}_2 - l\text{sgn}(\hat{s})) \right. \\
&\quad \left. -y_d^{(n)} + c_{n-1}e_n + \cdots + c_1 e_2 \right) \\
&= s\left(f(x) - \hat{f}(x) - \sum_{i=2}^{n} c_{i-1}(\hat{x}_i - x_i) - l\text{sgn}(\hat{s}) \right. \\
&\quad \left. + \frac{g(x) - g(\hat{x})}{g(\hat{x})}(-\hat{f}(x) + y_d^{(n)} - c_{n-1}\hat{e}_n - \cdots - c_1\hat{e}_2 - l\text{sgn}(\hat{s})) \right)
\end{aligned}$$

Therefore,

$$\dot{V} = s(f(x) - \hat{f}(x)) - s\sum_{i=2}^{n} c_{i-1}(\hat{x}_i - x_i) - \hat{s}l\text{sgn}(\hat{s}) - (s - \hat{s})l\text{sgn}(\hat{s})$$

$$+ \frac{g(x) - g(\hat{x})}{g(\hat{x})} s(-\hat{f}(x) + y_d^{(n)} - c_{n-1}\hat{e}_n - \cdots - c_1\hat{e}_2 - l\text{sgn}(\hat{s}))$$

$$= \hat{s}(f(x) - \hat{f}(x)) + (s - \hat{s})(f(x) - \hat{f}(x)) - \hat{s}\sum_{i=2}^{n} c_{i-1}(\hat{x}_i - x_i) - (s - \hat{s})\sum_{i=2}^{n} c_{i-1}(\hat{x}_i - x_i)$$

$$+ \frac{g(x) - g(\hat{x})}{g(\hat{x})} \hat{s}(-\hat{f}(x) + y_d^{(n)} - c_{n-1}\hat{e}_n - \cdots - c_1\hat{e}_2 - l\text{sgn}(\hat{s}))$$

$$+ \frac{g(x) - g(\hat{x})}{g(\hat{x})} (s - \hat{s})[-\hat{f}(x) + y_d^{(n)} - c_{n-1}\hat{e}_n - \cdots - c_1\hat{e}_2 - l\text{sgn}(\hat{s})]$$

$$- \hat{s}l\text{sgn}(\hat{s}) - (s - \hat{s})l\text{sgn}(\hat{s})$$

Therefore, we have

$$\dot{V} \leqslant |f(x) - \hat{f}(x)||\hat{s}| + |s - \hat{s}||f(x) - \hat{f}(x)| + |\hat{s}|\sum_{i=2}^{n} |c_{i-1}||\hat{x}_i - x_i|$$

$$+ |s - \hat{s}|\sum_{i=2}^{n} |c_{i-1}||\hat{x}_i - x_i| + \frac{|g(x) - g(\hat{x})|}{|g(\hat{x})|}|\hat{s}||-\hat{f}(x) + y_d^{(n)} - c_{n-1}\hat{e}_n - \cdots$$

$$- c_1\hat{e}_2 - l\text{sgn}(\hat{s})| + \frac{|g(x) - g(\hat{x})|}{|g(\hat{x})|}|s - \hat{s}||-\hat{f}(x) + y_d^{(n)} - c_{n-1}\hat{e}_n - \cdots$$

$$- c_1\hat{e}_2 - l\text{sgn}(\hat{s})| + l|s - \hat{s}| - l|\hat{s}|$$

$$\leqslant |f(x) - \hat{f}(x)||\hat{s}| + |s - \hat{s}||f(x) - \hat{f}(x)| + |\hat{s}|\sum_{i=2}^{n} |c_{i-1}||\hat{x}_i - x_i|$$

$$+ |s - \hat{s}|\sum_{i=2}^{n} |c_{i-1}||\hat{x}_i - x_i| + \frac{l_g|\hat{x} - x|}{l_{\text{inf}}}|\hat{s}||-\hat{f}(x) + y_d^{(n)} - c_{n-1}\hat{e}_n - \cdots$$

$$- c_1\hat{e}_2 - l\text{sgn}(\hat{s})| + \frac{l_g|\hat{x} - x|}{l_{\text{inf}}}|s - \hat{s}||-\hat{f}(x) + y_d^{(n)} - c_{n-1}\hat{e}_n - \cdots$$

$$- c_1\hat{e}_2 - l\text{sgn}(\hat{s})| + l|s - \hat{s}| - l|\hat{s}|$$

When ε is sufficient small, we have

$$\lim_{\varepsilon \to 0} |s - \hat{s}| = 0, \quad \lim_{\varepsilon \to 0} |\hat{x}_i - x_i| = 0, \quad \lim_{\varepsilon \to 0} |\dot{x}_n - \hat{x}_{n+1}| = 0$$

and from Eq. (8.47), we have

8 Sliding Mode Control Based on Observer

$$\lim_{\varepsilon \to 0} | f(x) - \hat{f}(x) | = 0$$

Finally, we have $\dot{V} \leq 0$. Therefore, $x_i \to y_d^{(i-1)}$, $i = 1, 2, \cdots, n$, as $t \to \infty$. This concludes the proof.

8.6.3 Simulation Example

Consider the following inverted pendulum:

$$\begin{cases} \dot{x}_1 = x_2 \\ \dot{x}_2 = \dfrac{g \sin x_1 - m l x_2^2 \cos x_1 \sin x_1 /(m_c + m)}{l(4/3 - m \cos^2 x_1 /(m_c + m))} + \dfrac{\cos x_1 /(m_c + m)}{l(4/3 - m \cos^2 x_1 /(m_c + m))} u \end{cases}$$

where x_1 and x_2 are the swing angle and swing rate respectively. $g = 9.8 \, \text{m/s}^2$, $m_c = 1 \, \text{kg}$ is the vehicle mass, $m = 0.1 \, \text{kg}$ is the mass of pendulum. $l = 0.5 \, \text{m}$ is one half of the pendulum length, and u is the control input. The desired trajectory is $y_d(t) = 0.1 \sin(\pi t)$.

The integral-chain differentiator is designed as

$$\dot{\hat{x}}_1 = \hat{x}_2$$
$$\dot{\hat{x}}_2 = \hat{x}_3$$
$$\dot{\hat{x}}_3 = -\frac{a_1}{\varepsilon^3}(\hat{x}_1 - x_1) - \frac{a_2}{\varepsilon^2}\hat{x}_2 - \frac{a_3}{\varepsilon}\hat{x}_3$$

where $\varepsilon = 0.01$, $a_1 = a_2 = a_3 = 10$. The controller is selected as Eq. (8.50), and $k_1 = 20$, $k_2 = 10$. The curves of position tracking, velocity estimation and uncertainty approximation using integral-chain differentiator are in Fig. 8.15 – Fig. 8.17.

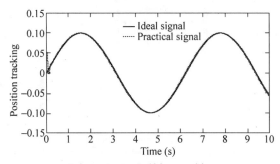

Figure 8.15 Position tracking

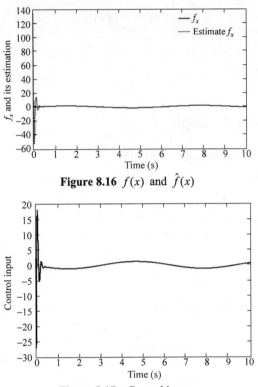

Figure 8.16 $f(x)$ and $\hat{f}(x)$

Figure 8.17 Control input u

Simulation programs:

(1) Main Simulink program: chap8_7sim.mdl

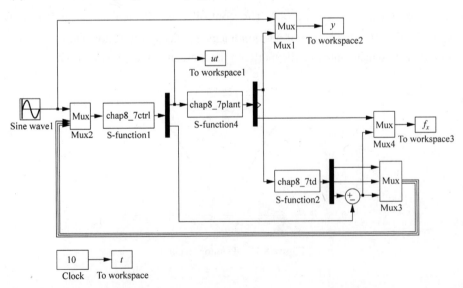

8 Sliding Mode Control Based on Observer

(2) Sliding mode controller: chap8_7ctrl.m

```
function [sys,x0,str,ts] = spacemodel(t,x,u,flag)
switch flag,
case 0,
    [sys,x0,str,ts]=mdlInitializeSizes;
case 3,
    sys=mdlOutputs(t,x,u);
case {1,2,4,9}
    sys=[];
otherwise
    error(['Unhandled flag = ',num2str(flag)]);
end
function [sys,x0,str,ts]=mdlInitializeSizes
sizes = simsizes;
sizes.NumContStates  = 0;
sizes.NumDiscStates  = 0;
sizes.NumOutputs     = 2;
sizes.NumInputs      = 4;
sizes.DirFeedthrough = 1;
sizes.NumSampleTimes = 0;
sys = simsizes(sizes);
x0  = [];
str = [];
ts  = [];
function sys=mdlOutputs(t,x,u)
yd=0.1*sin(t);
dyd=0.1*cos(t);
ddyd=-0.1*sin(t);

x1p=u(2);
x2p=u(3);
fxp=u(4);

e1p=x1p-yd;
e2p=x2p-dyd;

c=30;
sp=e2p+c*e1p;
delta=0.05;
k=1/delta;
if abs(sp)>=delta
   sat=sign(sp);
else
   sat=k*sp;
end

g=9.8;mc=1.0;m=0.1;l=0.5;
S=l*(4/3-m*(cos(x1p))^2/(mc+m));
```

203

```
fx=g*sin(x1p)-m*l*x2p^2*cos(x1p)*sin(x1p)/(mc+m);
fxp=fx/S;
gx=cos(x1p)/(mc+m);
gxp=gx/S;

%ut=1/gxp*(-fxp+ddyd-c*e2p-l*sign(sp));
l=0.20;
ut=1/gxp*(-fxp+ddyd-c*e2p-l*sat);

sys(1)=ut;
sys(2)=gxp*ut;
```

(3) TD differentiator program: chap8_7td.m

```
function [sys,x0,str,ts] = Differentiator(t,x,u,flag)
switch flag,
case 0,
    [sys,x0,str,ts]=mdlInitializeSizes;
case 1,
    sys=mdlDerivatives(t,x,u);
case 3,
    sys=mdlOutputs(t,x,u);
case {2, 4, 9 }
    sys = [];
otherwise
    error(['Unhandled flag = ',num2str(flag)]);
end
function [sys,x0,str,ts]=mdlInitializeSizes
sizes = simsizes;
sizes.NumContStates  = 3;
sizes.NumDiscStates  = 0;
sizes.NumOutputs     = 3;
sizes.NumInputs      = 1;
sizes.DirFeedthrough = 1;
sizes.NumSampleTimes = 1;
sys = simsizes(sizes);
x0  = [0 0 0];
str = [];
ts  = [0 0];
function sys=mdlDerivatives(t,x,u)
vt=u(1);
epc=0.01;

alfa1=1;alfa2=3;alfa3=3;
e=x(1)-vt;

sys(1)=x(2);
sys(2)=x(3);
sys(3)=-alfa1/epc^3*e-alfa2/epc^2*x(2)-alfa3/epc*x(3);
```

8 Sliding Mode Control Based on Observer

```
function sys=mdlOutputs(t,x,u)
sys = x;
```

(4) Plant program: chap8_7plant.m

```
function [sys,x0,str,ts]=s_function(t,x,u,flag)
switch flag,
case 0,
    [sys,x0,str,ts]=mdlInitializeSizes;
case 1,
    sys=mdlDerivatives(t,x,u);
case 3,
    sys=mdlOutputs(t,x,u);
case {2, 4, 9 }
    sys = [];
otherwise
    error(['Unhandled flag = ',num2str(flag)]);
end
function [sys,x0,str,ts]=mdlInitializeSizes
sizes = simsizes;
sizes.NumContStates  = 2;
sizes.NumDiscStates  = 0;
sizes.NumOutputs     = 3;
sizes.NumInputs      = 1;
sizes.DirFeedthrough = 0;
sizes.NumSampleTimes = 0;
sys=simsizes(sizes);
x0=[pi/60 0];
str=[];
ts=[];
function sys=mdlDerivatives(t,x,u)
g=9.8;mc=1.0;m=0.1;l=0.5;
S=l*(4/3-m*(cos(x(1)))^2/(mc+m));
fx=g*sin(x(1))-m*l*x(2)^2*cos(x(1))*sin(x(1))/(mc+m);
fx=fx/S;
gx=cos(x(1))/(mc+m);
gx=gx/S;

sys(1)=x(2);
sys(2)=fx+gx*u;
%sys(2)=-25*x(2)+133*u;
function sys=mdlOutputs(t,x,u)
g=9.8;mc=1.0;m=0.1;l=0.5;
S=l*(4/3-m*(cos(x(1)))^2/(mc+m));
fx=g*sin(x(1))-m*l*x(2)^2*cos(x(1))*sin(x(1))/(mc+m);
fx=fx/S;

sys(1)=x(1);
sys(2)=x(2);
sys(3)=fx;
```

(5) Position tracking plot program: chap8_7plot.m

```
close all;

figure(1);
plot(t,y(:,1),'k',t,y(:,2),'k:','linewidth',2);
xlabel('time(s)');ylabel('Position tracking');
legend('ideal signal','practical signal');

figure(2);
plot(t,fx(:,1),'k',t,fx(:,2),'k:','linewidth',2);
xlabel('time(s)');ylabel('fx and its estimation');
legend('fx','estimated fx');

figure(3);
plot(t,ut(:,1),'k','linewidth',2);
xlabel('time(s)');ylabel('Control input');
```

8.7 Design and Analysis of Slow Time-Varying Disturbance Observer

8.7.1 System Description

Consider a second-order system with slow time-varying disturbance as follows:

$$\ddot{\theta} = -b\dot{\theta} + au - d \tag{8.51}$$

where θ is the angle signal, $b > 0$, $a > 0$, a and b are all known, d is a slow time-varying disturbance.

8.7.2 Disturbance Observer Design

Atsuo et al. proposed an observer[8] for the system (8.51) with time-varying disturbance as:

$$\dot{\hat{d}} = k_1(\hat{\omega} - \dot{\theta}) \tag{8.52}$$

$$\dot{\hat{\omega}} = -\hat{d} + au - k_2(\hat{\omega} - \dot{\theta}) - b\dot{\theta} \tag{8.53}$$

where $\hat{d}$ is the estimation of d, and $\hat{\omega}$ is the estimation of $\dot{\theta}$, $k_1 > 0$, $k_2 > 0$.

8 Sliding Mode Control Based on Observer

Analysis of stability:

Select the Lyapunov function as

$$V = \frac{1}{2k_1}\tilde{d}^2 + \frac{1}{2}\tilde{\omega}^2 \tag{8.54}$$

where $\tilde{d} = d - \hat{d}$, $\tilde{\omega} = \dot{\theta} - \hat{\omega}$.

Therefore, we have

$$\dot{V} = \frac{1}{k_1}\tilde{d}\dot{\tilde{d}} + \tilde{\omega}\dot{\tilde{\omega}} = \frac{1}{k_1}\tilde{d}(\dot{d} - \dot{\hat{d}}) + \tilde{\omega}(\ddot{\theta} - \dot{\hat{\omega}})$$

Suppose $\dot{d}$ is bounded, and when k_1 is selected as a relative large value, we have

$$\frac{1}{k_1}\dot{d} \approx 0 \tag{8.55}$$

From above, we have:

$$\begin{aligned}
\dot{V} &= \frac{1}{k_1}\tilde{d}\dot{d} - \frac{1}{k_1}\tilde{d}\dot{\hat{d}} + \tilde{\omega}(\ddot{\theta} - (-\hat{d} + au - k_2(\hat{\omega} - \dot{\theta}) - b\dot{\theta})) \\
&= \frac{1}{k_1}\tilde{d}\dot{d} - \frac{1}{k_1}\tilde{d}k_1(\hat{\omega} - \dot{\theta}) + \tilde{\omega}(-b\dot{\theta} + au - d - (-\hat{d} + au - k_2(\hat{\omega} - \dot{\theta}) - b\dot{\theta})) \\
&= \frac{1}{k_1}\tilde{d}\dot{d} - \tilde{d}(\hat{\omega} - \dot{\theta}) + \tilde{\omega}(-d + \hat{d} + k_2(\hat{\omega} - \dot{\theta})) \\
&= \frac{1}{k_1}\tilde{d}\dot{d} + \tilde{d}\tilde{\omega} + \tilde{\omega}(-\tilde{d} - k_2\tilde{\omega}) = \frac{1}{k_1}\tilde{d}\dot{d} - k_2\tilde{\omega}^2 \leqslant 0
\end{aligned}$$

Obviously, the disturbance d can be estimated by this observer, and the compensation will be realized in the feedback control.

8.7.3 Simulation Example

The kinetic equation of system is considered as:

$$\ddot{\theta} = -b\dot{\theta} + au - d$$

where $a = 5$, $b = 0.15$, $d = 150\sin(0.1t)$.

The observer is given in Eqs. (8.52) and (8.53), and $k_1 = 500$, $k_2 = 200$. The simulation result is shown in Fig. 8.18.

207

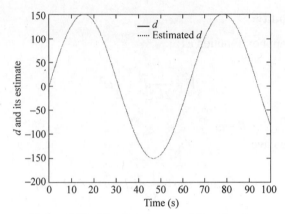

Figure 8.18 The disturbance and its estimation

Simulation programs:

(1) Simulink main program: chap8_8sim.mdl

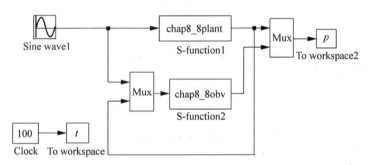

(2) Observer S-function: chap8_8obv.m

```
function [sys,x0,str,ts]=s_function(t,x,u,flag)
switch flag,
case 0,
    [sys,x0,str,ts]=mdlInitializeSizes;
case 1,
    sys=mdlDerivatives(t,x,u);
case 3,
    sys=mdlOutputs(t,x,u);
case {2, 4, 9 }
    sys = [];
otherwise
    error(['Unhandled flag = ',num2str(flag)]);
end
function [sys,x0,str,ts]=mdlInitializeSizes
sizes = simsizes;
sizes.NumContStates  = 2;
sizes.NumDiscStates  = 0;
```

8 Sliding Mode Control Based on Observer

```
sizes.NumOutputs      = 2;
sizes.NumInputs       = 4;
sizes.DirFeedthrough = 0;
sizes.NumSampleTimes = 0;
sys=simsizes(sizes);
x0=[0;0];
str=[];
ts=[];
function sys=mdlDerivatives(t,x,u)
ut=u(1);
dth=u(3);

k1=1000;
k2=200;

a=5;b=0.15;
sys(1)=k1*(x(2)-dth);
sys(2)=-x(1)+a*ut-k2*(x(2)-dth)-b*dth;
function sys=mdlOutputs(t,x,u)
sys(1)=x(1);     %d estimate
sys(2)=x(2);     %speed estimate
```

(3) S-function of the plant: chap8_8plant.m

```
function [sys,x0,str,ts]=s_function(t,x,u,flag)
switch flag,
case 0,
    [sys,x0,str,ts]=mdlInitializeSizes;
case 1,
    sys=mdlDerivatives(t,x,u);
case 3,
    sys=mdlOutputs(t,x,u);
case {2, 4, 9 }
    sys = [];
otherwise
    error(['Unhandled flag = ',num2str(flag)]);
end
function [sys,x0,str,ts]=mdlInitializeSizes
sizes = simsizes;
sizes.NumContStates = 2;
sizes.NumDiscStates = 0;
sizes.NumOutputs     = 3;
sizes.NumInputs      = 1;
sizes.DirFeedthrough = 0;
sizes.NumSampleTimes = 0;
sys=simsizes(sizes);
x0=[0;0];
str=[];
ts=[];
function sys=mdlDerivatives(t,x,u)
```

Advanced Sliding Mode Control for Mechanical Systems: Design, Analysis and MATLAB Simulation

```
ut=u(1);
b=0.15;
a=5;

d=150*sin(0.1*t);
ddth=-b*x(2)+a*ut-d;

sys(1)=x(2);
sys(2)=ddth;
function sys=mdlOutputs(t,x,u)
d=150*sin(0.1*t);
sys(1)=x(1);
sys(2)=x(2);
sys(3)=d;
```

(4) plot program: chap8_8plot.m

```
close all;
figure(1);
plot(t,p(:,3),'r',t,p(:,4),'b');
xlabel('time(s)');ylabel('d and its estimate');
legend('d','Estimated d');
```

8.8 Sliding Mode Control Based on Disturbance Observer

8.8.1 Problem Statement

A second-order system is given as follow:

$$G(s) = \frac{a}{s^2 + bs} \tag{8.56}$$

and considering disturbances, the system (8.56) can be written as

$$\ddot{\theta} = -b\dot{\theta} + au - d$$

where θ is the angle signal, a and b are all known positive constant, d is the slow time-varying disturbance.

8.8.2 Design and Analysis of Disturbance Observer

For the system (8.51), the observer proposed by Atsuo et al. as:

$$\dot{\hat{d}} = k_1(\hat{\omega} - \dot{\theta}) \tag{8.57}$$

210

8 Sliding Mode Control Based on Observer

$$\dot{\hat{\omega}} = -\hat{d} + au - k_2(\hat{\omega} - \dot{\theta}) - b\dot{\theta} \tag{8.58}$$

where $\hat{d}$ is the estimation of d, and $\hat{\omega}$ is the estimation of $\dot{\theta}$, $k_1 > 0$, $k_2 > 0^{[9]}$.

Select the Lyapunov function as

$$V_1 = \frac{1}{2k_1}\tilde{d}^2 + \frac{1}{2}\tilde{\omega}^2 \tag{8.59}$$

where $\tilde{d} = d - \hat{d}$, $\tilde{\omega} = \dot{\theta} - \hat{\omega}$.

Therefore, we have

$$\dot{V}_1 = \frac{1}{k_1}\tilde{d}\dot{\tilde{d}} + \tilde{\omega}\dot{\tilde{\omega}} = \frac{1}{k_1}\tilde{d}(\dot{d} - \dot{\hat{d}}) + \tilde{\omega}(\ddot{\theta} - \dot{\hat{\omega}})$$

From Eqs. (8.57) and (8.58), we have:

$$\dot{V}_1 = \frac{1}{k_1}\tilde{d}\dot{d} - \frac{1}{k_1}\tilde{d}\dot{\hat{d}} + \tilde{\omega}(\ddot{\theta} - (-\hat{d} + au - k_2(\hat{\omega} - \dot{\theta}) - b\dot{\theta}))$$

$$= \frac{1}{k_1}\tilde{d}\dot{d} - \frac{1}{k_1}\tilde{d}k_1(\hat{\omega} - \dot{\theta}) + \tilde{\omega}(-b\dot{\theta} + au - d - (-\hat{d} + au - k_2(\hat{\omega} - \dot{\theta}) - b\dot{\theta}))$$

$$= \frac{1}{k_1}\tilde{d}\dot{d} - \tilde{d}(\hat{\omega} - \dot{\theta}) + \tilde{\omega}(-d + \hat{d} + k_2(\hat{\omega} - \dot{\theta}))$$

$$= \frac{1}{k_1}\tilde{d}\dot{d} + \tilde{d}\tilde{\omega} + \tilde{\omega}(-\tilde{d} - k_2\tilde{\omega}) = \frac{1}{k_1}\tilde{d}\dot{d} - k_2\tilde{\omega}^2 \leqslant 0$$

Suppose the disturbance d be a slow time-varying signal, and d is bounded. When k_1 is relative large, we can get $\frac{1}{k_1}\dot{d} \approx 0$. At the same time, k_2 is also relative large, we can get:

$$\dot{V}_1 = \frac{1}{k_1}\tilde{d}\dot{d} - k_2\tilde{\omega}^2 \leqslant 0 \tag{8.60}$$

The disturbance d can be estimated by the designed disturbance observer, and the compensation will be realized in the feedback control.

8.8.3 Sliding Mode Controller Design

For system (8.56), let desired position input be θ_d, and $e = \theta_d - \theta$. The sliding variable is selected as

$$s = \dot{e} + ce \tag{8.61}$$

where $c > 0$. Therefore,

$$\dot{s} = \ddot{e} + c\dot{e} = \ddot{\theta}_d - \ddot{\theta} + c\dot{e} = \ddot{\theta}_d + b\dot{\theta} - au + d + c\dot{e}$$

The controller is adopted as

$$u = \frac{1}{a}[\ddot{\theta}_d + b\dot{\theta} + c\dot{e} + \hat{d} + \eta \operatorname{sgn}(s)] \qquad (8.62)$$

where $d = d - \hat{d}$, $\eta \geqslant |\tilde{d}|$.

Select the Lyapunov function as

$$V_2 = \frac{1}{2} s^2$$

Therefore, we have

$$\begin{aligned}
\dot{V}_2 &= s\dot{s} = s(\ddot{\theta}_d + b\dot{\theta} - au + d + c\dot{e}) \\
&= s(\ddot{\theta}_d + b\dot{\theta} - (\ddot{\theta}_d + b\dot{\theta} + c\dot{e} + \hat{d} + \eta \operatorname{sgn}(s)) + d + c\dot{e}) \qquad (8.63) \\
&= s(d - \hat{d} - \eta \operatorname{sgn}(s)) = \tilde{d}s - \eta |s| \leqslant 0
\end{aligned}$$

The Lyapunov function of the whole closed system can be described as

$$V = V_1 + V_2 = \frac{1}{2k_1} \tilde{d}^2 + \frac{1}{2} \tilde{\omega}^2 + \frac{1}{2} s^2$$

From Eqs. (8.60) and (8.63), we can get $\dot{V} \leqslant 0$.

In order to restrain the chattering phenomenon, the saturated function $\operatorname{sat}(s)$ is adopted instead of $\operatorname{sgn}(s)$ in Eq. (8.62),

$$\operatorname{sat}(s) = \begin{cases} 1, & s > \Delta \\ ks, & |s| \leqslant \Delta, \quad k = 1/\Delta \\ -1, & s < -\Delta \end{cases} \qquad (8.64)$$

where Δ is the "boundary layer".

The nature of saturated function is: Out of the boundary layer, switch control is selected, in the boundary layer, the usual feedback control is adopted. Therefore, the chattering phenomenon can be restrained thoroughly.

8.8.4 Simulation Example

The kinetic equation of system is given as follow:

$$\ddot{\theta} = -b\dot{\theta} + au - d$$

8 Sliding Mode Control Based on Observer

where $a = 5$, $b = 0.15$, $d = 150\sin(0.5t)$.

Let the desired position trajectory be $\theta_d = \sin t$, and the observer is given in Eqs. (8.57) and (8.58). Let $k_1 = 500$, $k_2 = 200$. The controller is given in Eq. (8.62), According to the upper boundless of observing error, select $\eta = 5.0$, $c = 15$, $\Delta = 0.10$. The simulation results are shown in Fig. 8.19 – Fig. 8.21.

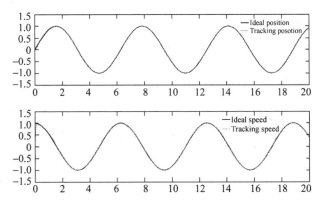

Figure 8.19 Position tracking and speed tracking

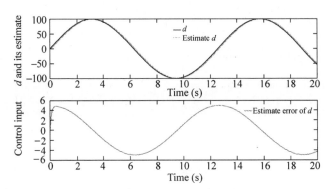

Figure 8.20 Disturbance and its observer value

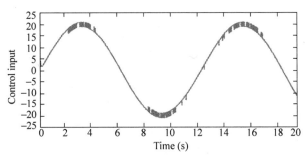

Figure 8.21 Control input

Advanced Sliding Mode Control for Mechanical Systems: Design, Analysis and MATLAB Simulation

Simulation programs:

(1) Simulink main program: chap8_9sim.mdl

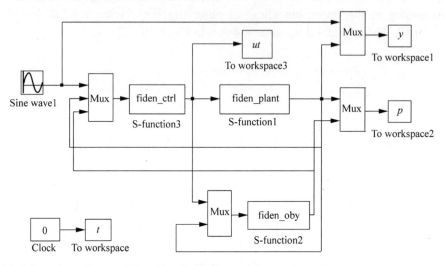

(2) S-function of controller: chap8_9ctrl.m

```
function [sys,x0,str,ts]=s_function(t,x,u,flag)
switch flag,
case 0,
    [sys,x0,str,ts]=mdlInitializeSizes;
case 1,
    sys=mdlDerivatives(t,x,u);
case 3,
    sys=mdlOutputs(t,x,u);
case {1, 2, 4, 9 }
    sys = [];
otherwise
    error(['Unhandled flag = ',num2str(flag)]);
end
function [sys,x0,str,ts]=mdlInitializeSizes
sizes = simsizes;
sizes.NumDiscStates  = 0;
sizes.NumOutputs     = 1;
sizes.NumInputs      = 5;
sizes.DirFeedthrough = 1;
sizes.NumSampleTimes = 0;
sys=simsizes(sizes);
x0=[];
str=[];
ts=[];
function sys=mdlOutputs(t,x,u)
thd=u(1);dthd=cos(t);ddthd=-sin(t);
th=u(2);
```

8　Sliding Mode Control Based on Observer

```
dth=u(3);
dp=u(5);
b=0.15;a=5;

e=thd-th;
de=dthd-dth;
c=15;
s=c*e+de;

xite=5.0;
M=2;
if M==1
    ut=1/a*(ddthd+b*dth+c*de+dp+xite*sign(s));
elseif M==2                  %Saturated function
        delta=0.10;
         kk=1/delta;
        if abs(s)>delta
          sats=sign(s);
        else
          sats=kk*s;
        end
    ut=1/a*(ddthd+b*dth+c*de+dp+xite*sign(s));
end
sys(1)=ut;
```

(3) Observer S-function: chap8_9obv.m

```
function [sys,x0,str,ts]=s_function(t,x,u,flag)
switch flag,
case 0,
    [sys,x0,str,ts]=mdlInitializeSizes;
case 1,
    sys=mdlDerivatives(t,x,u);
case 3,
    sys=mdlOutputs(t,x,u);
case {2, 4, 9 }
    sys = [];
otherwise
    error(['Unhandled flag = ',num2str(flag)]);
end
function [sys,x0,str,ts]=mdlInitializeSizes
sizes = simsizes;
sizes.NumContStates  = 2;
sizes.NumDiscStates  = 0;
sizes.NumOutputs     = 1;
sizes.NumInputs      = 4;
sizes.DirFeedthrough = 0;
sizes.NumSampleTimes = 0;
sys=simsizes(sizes);
x0=[0;0];
str=[];
```

```
ts=[];
function sys=mdlDerivatives(t,x,u)
ut=u(1);
dth=u(3);

k1=5000;
k2=500;

a=5;b=0.15;
sys(1)=k1*(x(2)-dth);
sys(2)=-x(1)+a*ut-k2*(x(2)-dth)-b*dth;
function sys=mdlOutputs(t,x,u)
sys(1)=x(1);    %d estimate
```

(4) S-function of the plant: chap8_9plant.m

```
function [sys,x0,str,ts]=s_function(t,x,u,flag)
switch flag,
case 0,
    [sys,x0,str,ts]=mdlInitializeSizes;
case 1,
    sys=mdlDerivatives(t,x,u);
case 3,
    sys=mdlOutputs(t,x,u);
case {2, 4, 9 }
    sys = [];
otherwise
    error(['Unhandled flag = ',num2str(flag)]);
end
function [sys,x0,str,ts]=mdlInitializeSizes
sizes = simsizes;
sizes.NumContStates  = 2;
sizes.NumDiscStates  = 0;
sizes.NumOutputs     = 3;
sizes.NumInputs      = 1;
sizes.DirFeedthrough = 0;
sizes.NumSampleTimes = 0;
sys=simsizes(sizes);
x0=[0;0];
str=[];
ts=[];
function sys=mdlDerivatives(t,x,u)
ut=u(1);
b=0.15;
a=5;

d=100*sin(0.5*t);
ddth=-b*x(2)+a*ut-d;

sys(1)=x(2);
```

8 Sliding Mode Control Based on Observer

```
sys(2)=ddth;
function sys=mdlOutputs(t,x,u)
d=100*sin(0.5*t);
sys(1)=x(1);
sys(2)=x(2);
sys(3)=d;
```

(5) plot program: chap8_9plot.m

```
close all;

figure(1);
subplot(211);
plot(t,y(:,1),'k',t,y(:,2),'r:','linewidth',2);
legend('ideal position','tracking position');
subplot(212);
plot(t,cos(t),'k',t,y(:,3),'r:','linewidth',2);
legend('ideal speed','tracking speed');

figure(2);
subplot(211);
plot(t,p(:,3),'k',t,p(:,4),'r:','linewidth',2);
xlabel('time(s)');ylabel('d and its estimate');
legend('d','Estimate d');
subplot(212);
plot(t,p(:,3)-p(:,4),'r','linewidth',2);
xlabel('time(s)');ylabel('error between d and its estimate');
legend('Estimate error of d');

figure(3);
plot(t,ut(:,1),'r','linewidth',2);
xlabel('time(s)');ylabel('Control input');
```

8.9 Delayed Output Observer

8.9.1 System Description

Consider a second order transfer function as

$$G(s) = \frac{1}{s^2 + 10s + 1} \tag{8.65}$$

The system (8.65) can be described as

$$\begin{aligned} \dot{\theta} &= \omega \\ \dot{\omega} &= -10\dot{\theta} - \theta + u \end{aligned} \tag{8.66}$$

217

Advanced Sliding Mode Control for Mechanical Systems: Design, Analysis and MATLAB Simulation

where $\theta(t)$ denote angle at time t; u are the input signal, $y(t) = \theta(t)$.

Denote:

$$z(t) = [\theta(t) \quad \omega(t)]^{\mathrm{T}}$$

The goal is to observe that

$$\hat{\theta}(t) \to \theta(t), \hat{\omega}(t) \to \omega(t) \text{ as } t \to \infty.$$

where Δ is the time delay brought from measurement delay.

8.9.2 Delayed Output Observer Design

We rewrite system (8.65) as:

$$\dot{z}(t) = Az(t) + Hu(t) \tag{8.67}$$

where A is a Hurwitz matrix, and $A = \begin{bmatrix} 0 & 1 \\ -1 & -10 \end{bmatrix}$, $H = \begin{bmatrix} 0 \\ 1 \end{bmatrix}$.

The measurement outputs are:

$$\bar{y}(t) = \theta(t - \Delta) = Cz(t - \Delta) \tag{8.68}$$

where $C = (1 \quad 0)$.

We design an observer[9] for system (8.67) as follow:

$$\dot{\hat{z}}(t) = A\hat{z}(t) + Hu(t) + e^{A\Delta}K[\bar{y}(t) - C\hat{z}(t - \Delta)] \tag{8.69}$$

$$\dot{\hat{z}}(t - \Delta) = A\hat{z}(t - \Delta) + Hu(t - \Delta) + K[\bar{y}(t) - C\hat{z}(t - \Delta)] \tag{8.70}$$

where A must be Hurwitz, K is selected to make $A - KC$ Hurwitz, and

$$e^{A\Delta} = I + A\Delta + \frac{1}{2!}A^2\Delta^2 + \cdots = \begin{bmatrix} 1 & \Delta \\ 0 & 1 \end{bmatrix}$$

Denote

$$\delta(t) = [\delta_1(t) \quad \delta_2(t)]^{\mathrm{T}} = [\hat{\theta}(t) - \theta(t) \quad \hat{\omega}(t) - \omega(t)]^{\mathrm{T}} \tag{8.71}$$

8.9.3 Delayed Output Observer Analysis

From Eq. (8.67), we have

218

8 Sliding Mode Control Based on Observer

$$\dot{z}(t-\Delta) = Az(t-\Delta) + Hu(t-\Delta) \tag{8.72}$$

From Eqs. (8.67) and (8.71), we get

$$\delta(t-\Delta) = \hat{z}(t-\Delta) - z(t-\Delta) \tag{8.73}$$

Therefore, from Eqs. (8.70) and (8.73), we get

$$\dot{\delta}(t-\Delta) = (A-KC)\delta(t-\Delta) \tag{8.74}$$

The solution of Eq. (8.74) is

$$\delta(t-\Delta) = \delta(t_0 - \Delta)e^{(A-KC)(t-t_0)} \tag{8.75}$$

where t_0 is the initial time.

We select K such that $A - KC$ is Hurwitz. From Eq. (8.75), there exist positive constants λ and l such that

$$\| \delta(t-\Delta) \| \leqslant l \| \delta(t_0 - \Delta) \| e^{-\lambda(t-t_0)} \tag{8.76}$$

Lemma 1[9]: The observer (8.79) is equivalent to the following relations:

$$\hat{z}(t) = e^{A\Delta}\hat{z}(t-\Delta) + \int_{t-\Delta}^{t} e^{A(t-\tau)} Hu(\tau)\mathrm{d}\tau \tag{8.77}$$

Proof: For Eq. (8.77), after an application of Leibniz integral rule, we obtain

$$
\begin{aligned}
\dot{\hat{z}}(t) &= e^{A\Delta}\dot{\hat{z}}(t-\Delta) + A\int_{t-\Delta}^{t} e^{A(t-\tau)} Hu(\tau)\mathrm{d}\tau + Hu(t) - e^{A\Delta} Hu(t-\Delta) \\
&= e^{A\Delta}\dot{\hat{z}}(t-\Delta) + A(\hat{z}(t) - e^{A\Delta}\hat{z}(t-\Delta)) + Hu(t) - e^{A\Delta} Hu(t-\Delta) \\
&= A\hat{z}(t) + Hu(t) + e^{A\Delta}(\dot{\hat{z}}(t-\Delta) - A\hat{z}(t-\Delta) - Hu(t-\Delta))
\end{aligned} \tag{8.78}
$$

From there it follows, after rearranging the terms in Eq. (8.78), we get

$$\dot{\hat{z}}(t) = A\hat{z}(t) + Hu(t) + e^{A\Delta} K(\bar{y}(t) - C\hat{z}(t-\Delta)) \tag{8.79}$$

This concludes Lemma 1.

Theorem 3[9]: For system (8.73) with Eq. (8.74), and the designed observers (8.69) and (8.70), there exist positive constants λ and l such that

$$\| \delta(t) \| \leqslant l \| e^{A\Delta} \| \| \delta(t_0 - \Delta) \| e^{-\lambda(t-t_0)} \tag{8.80}$$

where $\delta(t)$ is defined in Eq. (8.76).

Proof: From Eq. (8.73), we have

$$z(t) = e^{A\Delta} z(t-\Delta) + \int_{t-\Delta}^{t} e^{A(t-\tau)} Hu(\tau)\mathrm{d}\tau \tag{8.81}$$

219

From Eq. (8.77) in lemma 1 and Eq. (8.81), we can get

$$\delta(t) = e^{A\Delta}\delta(t-\Delta) \tag{8.82}$$

Therefore, from Eqs. (8.76) and (8.82), we have

$$\|\delta(t)\| \leqslant \|e^{A\Delta}\| \|\delta(t-\Delta)\| \leqslant l \|e^{A\Delta}\| \|\delta(t_0-\Delta)\| e^{-\lambda(t-t_0)} \tag{8.83}$$

This concludes the proof.

8.9.4 Simulation Example

Consider the system (8.65) with delayed output, choose $u(t) = \sin t$.
We select K to make $A - KC$ Hurwitz. Since

$$A - KC = \begin{bmatrix} 0 & 1 \\ -1 & -10 \end{bmatrix} - \begin{bmatrix} k_1 \\ k_2 \end{bmatrix} [1 \ 0] = \begin{bmatrix} -k_1 & 1 \\ -1-k_2 & -10 \end{bmatrix}$$

according to $|\lambda I - (A - KC)| = 0$, we can get $\begin{vmatrix} \lambda + k_1 & -1 \\ k_2 + 1 & \lambda + 10 \end{vmatrix} = 0$, that is
$\lambda^2 + (k_1 + 10)\lambda + k_2 + 1 + 10k_1 = 0$. From $(\lambda + a)^2 = 0$ and $a > 0$, we can get
$\lambda^2 + 2\lambda a + a^2 = 0$, then we can choose $k_1 + 10 = 2a$, $k_2 + 1 + 10k_1 = a^2$.

To guarantee $A - KC$ to be Hurwitz, we can choose $a = 10$, then $k_1 = 10$, $k_2 = -1$, and initial states of the plant and the observers (8.69) and (8.70) are $\theta(0) = 0.20$, $\omega(0) = 0$, $\hat{\theta}(0) = \hat{\omega}(0) = 0$, $\Delta = 3.0$. The simulation results are shown in Fig. 8.22 – Fig. 8.24. It is seen that the observer errors asymptotically converge to zero.

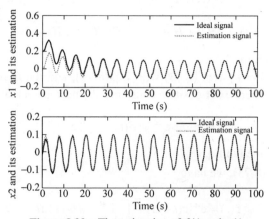

Figure 8.22 The estimation of $\theta(t)$ and $\omega(t)$

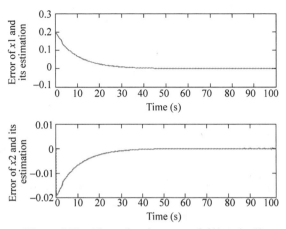

Figure 8.23 The estimation error of $\theta(t)$ and $\omega(t)$

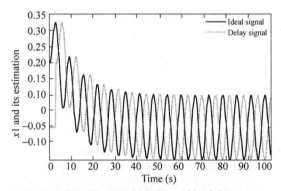

Figure 8.24 The practical $\theta(t)$ and its delay output

8.10 Design of Controller Based on Delayed Output Observer

8.10.1 Design of Controller

Let the desired trajectory be (θ_d, ω_d), and let

$$e_1 = \theta_1(t) - \theta_d, \quad e_2 = \omega(t) - \omega_d$$

and

$$\hat{e}_1 = \hat{\theta}_1(t) - \theta_d, \quad \hat{e}_2 = \hat{\omega}(t) - \omega_d$$

For the delayed output sub-observer (8.69), we rewrite it as

$$\left.\begin{array}{l}\dot{\hat{\theta}}(t)=\hat{\omega}(t)+(k_1+k_2\varDelta)(\theta(t-\varDelta)-\hat{\theta}(t-\varDelta))\\\dot{\hat{\omega}}(t)=-\hat{\theta}-10\hat{\omega}+u(t)+k_2(\theta(t-\varDelta)-\hat{\theta}(t-\varDelta))\end{array}\right\} \quad (8.84)$$

The tracking error system between the delayed output sub-observer (8.84) and the desired trajectory be (θ_d,ω_d) is

$$\dot{\hat{e}}_1(t)=\hat{e}_2(t)+(k_1+k_2\varDelta)(\theta(t-\varDelta)-\hat{\theta}(t-\varDelta))$$
$$\dot{\hat{e}}_2(t)=-\hat{\theta}-10\hat{\omega}+u(t)+k_2(\theta(t-\varDelta)-\hat{\theta}(t-\varDelta))-\omega_d$$

Let the observing sliding variable be

$$\hat{s}=\hat{e}_2+\lambda\hat{e}_1$$

where λ is a positive constant. The Lyapunov function is selected as

$$V=\frac{1}{2}\hat{s}^2$$

Therefore, we have

$$\dot{V}=\hat{s}(\dot{\hat{e}}_2+\lambda\dot{\hat{e}}_1)$$
$$=\hat{s}(-\hat{\theta}-10\hat{\omega}+u(t)+k_2(\theta(t-\varDelta)-\hat{\theta}(t-\varDelta))-\omega_d$$
$$+(\hat{e}_2(t)+(k_1+k_2\varDelta)(\theta(t-\varDelta)-\hat{\theta}(t-\varDelta))))$$

We select the controller as

$$u(t)=\hat{\theta}+10\hat{\omega}-l\mathrm{sgn}(\hat{s})+\omega_d-\lambda\hat{e}_2(t)-(\lambda(k_1+k_2\varDelta)+k_2)(\theta(t-\varDelta)-\hat{\theta}(t-\varDelta))$$

$$(8.85)$$

where λ is a positive constant. Therefore, we have

$$\dot{V}=-l\hat{s}\,\mathrm{sgn}(\hat{s})=-l\,|\,\hat{s}\,|\leqslant 0$$

Therefore, there exist t_s, for $t\geqslant t_s$, we have $\hat{s}=\hat{e}_2+\lambda\hat{e}_1=0$, i.e.,

$$\hat{e}_2\to 0 \text{ and } \hat{e}_1\to 0 \quad \text{as } t\to 0$$

From Theorem 3, it implies that Eqs. (8.69) and (8.70) are the global exponential observer. Therefore, $e_1(t)\to 0$, $e_2(t)\to 0$ as $t\to\infty$.

222

8.10.2 Simulation Example

Consider the system (8.65) with delayed output, choose $u(t) = \sin t$. In the observer (8.69) and (8.70), to guarantee $A - KC$ to be Hurwitz, we choose $a = 10$, then $k_1 = 10$, $k_2 = -1$, and initial states of the plant are $\theta(0) = 0.20$, $\omega(0) = 0$, $\hat{\theta}(0) = \hat{\omega}(0) = 0$, $\Delta = 3.0$. Using the observers (8.69) and (8.70) and the controller (8.85), the simulation results are shown in Fig. 8.25 – Fig. 8.27. It is seen that the tracking errors converge to very small.

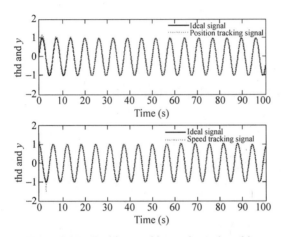

Figure 8.25 Position tracking and speed tracking

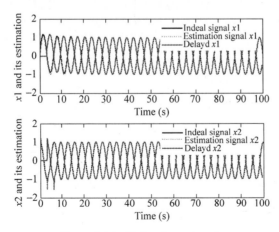

Figure 8.26 Estimation value of x

Advanced Sliding Mode Control for Mechanical Systems: Design, Analysis and MATLAB Simulation

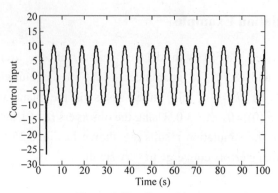

Figure 8.27 Control input

Simulation programs:

1. Observer program

(1) Simulink main program: chap8_10sim.mdl

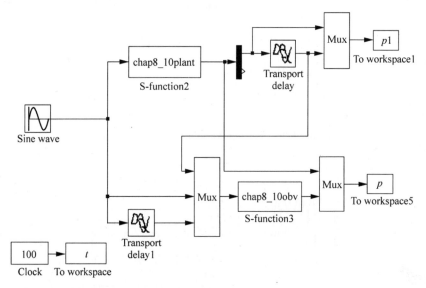

(2) S-function of observer: chap8_10obv.m

```
function [sys,x0,str,ts]=s_function(t,x,u,flag)
switch flag,
case 0,
    [sys,x0,str,ts]=mdlInitializeSizes;
case 1,
    sys=mdlDerivatives(t,x,u);
case 3,
    sys=mdlOutputs(t,x,u);
case {2, 4, 9 }
```

8 Sliding Mode Control Based on Observer

```
    sys = [];
otherwise
    error(['Unhandled flag = ',num2str(flag)]);
end
function [sys,x0,str,ts]=mdlInitializeSizes
sizes = simsizes;
sizes.NumContStates  = 4;
sizes.NumDiscStates  = 0;
sizes.NumOutputs     = 4;
sizes.NumInputs      = 3;
sizes.DirFeedthrough = 1;
sizes.NumSampleTimes = 1;
sys=simsizes(sizes);
x0=[0 0 0 0];
str=[];
ts=[-1 0];
function sys=mdlDerivatives(t,x,u)
tol=3.0;
th_tol=u(1);
y3p=th_tol;

ut=u(2);
ut_tol=u(3);
z3_tol=[x(3);x(4)];
thp_tol=x(3);
thp=x(1);wp=x(2);

%%%%%%%%%
A=[0 1;-1 -10];
C=[1 0];

H3=[0;1];

k1=1;k2=2;

k1=10;k2=-1;
K=[k1 k2]';
z3=[thp wp]';

%%%%%%%%%
E=[exp(-1*tol) 0;0 exp(-1*tol)];

dz3=A*z3+H3*ut+E*K*(y3p-C*z3_tol);
dz3_tol=A*z3_tol+H3*ut_tol+K*(y3p-C*z3_tol);

for i=1:2
    sys(i)=dz3(i);
```

Advanced Sliding Mode Control for Mechanical Systems: Design, Analysis and MATLAB Simulation

```
    sys(i+2)=dz3_tol(i);
end
function sys=mdlOutputs(t,x,u)
thp=x(1);wp=x(2);
thp_tol=x(3);wp_tol=x(4);

sys(1)=thp;
sys(2)=wp;
sys(3)=thp_tol;
sys(4)=wp_tol;
```

(3) S-function of plant: chap8_10plant.m

```
function [sys,x0,str,ts]=s_function(t,x,u,flag)
switch flag,
case 0,
    [sys,x0,str,ts]=mdlInitializeSizes;
case 1,
    sys=mdlDerivatives(t,x,u);
case 3,
    sys=mdlOutputs(t,x,u);
case {2, 4, 9 }
    sys = [];
otherwise
    error(['Unhandled flag = ',num2str(flag)]);
end
function [sys,x0,str,ts]=mdlInitializeSizes
sizes = simsizes;
sizes.NumContStates  = 2;
sizes.NumDiscStates  = 0;
sizes.NumOutputs     = 2;
sizes.NumInputs      =1;
sizes.DirFeedthrough = 1;
sizes.NumSampleTimes = 1;
sys=simsizes(sizes);
x0=[0.2 0];
str=[];
ts=[-1 0];
function sys=mdlDerivatives(t,x,u)
sys(1)=x(2);
sys(2)=-10*x(2)-x(1)+u(1);
function sys=mdlOutputs(t,x,u)
th=x(1);w=x(2);

sys(1)=th;
sys(2)=w;
```

(4) S-function of plot: chap8_10plot.m

```
close all;
```

226

8 Sliding Mode Control Based on Observer

```
figure(1);
subplot(211);
plot(t,p(:,1),'k',t,p(:,3),'r:','linewidth',2);
xlabel('time(s)');ylabel('x1 and its estimation');
legend('ideal signal','estimation signal');
subplot(212);
plot(t,p(:,2),'k',t,p(:,4),'r:','linewidth',2);
xlabel('time(s)');ylabel('x2 and its estimation');
legend('ideal signal','estimation signal');

figure(2);
subplot(211);
plot(t,p(:,1)-p(:,3),'r','linewidth',2);
xlabel('time(s)');ylabel('error of x1 and its estimation');
subplot(212);
plot(t,p(:,2)-p(:,4),'r','linewidth',2);
xlabel('time(s)');ylabel('error of x2 and its estimation');

figure(3);
plot(t,p1(:,1),'k',t,p1(:,2),'r:','linewidth',2);
xlabel('time(s)');ylabel('x1 and its estimation');
legend('ideal signal','delay signal');
```

2. Sliding mode controller

(1) Simulink main program: chap8_11sim.mdl

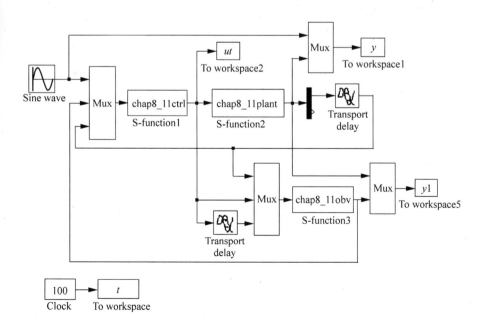

(2) S-function of controller: chap8_11ctrl.m

```matlab
function [sys,x0,str,ts]=s_function(t,x,u,flag)
switch flag,
case 0,
    [sys,x0,str,ts]=mdlInitializeSizes;
case 3,
    sys=mdlOutputs(t,x,u);
case {1,2, 4, 9 }
    sys = [];
otherwise
    error(['Unhandled flag = ',num2str(flag)]);
end
function [sys,x0,str,ts]=mdlInitializeSizes
sizes = simsizes;
sizes.NumContStates  = 0;
sizes.NumDiscStates  = 0;
sizes.NumOutputs     = 1;
sizes.NumInputs      = 6;
sizes.DirFeedthrough = 1;
sizes.NumSampleTimes = 1;
sys=simsizes(sizes);
x0=[];
str=[];
ts=[-1 0];
function sys=mdlOutputs(t,x,u)
tol=3;
thd=1*sin(t);
wd=1*cos(t);
ddthd=-sin(t);

k1=10;k2=-1;
nmn=15;
thp=u(2);
wp=u(3);
thp_tol=u(4);
th_tol=u(6);

e1p=thp-thd;
e2p=wp-wd;
sp=e2p+nmn*e1p;
l=3.0;

fai=0.05;
if sp/fai>1
   sat=1;
elseif abs(sp/fai)<=1
   sat=sp/fai;
elseif sp/fai<-1
```

8 Sliding Mode Control Based on Observer

```
    sat=-1;
end
%ut=thp+10*wp-1*sign(sp)+wd-nmn*e2p-(nmn*(k1+k2*tol)+k2)*(th_tol-thp_tol);
ut=thp+10*wp-1*sat+wd-nmn*e2p-(nmn*(k1+k2*tol)+k2)*(th_tol-thp_tol);


sys(1)=ut;
```

(3) S-function of observer: chap8_11obv.m

```
function [sys,x0,str,ts]=s_function(t,x,u,flag)
switch flag,
case 0,
    [sys,x0,str,ts]=mdlInitializeSizes;
case 1,
    sys=mdlDerivatives(t,x,u);
case 3,
    sys=mdlOutputs(t,x,u);
case {2, 4, 9 }
    sys = [];
otherwise
    error(['Unhandled flag = ',num2str(flag)]);
end
function [sys,x0,str,ts]=mdlInitializeSizes
sizes = simsizes;
sizes.NumContStates  = 4;
sizes.NumDiscStates  = 0;
sizes.NumOutputs     = 4;
sizes.NumInputs      = 3;
sizes.DirFeedthrough = 1;
sizes.NumSampleTimes = 1;
sys=simsizes(sizes);
x0=[0 0 0 0];
str=[];
ts=[-1 0];
function sys=mdlDerivatives(t,x,u)
tol=3.0;
th_tol=u(1);
y3p=th_tol;

ut=u(2);
ut_tol=u(3);
z3_tol=[x(3);x(4)];
thp_tol=x(3);
thp=x(1);wp=x(2);

%%%%%%%%
A=[0 1;-1 -10];
C=[1 0];
```

```
H3=[0;1];

k1=10;k2=-1;
K=[k1 k2]';
z3=[thp wp]';
%%%%%%%%
E=[exp(-1*tol) 0;0 exp(-1*tol)];

dz3=A*z3+H3*ut+E*K*(y3p-C*z3_tol);
dz3_tol=A*z3_tol+H3*ut_tol+K*(y3p-C*z3_tol);

for i=1:2
    sys(i)=dz3(i);
    sys(i+2)=dz3_tol(i);
end
function sys=mdlOutputs(t,x,u)
thp=x(1);wp=x(2);
thp_tol=x(3);wp_tol=x(4);

sys(1)=thp;
sys(2)=wp;
sys(3)=thp_tol;
sys(4)=wp_tol;
```

(4) S-function of plant: chap8_11plant.m

```
function [sys,x0,str,ts]=s_function(t,x,u,flag)
switch flag,
case 0,
    [sys,x0,str,ts]=mdlInitializeSizes;
case 1,
    sys=mdlDerivatives(t,x,u);
case 3,
    sys=mdlOutputs(t,x,u);
case {2, 4, 9 }
    sys = [];
otherwise
    error(['Unhandled flag = ',num2str(flag)]);
end
function [sys,x0,str,ts]=mdlInitializeSizes
sizes = simsizes;
sizes.NumContStates  = 2;
sizes.NumDiscStates  = 0;
sizes.NumOutputs     = 2;
sizes.NumInputs      =1;
sizes.DirFeedthrough = 1;
sizes.NumSampleTimes = 1;
sys=simsizes(sizes);
x0=[0.2 0];
```

8 Sliding Mode Control Based on Observer

```
str=[];
ts=[-1 0];
function sys=mdlDerivatives(t,x,u)
sys(1)=x(2);
sys(2)=-10*x(2)-x(1)+u(1);
function sys=mdlOutputs(t,x,u)
th=x(1);w=x(2);


sys(1)=th;
sys(2)=w;
```

(5) S-function of plot: chap8_11plot.m

```
close all;

figure(1);
subplot(211);
plot(t,y(:,1),'k',t,y(:,2),'r:','linewidth',2);
xlabel('time(s)');ylabel('thd and y');
legend('ideal signal','position tracking signal');
subplot(212);
plot(t,cos(t),'k',t,y(:,3),'r:','linewidth',2);
xlabel('time(s)');ylabel('thd and y');
legend('ideal signal','speed tracking signal');

figure(2);
subplot(211);
plot(t,y1(:,1),'k',t,y1(:,3),'r:',t,y1(:,5),'b','linewidth',2);
xlabel('time(s)');ylabel('x1 and its estimation');
legend('ideal signal x1','estimation signal x1','delayed x1');
subplot(212);
plot(t,y1(:,2),'k',t,y1(:,4),'r:',t,y1(:,6),'b','linewidth',2);
xlabel('time(s)');ylabel('x2 and its estimation');
legend('ideal signal x2','estimation signal x2','delayed x2');

figure(3);
plot(t,ut(:,1),'k','linewidth',2);
xlabel('time(s)');ylabel('Control input');
```

References

[1] Kahlil HK. Nonlinear Systems, 3nd ed. Englewood Cliffs, NJ: Prentice-Hall, 2002
[2] Khalil HK. High-gain observers in nonlinear feedback control, Int. Conf. on Control, Automation and Systems, Seoul, Korea, 2008
[3] Wang XH, Chen ZQ, Yuan ZZ. Output tracking based on extended observer for nonlinear uncertain systems, Control and Decision, 2004, 19(10): 1113 – 1116 (In Chinese)

[4] Khalil HK. Nonlinear Systems, Prentice Hall, Upper Saddle River, New Jersey, 3rd edition, 2002

[5] Wang XH and Liu JK. Differentiator Design and Application-Filtering and Differentiating for Signals (In Chinese)

[6] Ahrens JH, Khalil HK. High-gain observers in the presence of measurement noise: A switched-gain approach, Automatica, 2009, 45: 936 – 943

[7] Slotine JJ. and Li WP. Applied nonlinear control. Prentice-Hall, 1991

[8] Atsuo K, Hiroshi I, Kiyoshi S. Chattering reduction of disturbance observer based sliding mode control. IEEE Transactions on Industry Applications, 1994, 30(2): 456 – 461

[9] Wang XH, Liu JK, Cai KY. Tracking control for a velocity-sensorless VTOL aircraft with delayed outputs, Automatica, 2009, 45: 2876 – 2882

9 Fuzzy Sliding Mode Control

Jinkun Liu
Beijing University of Aeronautics and Astronautics
P.R.China
E-mail: ljk@buaa.edu.cn

Xinhua Wang
National University of Singapore
Singapore
E-mail: wangxinhua04@gmail.com

Abstract   This chapter introduces four kinds of fuzzy sliding mode controllers design, including fuzzy sliding mode control based on equivalent control, sliding mode control based on fuzzy switch-gain regulation, sliding mode control based on fuzzy system approximation and adaptive fuzzy control based on fuzzy compensation for manipulator.

Keywords   fuzzy sliding mode control, equivalent control, fuzzy switch-gain, fuzzy system approximation, adaptive fuzzy control

Section 9.1 deals with the control system that comprises a logic fuzzy control design and an equivalent control. We introduce a fuzzy sliding mode control based on the equivalent control scheme for a class of nonlinear systems. The sliding mode control law in the existing equivalent sliding mode control system is directly substituted by a fuzzy logic controller. Hence, a control input without chattering is obtained in the systems with uncertainties. The chattering phenomenon in the sliding mode control is attenuated.

A chattering-free fuzzy sliding-mode control strategy for uncertain systems is introduced in section 9.2. The discontinuous switch gain in the traditional sliding-mode control is replaced by a fuzzy logic control. Hence, a control input without chattering is obtained in the systems with uncertainties. Based on the Lyapunov stability theory, we address the design schemes of the fuzzy sliding-mode control where the fuzzy control is designed by a set of linguistic rules and the control input is chattering free.

Past research of the universal approximation theorem[1] shows that any nonlinear function over a compact set with arbitrary accuracy can be approximated by a

Advanced Sliding Mode Control for Mechanical Systems: Design, Analysis and MATLAB Simulation

fuzzy system. There have been significant research efforts on the adaptive fuzzy control for nonlinear systems[2]. Section 9.3 and section 9.4 propose an adaptive fuzzy sliding mode control algorithm for a class of continuous time unknown nonlinear systems. The unknown nonlinearities are approximated by the fuzzy system with a set of fuzzy IF-THEN rules whose parameters are adjusted on-line according to some adaptive laws. This aids in controlling the output of the nonlinear system to track a given trajectory. The Lyapunov synthesis approach is used to develop an adaptive control algorithm which is based on the adaptive fuzzy model. The chattering action is attenuated and robust performance can be ensured. The stability analysis for the proposed control algorithm is provided.

9.1 Fuzzy Sliding Mode Control Based on Equivalent Control

In section 6 of Chapter 1, the equivalent sliding mode control has been described. The control law consists of an equivalent control u_{eq} and a switch control u_s. System states are kept on the sliding surface by an equivalent control and system states attain the sliding surface by a switch control. Using fuzzy rules, the fuzzy system is established based on the equivalent control and the switch control.

The sliding mode control based on an equivalent control uses the switching-gain switch control to reduce the chattering phenomenon and guarantee the Lyapunov stability. The small switching-gain switch control is adopted when the magnitudes of disturbances are small and the large switching-gain switch control is adopted when magnitudes of disturbances are large. This function can be realized by fuzzy system with fuzzy rules[3].

9.1.1 Design of Fuzzy Control

Consider the following system with disturbances and uncertainties:

$$\ddot{x} = f(x,t) + g(x,t)u(t) + d(t) \tag{9.1}$$

Let the tracking error be $e = x_d - x$, and the switch function be

$$s = ce + \dot{e} \tag{9.2}$$

According to the sliding mode control theory, a sliding mode controller consists of equivalent sliding mode control and switch control. The control law is shown as follows:

$$\text{If } s(t) \text{ is } N \text{ then } \mu \text{ is } P \tag{9.3a}$$

$$\text{If } s(t) \text{ is } Z \text{ then } \mu \text{ is } Z \tag{9.3b}$$

234

9 Fuzzy Sliding Mode Control

$$\text{If } s(t) \text{ is } P \text{ then } \mu \text{ is } P \tag{9.3c}$$

where the fuzzy sets Z, N and P denote "zero", "negative", and "positive" respectively.

Fuzzy rule (9.3b) states that the fuzzy controller is the equivalent control u_{eq} when the switch function is equal to zero. Also, fuzzy rules (9.3a) and (9.3c) state that the fuzzy controller is the equivalent control $u_{eq} + \mu \times$ the switch control u_s when switch function is not equal to zero.

The output of the fuzzy deduce system is membership μ. Adopting reverse fuzzification method, the fuzzy control is designed as:

$$u = u_{eq} + \mu \cdot u_s \tag{9.4}$$

When $\mu = 1$, $u = u_{eq} + u_s$. Therefore, the control law is the traditional equivalent sliding mode control. When $\mu \neq 1$, the chattering phenomenon can be reduced by the variant membership μ.

9.1.2 Simulation Example

Consider the kinetic equation of a single-stage inverted pendulum as follows:

$$\begin{cases} \dot{x}_1 = x_2 \\ \dot{x}_2 = f(x) + g(x) \cdot u + d(t) \end{cases}$$

where

$$f(x) = \frac{g \sin x_1 - mlx_2^2 \cos x_1 \sin x_1 / (m_c + m)}{l(4/3 - m\cos^2 x_1 / (m_c + m))}$$

$$g(x) = \frac{\cos x_1 / (m_c + m)}{l(4/3 - m\cos^2 x_1 / (m_c + m))}$$

$x = [x_1 \quad x_2]$, x_1 and x_2 are the roll angle and roll rate respectively, $g = 9.8 \text{ m/s}^2$, u is the control input, $m_c = 1 \text{ kg}$ is the mass of the vehicle, $m = 0.1 \text{ kg}$ is the mass of the pendulum, $l = 0.5 \text{ m}$ is the length of one half of the pendulum.

Consider the disturbance $d(t)$ with the form of Gauss function in the following:

$$d(t) = 5\exp\left(-\frac{(t - c_i)^2}{2b_i^2}\right)$$

Let $b_i = 0.50$, $c_i = 5.0$ and $\eta = 0.15$. The upper bound of disturbance is $D = \max(|d(t)|) + \eta = 5.15$. The disturbance $d(t)$ is shown in Fig. 9.1. The desired position trajectory is $x_d = \sin t$.

235

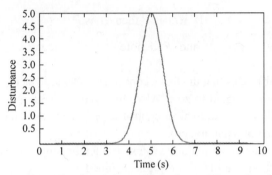

Figure 9.1 The disturbance with the form of Gauss function

The fuzzy system is established in S-function chap4_5s.m and the rule library is kept running by the command of persistent. The membership functions of input and output of fuzzy system are in Figs. 9.2 and 9.3 respectively. Fuzzy rule is designed as:

(1) If (s is N) then (Mu is P);
(2) If (s is Z) then (u is Z);
(3) If (s is P) then (Mu is P).

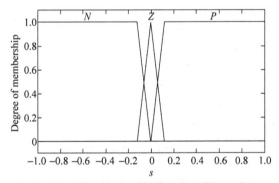

Figure 9.2 The membership function of fuzzy input s

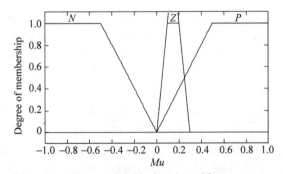

Figure 9.3 The membership function of fuzzy output μ

Use control law (9.4) with $\mu = 1$, and let $c = 25$, simulation results are shown in Fig. 9.4 and Fig. 9.5. Using control law (9.4) with $\mu \neq 1$, and let $c = 25$, simulation results are shown in Fig. 9.6 – Fig. 9.8. It can be found that the chattering

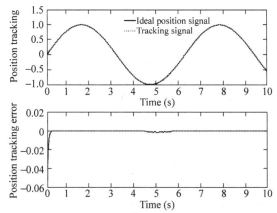

Figure 9.4 Position tracking by equivalent sliding mode control ($\mu = 1$)

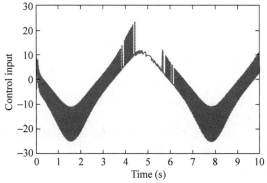

Figure 9.5 Control input ($\mu = 1$)

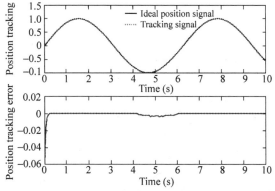

Figure 9.6 Position tracking by fuzzy sliding mode control ($\mu \neq 1$)

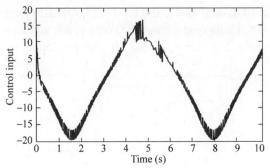

Figure 9.7 Control input ($\mu \neq 1$)

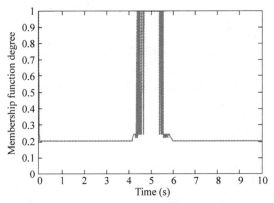

Figure 9.8 Membership function $\mu_{NZ}(s)$ ($\mu \neq 1$)

phenomenon can be reduced effectively when the fuzzy sliding mode control based on an equivalent control is adopted.

Simulation programs:

(1) Fuzzy logic system program: chap9_1fuzz.m

```
close all
clear all;

a=newfis('fuzz_smc');

a=addvar(a,'input','s',1/25*[-25,25]);
a=addmf(a,'input',1,'N','trapmf',1/25*[-25,-25,-3,0]);
a=addmf(a,'input',1,'Z','trimf',1/25*[-3,0,3]);
a=addmf(a,'input',1,'P','trapmf',1/25*[0,3,25,25]);

% a=addvar(a,'output','Mu',20*[-5,5]);
% a=addmf(a,'output',1,'N','trapmf',20*[-5,-5,-3,0]);
% a=addmf(a,'output',1,'Z','trimf',20*[-3,0,3]);
% a=addmf(a,'output',1,'P','trapmf',20*[0,3,5,5]);
```

```
a=addvar(a,'output','Mu',[-1,1]);
a=addmf(a,'output',1,'N','trapmf',[-1,-1,-0.5,0]);
a=addmf(a,'output',1,'Z','trapmf',[0,0.1,0.2,0.3]);
a=addmf(a,'output',1,'P','trapmf',[0,0.5,1,1]);

rulelist=[1 3 1 1;
          2 2 1 1;
          3 3 1 1];

a=addrule(a,rulelist);
showrule(a)                    %Show fuzzy rule base

a1=setfis(a,'DefuzzMethod','centroid');   %Defuzzy
a1=setfis(a,'DefuzzMethod','lom');   %Defuzzy
writefis(a1,'fsmc');                %Save fuzzy system as "fsmc.fis"
a2=readfis('fsmc');
ruleview(a2);

figure(1);
plotmf(a,'input',1);
figure(2);
plotmf(a,'output',1);
```

(2) Simulink main program: chap9_1sim.mdl

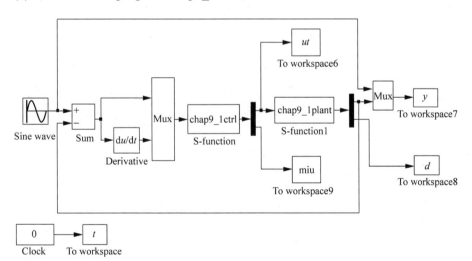

(3) S-function of controller: chap9_1ctrl.m

```
function [sys,x0,str,ts]=s_function(t,x,u,flag)
switch flag,
case 0,
    [sys,x0,str,ts]=mdlInitializeSizes;
case 3,
    sys=mdlOutputs(t,x,u);
case {2, 4, 9 }
```

```
    sys = [];
otherwise
    error(['Unhandled flag = ',num2str(flag)]);
end
function [sys,x0,str,ts]=mdlInitializeSizes
sizes = simsizes;
sizes.NumContStates  = 0;
sizes.NumDiscStates  = 0;
sizes.NumOutputs     = 2;
sizes.NumInputs      = 2;
sizes.DirFeedthrough = 1;
sizes.NumSampleTimes = 0;
sys=simsizes(sizes);
x0=[];
str=[];
ts=[];
function sys=mdlOutputs(t,x,u)
persistent a2

if t==0
   a2=readfis('fsmc.fis');
end
xd=sin(t);
dxd=cos(t);
ddxd=-sin(t);

e=u(1);
de=u(2);

c=25;
s=c*e+de;

x1=xd-e;
x2=dxd-de;

g=9.8;mc=1.0;m=0.1;l=0.5;
S=l*(4/3-m*(cos(x1))^2/(mc+m));
fx=g*sin(x1)-m*l*x2^2*cos(x1)*sin(x1)/(mc+m);
fx=fx/S;
gx=cos(x1)/(mc+m);
gx=gx/S;

ueq=1/gx*(c*de+ddxd-fx);
D=5;
xite=D+0.15;
us=1/gx*xite*sign(s);

M=2;
if M==1        % Using conventional equavalent sliding mode control
   Mu=1.0;
elseif M==2
    Mu=evalfis([s],a2);  % Using fuzzy equavalent sliding mode control
```

9 Fuzzy Sliding Mode Control

```
end
ut=ueq+Mu*us;

sys(1)=ut;
sys(2)=Mu;
```

(4) S-function of the plant: chap9_1plant.m

```
function [sys,x0,str,ts]=s_function(t,x,u,flag)
switch flag,
case 0,
    [sys,x0,str,ts]=mdlInitializeSizes;
case 1,
    sys=mdlDerivatives(t,x,u);
case 3,
    sys=mdlOutputs(t,x,u);
case {2, 4, 9 }
    sys = [];
otherwise
    error(['Unhandled flag = ',num2str(flag)]);
end
function [sys,x0,str,ts]=mdlInitializeSizes
sizes = simsizes;
sizes.NumContStates  = 2;
sizes.NumDiscStates  = 0;
sizes.NumOutputs     = 2;
sizes.NumInputs      = 1;
sizes.DirFeedthrough = 0;
sizes.NumSampleTimes = 0;
sys=simsizes(sizes);
x0=[pi/60 0];
str=[];
ts=[];
function sys=mdlDerivatives(t,x,u)
g=9.8;mc=1.0;m=0.1;l=0.5;
S=l*(4/3-m*(cos(x(1)))^2/(mc+m));
fx=g*sin(x(1))-m*l*x(2)^2*cos(x(1))*sin(x(1))/(mc+m);
fx=fx/S;
gx=cos(x(1))/(mc+m);
gx=gx/S;
%%%%%%%%%
bi=0.50;ci=5;
dt=5*exp(-(t-ci)^2/(2*bi^2));   %rbf_func.m
%%%%%%%%%

sys(1)=x(2);
sys(2)=fx+gx*u+dt;
function sys=mdlOutputs(t,x,u)
bi=0.50;ci=5;
dt=5*exp(-(t-ci)^2/(2*bi^2));   %rbf_func.m

sys(1)=x(1);
sys(2)=dt;
```

241

(5) Plot program: chap9_1plot.m

```
close all;

figure(1);
subplot(211);
plot(t,y(:,1),'k',t,y(:,2),'r:','linewidth',2);
xlabel('time(s)');ylabel('Position tracking');
legend('Ideal position signal','tracking signal');
subplot(212);
plot(t,y(:,1)-y(:,2),'linewidth',2);
xlabel('time(s)');ylabel('Position tracking error');

figure(2);
plot(t,ut,'r','linewidth',2);
xlabel('time(s)');ylabel('control input');

figure(3);
plot(t,d(:,1),'r','linewidth',2);
xlabel('time(s)');ylabel('Disturbance');

figure(4);
plot(t,miu(:,1),'r','linewidth',2);
xlabel('time(s)');ylabel('Membership function degree');
```

9.2 Sliding Mode Control Based on Fuzzy Switch-Gain Regulation

Fuzzy rule is adopted and the switch gain is estimated effectively according to the attaining condition of sliding mode. Thus, the disturbances and chattering phenomenon are reduced using switch gain.

9.2.1 System Description

Consider the uncertain system as follows:

$$\ddot{\theta} = f(\theta,\dot{\theta}) + b\,(u(t) + E(t)) \tag{9.5}$$

where $u(t) \in \mathbf{R}$ is control input $f(\theta,\dot{\theta})$ is known, $b > 0$, $E(t)$ is the unknown disturbance.

9.2.2 Design of Sliding Mode Controller

Select sliding mode variable as

$$s = \dot{e} + ce, \quad c > 0 \tag{9.6}$$

where e is the tracking error and $e = \theta_{\mathrm{d}} - \theta$, θ_{d} is the desired trajectory.

Sliding mode controller is designed as

$$u = \frac{1}{b}(-f(\theta) + \ddot{\theta}_{\mathrm{d}} + c\dot{e} + K(t)\mathrm{sgn}(s)) \tag{9.7}$$

and select

$$K(t) = \max|E(t)| + \eta \tag{9.8}$$

where $\eta > 0$.

Analysis of stability:

Select the Lyapunov function as

$$V = \frac{1}{2}s^2$$

Therefore, we have

$$\dot{V} = s\dot{s} = s(\ddot{e} + c\dot{e}) = s(\ddot{\theta}_{\mathrm{d}} - \ddot{\theta} + c\dot{e}) = s(\ddot{\theta}_{\mathrm{d}} - f(\theta) - bu - E(t) + c\dot{e})$$

From Eq. (9.7), we have

$$\dot{V} = s(-K(t)\mathrm{sgn}(s) - E(t)) = -K(t)|s| - E(t)s \leqslant -\eta|s|$$

In Eq. (9.7), $K(t)$ is used to compensate the uncertainty $E(t)$ and guarantee the existing condition of the sliding mode. The switch gain $K(t)$ brings out chattering phenomenon. If $E(t)$ is time variant, then, in order to bring out the chattering phenomenon, $K(t)$ should be the time variant.

Using fuzzy rule and designing the fuzzy system, the estimation of $K(t)$ can be obtained.

9.2.3 Design of Fuzzy System

Existing condition of the sliding mode:

$$s\dot{s} < 0 \tag{9.9}$$

If Eq. (9.9) is satisfied, then the system states are on the sliding surface when the system states attain on the sliding surface. The selection of $K(t)$ must remove the effect of uncertainties in order to make system state attain sliding surface.

In order to guarantee the existence condition of sliding mode, fuzzy rule is given as follows:

If $s\dot{s} > 0$ then $K(t)$ should be increased;

If $s\dot{s} < 0$ then $K(t)$ should be decreased.

From the rule above, the fuzzy system of the relation between $s\dot{s}$ and $\Delta K(t)$ can be designed. In this system, $s\dot{s}$ is the input, and $\Delta K(t)$ is the output. The fuzzy sets of the input and output are defined respectively as follows:

$$s\dot{s} = \{NB \quad NM \quad ZO \quad PM \quad PB\}$$
$$\Delta K = \{NB \quad NM \quad ZO \quad PM \quad PB\}$$

where NB is negative and large, NM is negative and mid, ZO is zero, PM is the right mid, PB is positive and large.

The membership functions of the input and output of fuzzy system are shown in Fig. 9.9 and Fig. 9.10 respectively.

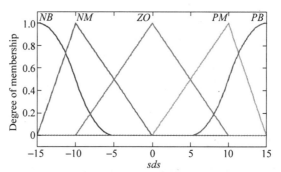

Figure 9.9 The membership function of fuzzy input

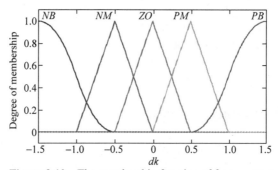

Figure 9.10 The membership function of fuzzy output

Fuzzy rule is selected as:

R1: IF $s\dot{s}$ is PB THEN ΔK is PB

R2: IF $s\dot{s}$ is PM THEN ΔK is PM

R3: IF $s\dot{s}$ is ZO THEN ΔK is ZO

R4: IF $s\dot{s}$ is NM THEN ΔK is NM

R5: IF $s\dot{s}$ is NB THEN ΔK is NB

9 Fuzzy Sliding Mode Control

Using integral method, the supper bound of $\hat{K}(t)$ is estimated:

$$\hat{K}(t) = G \int_0^t \Delta K \, dt \tag{9.10}$$

where G is proportionality coefficient and is decided according to the experiences. $\hat{K}(t)$ is used in Eq. (9.7) instead of $K(t)$, therefore, the controller is designed as:

$$u = \frac{1}{b}(-f(\theta) + \ddot{\theta}_d + c\dot{e} + \hat{K}(t)\text{sgn}(s)) \tag{9.11}$$

Replace Eq. (9.7) with Eq. (9.11), we have

$$\dot{V} = s(-K(t)\text{sgn}(s) - E(t)) = -K(t)|s| - E(t)s \leqslant -\eta|s|$$

9.2.4 Simulation Example

Consider the system as follows:

$$\ddot{\theta} = f(\theta) + b(u(t) + E(t))$$

where $f(\theta) = -25\dot{\theta}$, $b = 133$. The uncertainty $E(t)$ is the form of Gauss function:

$$E(t) = 200 \exp\left(-\frac{(t-c_i)^2}{2b_i^2}\right)$$

Select $b_i = 0.50$, $c_i = 5.0$, $\eta = 1.0$. Therefore, the switch gain of the controller is $\hat{K}(t) = \max(|E(t)|) + \eta = 201$. $E(t)$ is shown in Fig.9.11.

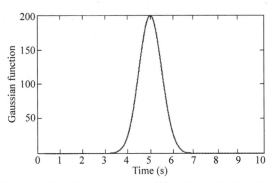

Figure 9.11 The uncertainty $E(t)$ of Gaussian function

Program of Gaussian function: chap4_3func.m

Desired position trajectory is $\theta_d = \sin(2\pi t)$. Fuzzy system is established using S-function program chap4_3rule.m, and the membership functions are shown in Fig. 9.9 and Fig. 9.10.

245

Firstly, $M=2$ is selected, the controller is given in Eq. (9.11), and $G=400$, $c=150$. The simulation results are shown in Fig. 9.12 – Fig. 9.14. $M=1$ is selected, the controller is given in Eq. (9.7), $D=200$, and $c=150$. The simulation results are shown in Fig. 9.15 and Fig. 9.16.

From the simulation, we can find that the fuzzy sliding mode control method based fuzzy rule can reduce effectively disturbances by switch gain.

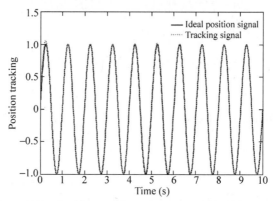

Figure 9.12 Position tracking using controller with Eq. (9.11)

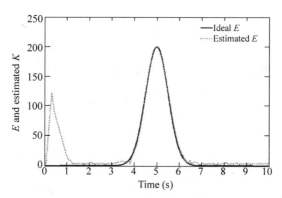

Figure 9.13 $E(t)$ and its $\hat{K}(t)$

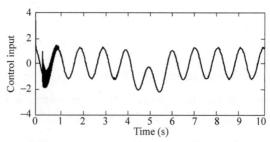

Figure 9.14 Control input with Eq. (9.11)

9 Fuzzy Sliding Mode Control

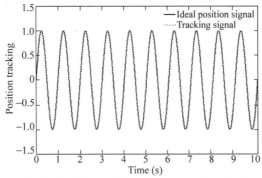

Figure 9.15 Position tracking using controller with Eq. (9.7)

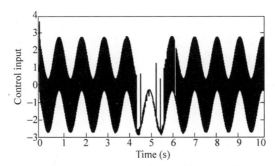

Figure 9.16 Control input with Eq. (9.7)

Simulation programs:

(1) Simulink main program: chap9_2sim.mdl

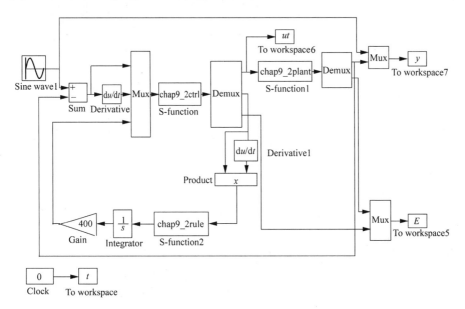

(2) S-function of controller: chap9_2ctrl.m

```
function [sys,x0,str,ts]=s_function(t,x,u,flag)
switch flag,
case 0,
    [sys,x0,str,ts]=mdlInitializeSizes;
case 3,
    sys=mdlOutputs(t,x,u);
case {2, 4, 9 }
    sys = [];
otherwise
    error(['Unhandled flag = ',num2str(flag)]);
end
function [sys,x0,str,ts]=mdlInitializeSizes
sizes = simsizes;
sizes.NumContStates  = 0;
sizes.NumDiscStates  = 0;
sizes.NumOutputs     = 3;
sizes.NumInputs      = 3;
sizes.DirFeedthrough = 1;
sizes.NumSampleTimes = 0;
sys=simsizes(sizes);
x0=[];
str=[];
ts=[];
function sys=mdlOutputs(t,x,u)
persistent s0
e=u(1);
de=u(2);

c=150;
thd=sin(2*pi*t);
dthd=2*pi*cos(2*pi*t);
ddthd=-(2*pi)^2*sin(2*pi*t);

x1=thd-e;
x2=dthd-de;

fx=-25*x2;b=133;

s=c*e+de;

D=200;xite=1.0;

M=2;
if M==1
   K=D+xite;
elseif M==2    %Estimation for K with fuzzy
   K=abs(u(3))+xite;
end
```

248

9 Fuzzy Sliding Mode Control

```
ut=1/b*(-fx+ddthd+c*de+K*sign(s));

sys(1)=ut;
sys(2)=s;
sys(3)=K;
```

(3) S-function of the plant: chap9_2plant.m

```
function [sys,x0,str,ts]=s_function(t,x,u,flag)
switch flag,
case 0,
    [sys,x0,str,ts]=mdlInitializeSizes;
case 1,
    sys=mdlDerivatives(t,x,u);
case 3,
    sys=mdlOutputs(t,x,u);
case {2, 4, 9 }
    sys = [];
otherwise
    error(['Unhandled flag = ',num2str(flag)]);
end
function [sys,x0,str,ts]=mdlInitializeSizes
sizes = simsizes;
sizes.NumContStates  = 2;
sizes.NumDiscStates  = 0;
sizes.NumOutputs     = 2;
sizes.NumInputs      = 1;
sizes.DirFeedthrough = 0;
sizes.NumSampleTimes = 0;
sys=simsizes(sizes);
x0=[0.15,0];
str=[];
ts=[];
function sys=mdlDerivatives(t,x,u)
%bi=0.05;ci=5;
bi=0.5;ci=5;
dt=200*exp(-(t-ci)^2/(2*bi^2));   %rbf_func.m
%dt=0;

sys(1)=x(2);
sys(2)=-25*x(2)+133*u+dt;
function sys=mdlOutputs(t,x,u)
%bi=0.05;ci=5;
bi=0.5;ci=5;
dt=200*exp(-(t-ci)^2/(2*bi^2));   %rbf_func.m
%dt=0;

sys(1)=x(1);
sys(2)=dt;
```

249

Advanced Sliding Mode Control for Mechanical Systems: Design, Analysis and MATLAB Simulation

(4) S-function of fuzzy system: chap9_2rule.m

```
function [sys,x0,str,ts]=s_function(t,x,u,flag)
switch flag,
case 0,
    [sys,x0,str,ts]=mdlInitializeSizes;
case 3,
    sys=mdlOutputs(t,x,u);
case {2, 4, 9 }
    sys = [];
otherwise
    error(['Unhandled flag = ',num2str(flag)]);
end
function [sys,x0,str,ts]=mdlInitializeSizes
sizes = simsizes;
sizes.NumContStates  = 0;
sizes.NumDiscStates  = 0;
sizes.NumOutputs     = 1;
sizes.NumInputs      = 1;
sizes.DirFeedthrough = 1;
sizes.NumSampleTimes = 0;
sys=simsizes(sizes);
x0=[];
str=[];
ts=[];
function sys=mdlOutputs(t,x,u)
warning off;
persistent a1
if t==0
    a1=readfis('smc_fuzz');
end

sys(1)=evalfis([u(1)],a1);
```

(5) Plot program: chap9_2plot.m

```
close all;

figure(1);
plot(t,y(:,1),'k',t,y(:,2),'r:','linewidth',2);
xlabel('time(s)');ylabel('Position tracking');
legend('Ideal position signal','tracking signal');

figure(2);
plot(t,E(:,1),'k',t,E(:,2),'r:','linewidth',2);
xlabel('time(s)');ylabel('E and estimated K');
legend('Ideal E','estimated E');

figure(3);
plot(t,ut(:,1),'k','linewidth',2);
xlabel('time(s)');ylabel('Control input');
```

9.3 Sliding Mode Control Based on Fuzzy System Approximation

9.3.1 Problem Statement

Consider a second-order nonlinear system as follows:

$$\ddot{\theta} = f(\theta,\dot{\theta}) + g(\theta,\dot{\theta})u + d(t) \tag{9.12}$$

where f and g are all nonlinear functions, $u \in \mathbf{R}$ and is the input control, $d(t)$ is the outer disturbance, and $|d(t)| \leqslant D$.

Let the desired output be θ_d, and denote

$$e = \theta_d - \theta$$

Design the sliding mode function as

$$s = \dot{e} + ce \tag{9.13}$$

where $c > 0$, then

$$\dot{s} = \ddot{e} + c\dot{e} = \ddot{\theta}_d - \ddot{\theta} + c\dot{e} = \ddot{\theta}_d - f - gu - d(t) + c\dot{e} \tag{9.14}$$

If f and g are known, we can design control law as

$$u = \frac{1}{g}[-f + \ddot{\theta}_d + c\dot{e} + \eta \operatorname{sgn}(s)] \tag{9.15}$$

Then Eq. (9.14) becomes

$$\dot{s} = \ddot{e} + c\dot{e} = \ddot{\theta}_d - \ddot{\theta} + c\dot{e} = \ddot{\theta}_d - f - gu - d(t) + c\dot{e} = -\eta \operatorname{sgn}(s) - d(t)$$

Therefore, if $\eta \geqslant D$, we have

$$s\dot{s} = -\eta|s| - s \cdot d(t) \leqslant 0$$

If $f(x)$ is unknown, we should estimate $f(x)$ by some algorithms. In the following, we will simply recall fuzzy systems approximate uncertain item $f(x)$.

9.3.2 Controller Design Based on Fuzzy System

9.3.2.1 Uncertainty Approximation Using Fuzzy System

If $f(x)$ is unknown, we can replace $f(x)$ with the fuzzy estimation $\hat{f}(x)$ to realize feedback control[1]. The universal approximation theorem is described as

Step one: For x_i ($i = 1, 2, \cdots, n$), define the fuzzy sets $A_i^{l_i}$, $l_i = 1, 2, \cdots, p_i$.

Step two: Adopt $\prod_{i=1}^{n} p_i$ fuzzy rules to construct fuzzy system $\hat{f}(x | \theta_f)$:

$$R^{(j)}: \text{If } x_1 \text{ is } A_1^{l_1} \text{ and } \dots \text{ and } x_n \text{ is } A_1^{l_n} \text{ then } \hat{f} \text{ is } E^{l_1, \cdots, l_n} \tag{9.16}$$

where $l_i = 1, 2, \cdots, p_i$, $i = 1, 2, \cdots, n$.

Therefore, the output of fuzzy system is

$$\hat{f}(x | \theta_f) = \frac{\sum_{l_1=1}^{p_1} \cdots \sum_{l_n=1}^{p_n} \overline{y}_f^{l_1, \cdots, l_n} \left(\prod_{i=1}^{n} \mu_{A_i^{l_i}}(x_i) \right)}{\sum_{l_1=1}^{p_1} \cdots \sum_{l_n=1}^{p_n} \left(\prod_{i=1}^{n} \mu_{A_i^{l_i}}(x_i) \right)} \tag{9.17}$$

where $\mu_{A_i^{l_i}}(x_i)$ is the membership function of x_i. All the states are required known. Moreover, if there are noises in the measurement output $y = x_1$, the computation of $\mu_{A_i^{l_i}}(x_i)$ is affected seriously, therefore, fuzzy system is contaminated.

Let $\overline{y}_f^{l_1, \cdots, l_n}$ be a free parameter and be put in the set $\hat{\theta}_f \in \mathbf{R}^{\prod_{i=1}^{n} p_i}$. Column vector $\xi(x)$ is introduced and Eq. (9.17) can be written as:

$$\hat{f}(x | \theta_f) = \hat{\theta}_f^{\mathrm{T}} \xi(x) \tag{9.18}$$

where $\xi(x)$ is the $\prod_{i=1}^{n} p_i$-dimensional column vector, and $l_1, \cdots, l_n$ elements are respectively

$$\xi_{l_1, \cdots, l_n}(x) = \frac{\prod_{i=1}^{n} \mu_{A_i^{l_i}}(x_i)}{\sum_{l_1=1}^{p_1} \cdots \sum_{l_n=1}^{p_n} \left(\prod_{i=1}^{n} \mu_{A_i^{l_i}}(x_i) \right)} \tag{9.19}$$

The membership functions are needed to be selected according to experiences. Moreover, all the states must be known.

9.3.2.2 Design of Adaptive Fuzzy Sliding Mode Controller

Suppose the optimal parameter as

$$\theta_f^* = \arg \min_{\theta_f \in \Omega_f} \left(\sup_{x \in R^n} | \hat{f}(x | \theta_f) - f(x) | \right)$$

where Ω_f is the set of θ_f, i.e. $\theta_f \in \Omega_f$.

The term f can be expressed as

$$f = \boldsymbol{\theta}_f^{*\mathrm{T}} \boldsymbol{\xi}(\boldsymbol{x}) + \varepsilon \tag{9.20}$$

where x is the input signal of the fuzzy system, where $\boldsymbol{\xi}(\boldsymbol{x})$ is the fuzzy vector, ε is approximation error of fuzzy system, and $\varepsilon \leqslant \varepsilon_{\mathrm{N}}$.

The fuzzy system is used to approximate f. The fuzzy system input is selected as $\boldsymbol{x} = [e \quad \dot{e}]^{\mathrm{T}}$, and the output of the fuzzy system is

$$\hat{f}(\boldsymbol{x} \mid \boldsymbol{\theta}_f) = \hat{\boldsymbol{\theta}}_f^{\mathrm{T}} \boldsymbol{\xi}(\boldsymbol{x}) \tag{9.21}$$

The control input Eq. (9.15) is written as

$$u = \frac{1}{g}(-\hat{f} + \ddot{\theta}_{\mathrm{d}} + c\dot{e} + \eta \, \mathrm{sgn}(s)) \tag{9.22}$$

Submitting Eqs. (9.22) to (9.14), we have

$$\dot{s} = \ddot{\theta}_{\mathrm{d}} - f - gu - d(t) + c\dot{e} = \ddot{\theta}_{\mathrm{d}} - f - (-\hat{f} + \ddot{\theta}_{\mathrm{d}} + c\dot{e} + \eta \, \mathrm{sgn}(s)) - d(t) + c\dot{e}$$
$$= -f + \hat{f} - \eta \, \mathrm{sgn}(s) - d(t) = -\tilde{f} - d(t) - \eta \, \mathrm{sgn}(s) \tag{9.23}$$

Since

$$\tilde{f} = f - \hat{f} = f = \boldsymbol{\theta}_f^{*\mathrm{T}} \boldsymbol{\xi}(\boldsymbol{x}) + \varepsilon - \hat{\boldsymbol{\theta}}_f^{\mathrm{T}} \boldsymbol{\xi}(\boldsymbol{x}) = \tilde{\boldsymbol{\theta}}_f^{\mathrm{T}} \boldsymbol{\xi}(\boldsymbol{x}) + \varepsilon \tag{9.24}$$

where $\tilde{\boldsymbol{\theta}}_f = \boldsymbol{\theta}_f^* - \hat{\boldsymbol{\theta}}_f$.

Define the Lyapunov function as

$$L = \frac{1}{2}s^2 + \frac{1}{2}\gamma \tilde{\boldsymbol{\theta}}_f^{\mathrm{T}} \tilde{\boldsymbol{\theta}}_f$$

where $\gamma > 0$.

Derivative L, and from Eqs. (9.23) and (9.24), we have

$$\dot{L} = s\dot{s} + \gamma \tilde{\boldsymbol{\theta}}_f^{\mathrm{T}} \dot{\tilde{\boldsymbol{\theta}}}_f = s(-\tilde{f} - d(t) - \eta \, \mathrm{sgn}(s)) - \gamma \tilde{\boldsymbol{\theta}}_f^{\mathrm{T}} \dot{\hat{\boldsymbol{\theta}}}_f$$
$$= s(-\tilde{\boldsymbol{\theta}}_f^{\mathrm{T}} \boldsymbol{\xi}(\boldsymbol{x}) - \varepsilon - d(t) - \eta \, \mathrm{sgn}(s)) - \gamma \tilde{\boldsymbol{\theta}}_f^{\mathrm{T}} \dot{\hat{\boldsymbol{\theta}}}_f$$
$$= -\tilde{\boldsymbol{\theta}}_f^{\mathrm{T}}(s\boldsymbol{\xi}(\boldsymbol{x}) + \gamma \dot{\hat{\boldsymbol{\theta}}}_f) - s(\varepsilon + d(t) + \eta \, \mathrm{sgn}(s))$$

Let the adaptive rule be

$$\dot{\hat{\boldsymbol{\theta}}}_f = -\frac{1}{\gamma} s\boldsymbol{\xi}(\boldsymbol{x}) \tag{9.25}$$

Then

$$\dot{L} = -s(\varepsilon + d(t) + \eta \operatorname{sgn}(s)) = -s(\varepsilon + d(t)) - \eta|s|$$

Due to the approximation error ε is sufficiently small, design $\eta \geq \varepsilon_N + D$, we can obtain approximately $\dot{L} \leq 0$.

9.3.3 Simulation Example

Consider the following inverted pendulum:

$$\begin{cases} \dot{x}_1 = x_2 \\ \dot{x}_2 = \dfrac{g \sin x_1 - m l x_2^2 \cos x_1 \sin x_1 / (m_c + m)}{l(4/3 - m \cos^2 x_1 / (m_c + m))} + \dfrac{\cos x_1 / (m_c + m)}{l(4/3 - m \cos^2 x_1 / (m_c + m))} u \end{cases}$$

where x_1 and x_2 are the swing angle and swing rate respectively. $g = 9.8$ m/s^2, $m_c = 1$ kg is the vehicle mass, $m = 0.10$ is the mass of the pendulum. $l = 0.50$ is one half of the pendulum length, and u is the control input.

W select the following five membership functions as:

$$\mu_{NM}(x_i) = \exp[-((x_i + \pi/6)/(\pi/24))^2], \mu_{NS}(x_i) = \exp[-((x_i + \pi/12)/(\pi/24))^2],$$
$$\mu_Z(x_i) = \exp[-(x_i/(\pi/24))^2], \mu_{PS}(x_i) = \exp[-((x_i - \pi/12)/(\pi/24))^2],$$
$$\mu_{PM}(x_i) = \exp[-((x_i - \pi/6)/(\pi/24))^2]$$

The membership functions curves are shown in Fig. 9.17.

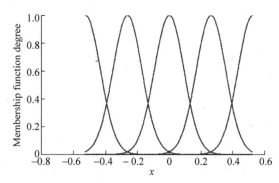

Figure 9.17　The membership function of x_i

Choosing $x_1 = \theta$, The desired trajectory is $\theta_d(t) = 0.1 \sin t$. The initial state is $[\pi/60 \ 0]$, $\theta_f(0) = 0.1$. We adapt control law as Eq. (9.22) and adaptive law as Eq. (9.25), choosing $\eta = 0.1$, $k_1 = 20$, $k_2 = 10$ and adaptive parameter $\gamma = 0.05$.

9　Fuzzy Sliding Mode Control

The curves of position tracking and uncertainty approximation are shown in Fig. 9.18 – Fig. 9.20.

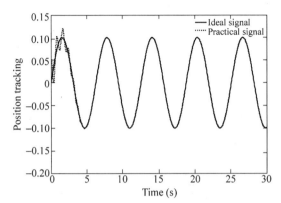

Figure 9.18　Position tracking

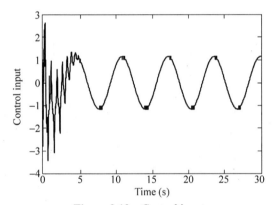

Figure 9.19　Control input

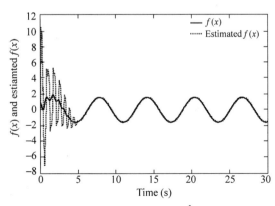

Figure 9.20　$f(x)$ and $\hat{f}(x)$

255

Simulation programs:

(1) Main Simulink program: chap9_3sim.mdl

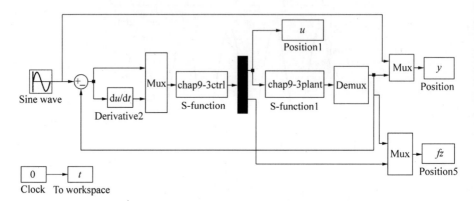

(2) Control law program: chap9_3ctrl.m

```
function [sys,x0,str,ts] = spacemodel(t,x,u,flag)
switch flag,
case 0,
    [sys,x0,str,ts]=mdlInitializeSizes;
case 1,
    sys=mdlDerivatives(t,x,u);
case 3,
    sys=mdlOutputs(t,x,u);
case {2,4,9}
    sys=[];
otherwise
    error(['Unhandled flag = ',num2str(flag)]);
end
function [sys,x0,str,ts]=mdlInitializeSizes
sizes = simsizes;
sizes.NumContStates  = 25;
sizes.NumDiscStates  = 0;
sizes.NumOutputs     = 2;
sizes.NumInputs      = 2;
sizes.DirFeedthrough = 1;
sizes.NumSampleTimes = 0;
sys = simsizes(sizes);
x0  = [zeros(25,1)];
str = [];
ts  = [];
function sys=mdlDerivatives(t,x,u)
gama=0.005;
r=0.1*sin(t);
dr=0.1*cos(t);
ddr=-0.1*sin(t);
```

9 Fuzzy Sliding Mode Control

```
e=u(1);
de=u(2);
n=25;
s=n*e+de;

x1=e;
x2=de;

for i=1:1:25
    thtaf(i,1)=x(i);
end
%%%%%%%%%%%%%%%%%%%%%%%%%%%%%%%%%%%%%%%%
FS1=0;
for l1=1:1:5
    gs1=-[(x1+pi/6-(l1-1)*pi/12)/(pi/24)]^2;
    u1(l1)=exp(gs1);
end

for l2=1:1:5
    gs2=-[(x2+pi/6-(l2-1)*pi/12)/(pi/24)]^2;
    u2(l2)=exp(gs2);
end
for l1=1:1:5
    for l2=1:1:5
        FS2(5*(l1-1)+l2)=u1(l1)*u2(l2);
        FS1=FS1+u1(l1)*u2(l2);
    end
end

FS=FS2/FS1;
for i=1:1:25
    sys(i)=-1/gama*s*FS(i);
end
function sys=mdlOutputs(t,x,u)
r=0.1*sin(t);
dr=0.1*cos(t);
ddr=-0.1*sin(t);

e=u(1);
de=u(2);
n=25;
s=n*e+de;

x1=e;
x2=de;
for i=1:1:25
    thtaf(i,1)=x(i);
end
```

```
FS1=0;
for l1=1:1:5
   gs1=-[(x1+pi/6-(l1-1)*pi/12)/(pi/24)]^2;
   u1(l1)=exp(gs1);
end

for l2=1:1:5
   gs2=-[(x2+pi/6-(l2-1)*pi/12)/(pi/24)]^2;
   u2(l2)=exp(gs2);
end

for l1=1:1:5
   for l2=1:1:5
        FS2(5*(l1-1)+l2)=u1(l1)*u2(l2);
        FS1=FS1+u1(l1)*u2(l2);
   end
end
FS=FS2/FS1;

fxp=thtaf'*FS';

g=9.8;mc=1.0;m=0.1;l=0.5;
S=l*(4/3-m*(cos(x1))^2/(mc+m));
gx=cos(x1)/(mc+m);
gx=gx/S;

if t<=1.0
    xite=1.0;
else
    xite=0.10;
end

ut=1/gx*(-fxp+ddr+n*de+xite*sign(s));
sys(1)=ut;
sys(2)=fxp;
```

(3) Membership function program: chap9_3mf.m

```
clear all;
close all;

L1=-pi/6;
L2=pi/6;
L=L2-L1;

T=L*1/1000;

x=L1:T:L2;
figure(1);
for i=1:1:5
```

9 Fuzzy Sliding Mode Control

```
    gs=-[(x+pi/6-(i-1)*pi/12)/(pi/24)].^2;
    u=exp(gs);
    hold on;
    plot(x,u);
end
xlabel('x');ylabel('Membership function degree');
```

(4) Plant program: chap9_3plant.m

```
function [sys,x0,str,ts]=s_function(t,x,u,flag)
switch flag,
case 0,
    [sys,x0,str,ts]=mdlInitializeSizes;
case 1,
    sys=mdlDerivatives(t,x,u);
case 3,
    sys=mdlOutputs(t,x,u);
case {2, 4, 9 }
    sys = [];
otherwise
    error(['Unhandled flag = ',num2str(flag)]);
end
function [sys,x0,str,ts]=mdlInitializeSizes
sizes = simsizes;
sizes.NumContStates  = 2;
sizes.NumDiscStates  = 0;
sizes.NumOutputs     = 2;
sizes.NumInputs      = 1;
sizes.DirFeedthrough = 0;
sizes.NumSampleTimes = 0;
sys=simsizes(sizes);
x0=[pi/60 0];
str=[];
ts=[];
function sys=mdlDerivatives(t,x,u)
g=9.8;mc=1.0;m=0.1;l=0.5;
S=l*(4/3-m*(cos(x(1)))^2/(mc+m));
fx=g*sin(x(1))-m*l*x(2)^2*cos(x(1))*sin(x(1))/(mc+m);
fx=fx/S;
gx=cos(x(1))/(mc+m);
gx=gx/S;
%%%%%%%%%
dt=0*10*sin(t);
%%%%%%%%%

sys(1)=x(2);
sys(2)=fx+gx*u+dt;
function sys=mdlOutputs(t,x,u)
g=9.8;
mc=1.0;
```

```
m=0.1;
l=0.5;

S=l*(4/3-m*(cos(x(1)))^2/(mc+m));
fx=g*sin(x(1))-m*l*x(2)^2*cos(x(1))*sin(x(1))/(mc+m);
fx=fx/S;

sys(1)=x(1);
sys(2)=fx;
```

(5) Plot program: chap9_3plot.m

```
close all;

figure(1);
plot(t,y(:,1),'k',t,y(:,2),'k:','linewidth',2);
xlabel('time(s)');ylabel('Position tracking');
legend('ideal signal','practical signal');

figure(2);
plot(t,u(:,1),'k','linewidth',2);
xlabel('time(s)');ylabel('Control input');

figure(3);
plot(t,fx(:,1),'k',t,fx(:,2),'k:','linewidth',2);
xlabel('time(s)');ylabel('fx and estiamted fx');
legend('fx','estiamted fx');
```

9.4 Adaptive Fuzzy Control Based on Fuzzy Compensation for Manipulator

9.4.1 System Description

Dynamic equation of manipulator:

$$H(q)\ddot{q} + C(q,\dot{q})\dot{q} + G(q) + F(q,\dot{q},\ddot{q}) = \tau \tag{9.26}$$

where $H(q)$ is the inertia matrix, $C(q,\dot{q})$ is the matrix resulting from Coriolis and centrifugal forces, $G(q)$ is the gravity. $F(q,\dot{q},\ddot{q})$ is the uncertainty generated by F_r, τ is the control input, τ_d is the disturbance adding on the τ.

9.4.2 Control Based on Fuzzy Compensation

Suppose $H(q)$, $C(q,\dot{q})$ and $G(q)$ are known, and all the states are measured.

Select sliding variable as:

$$s = \dot{\tilde{q}} + \Lambda \tilde{q} \tag{9.27}$$

where Λ is positive-definite, $\tilde{q}(t)$ is the tracking error.

Denote:

$$\dot{q}_r(t) = \dot{q}_d(t) - \Lambda \tilde{q}(t) \tag{9.28}$$

and select the Lyapunov function as

$$V(t) = \frac{1}{2}\left(s^T H s + \sum_{i=1}^{n} \tilde{\Theta}_i^T \Gamma_i \tilde{\Theta}_i\right) \tag{9.29}$$

where $\tilde{\Theta}_i = \Theta_i^* - \Theta_i$, Θ_i^* is the desired parameter, $\Gamma_i > 0$.

Because $s = \dot{\tilde{q}} + \Lambda \tilde{q} = \dot{q} - \dot{q}_d + \Lambda \tilde{q} = \dot{q} - \dot{q}_r$, we have

$$s = \dot{\tilde{q}} + \Lambda \tilde{q} = \dot{q} - \dot{q}_d + \Lambda \tilde{q} = \dot{q} - \dot{q}_r$$
$$H\dot{s} = H\ddot{q} - H\ddot{q}_r = \tau - C\dot{q} - G - F - H\ddot{q}_r$$

Therefore,

$$\dot{V}(t) = s^T H\dot{s} + \frac{1}{2}s^T \dot{H}s + \sum_{i=1}^{n} \tilde{\Theta}_i^T \Gamma_i \dot{\tilde{\Theta}}_i$$

$$= -s^T(-\tau + C\dot{q} + G + F + H\ddot{q}_r - Cs) + \sum_{i=1}^{n} \tilde{\Theta}_i^T \Gamma_i \dot{\tilde{\Theta}}_i \tag{9.30}$$

$$= -s^T(H\ddot{q}_r + C\dot{q}_r + G + F - \tau) + \sum_{i=1}^{n} \tilde{\Theta}_i^T \Gamma_i \dot{\tilde{\Theta}}_i$$

where $F(q,\dot{q},\ddot{q})$ is unknown nonlinear function. MIMO fuzzy system $\hat{F}(q,\dot{q},\ddot{q}|\Theta)$ is adopted to approximate to $F(q,\dot{q},\ddot{q})$.

Fuzzy adaptive sliding mode controller is designed as:

$$\tau = H(q)\ddot{q}_r + C(q,\dot{q})\dot{q}_r + G(q) + \hat{F}(q,\dot{q},\ddot{q}|\Theta) - K_D s - W \operatorname{sgn}(s) \tag{9.31}$$

where $W = \operatorname{diag}[w_{m_1}, w_{m_2}, \cdots, w_{m_n}]$, $w_{m_i} \geqslant |\omega_i|$, $i = 1,2,\cdots,n$, $K_D = \operatorname{diag}(K_i)$, $K_i > 0$, $i = 1,2,\cdots,n$, and

$$\hat{F}(q,\dot{q},\ddot{q}|\Theta) = \begin{bmatrix} \hat{F}_1(q,\dot{q},\ddot{q}|\Theta_1) \\ \hat{F}_2(q,\dot{q},\ddot{q}|\Theta_2) \\ \vdots \\ \hat{F}_n(q,\dot{q},\ddot{q}|\Theta_n) \end{bmatrix} = \begin{bmatrix} \Theta_1^T \xi(q,\dot{q},\ddot{q}) \\ \Theta_2^T \xi(q,\dot{q},\ddot{q}) \\ \vdots \\ \Theta_n^T \xi(q,\dot{q},\ddot{q}) \end{bmatrix} \tag{9.32}$$

Fuzzy approximating error is

Advanced Sliding Mode Control for Mechanical Systems: Design, Analysis and MATLAB Simulation

$$\omega = F(q,\dot{q},\ddot{q}) - \hat{F}(q,\dot{q},\ddot{q} \mid \Theta^*)$$
(9.33)

From Eqs. (9.31) and (9.30), we have

$$\dot{V}(t) = -s^{\mathrm{T}}(F(q,\dot{q},\ddot{q}) - \hat{F}(q,\dot{q},\ddot{q} \mid \Theta) + K_{\mathrm{D}}s + W\,\mathrm{sgn}(s)) + \sum_{i=1}^{n} \tilde{\Theta}_i^{\mathrm{T}} \Gamma_i \dot{\tilde{\Theta}}_i$$

$$= -s^{\mathrm{T}}(F(q,\dot{q},\ddot{q}) - \hat{F}(q,\dot{q},\ddot{q} \mid \Theta) + \hat{F}(q,\dot{q},\ddot{q} \mid \Theta^*)$$

$$\quad - \hat{F}(q,\dot{q},\ddot{q} \mid \Theta^*) + K_{\mathrm{D}}s + W\,\mathrm{sgn}(s)) + \sum_{i=1}^{n} \tilde{\Theta}_i^{\mathrm{T}} \Gamma_i \dot{\tilde{\Theta}}_i$$

$$= -s^{\mathrm{T}}(\tilde{\Theta}^{\mathrm{T}} \xi(q,\dot{q},\ddot{q}) + \omega + K_{\mathrm{D}}s + W\,\mathrm{sgn}(s)) + \sum_{i=1}^{n} \tilde{\Theta}_i^{\mathrm{T}} \Gamma_i \dot{\tilde{\Theta}}_i$$

$$= -s^{\mathrm{T}} K_{\mathrm{D}}s - s^{\mathrm{T}}\omega - W \parallel s \parallel + \sum_{i=1}^{n} (\tilde{\Theta}_i^{\mathrm{T}} \Gamma_i \dot{\tilde{\Theta}}_i - s_i \tilde{\Theta}_i^{\mathrm{T}} \xi(q,\dot{q},\ddot{q}))$$

where $\tilde{\Theta} = \Theta^* - \Theta$, $\xi(q,\dot{q},\ddot{q})$ is the fuzzy system.

The adaptive rule is

$$\dot{\Theta}_i = -\Gamma_i^{-1} s_i \xi(q,\dot{q},\ddot{q}), \quad i = 1,2,\cdots,n$$
(9.34)

Therefore, we have

$$\dot{V}(t) = -s^{\mathrm{T}} K_{\mathrm{D}}s - s^{\mathrm{T}}\omega - W \parallel s \parallel \leqslant -s^{\mathrm{T}} K_{\mathrm{D}}s \leqslant 0$$

Suppose the joint number of manipulator is n, and if MIMO fuzzy system $\hat{F}(q,\dot{q},\ddot{q} \mid \Theta)$ is adopted to approximate to $F(q,\dot{q},\ddot{q})$, then for each joint, the number of input variables is 3. If k membership functions are designed for each input variable, then the whole number of rules is k^{3n} [4].

For instance, the joint number of the manipulator is 2, the number of input variable is 3, there are 5 membership functions, then the whole rule number is $5^{3\times 2} = 5^6 = 15625$. The two many rules will bring out excessive computation. In order to decrease the number of fuzzy rules, independent design should be adopted with respect to $F(q,\dot{q},\ddot{q},t)$.

9.4.3 Control Based on Friction Compensation

When $F(q,\dot{q},\ddot{q})$ only consists of F_{r}, we can consider the case of fuzzy compensation with respect to friction. Because the friction is relative to velocity, the fuzzy system which approximates friction can be written as $\hat{F}(\dot{q} \mid \theta)$.

The method based on traditional fuzzy compensation, i.e., Eqs. (9.31) and (9.34), is adopted to design the controller. The fuzzy adaptive sliding mode controller is designed as:

$$\tau = H(q)\ddot{q}_r + C(q,\dot{q})\dot{q}_r + G(q) + \hat{F}(\dot{q} \mid \theta) - K_D s - W \operatorname{sgn}(s) \tag{9.35}$$

The adaptive rule is

$$\dot{\theta}_i = -\Gamma_i^{-1} s_i \xi(\dot{q}), \ i = 1, 2, \cdots, n \tag{9.36}$$

and the fuzzy system is

$$\hat{F}(\dot{q} \mid \theta) = \begin{bmatrix} \hat{F}_1(\dot{q}_1) \\ \hat{F}_2(\dot{q}_2) \\ \vdots \\ \hat{F}_n(\dot{q}_n) \end{bmatrix} = \begin{bmatrix} \theta_1^T \xi^1(\dot{q}_1) \\ \theta_2^T \xi^2(\dot{q}_2) \\ \vdots \\ \theta_n^T \xi^n(\dot{q}_n) \end{bmatrix}$$

9.4.4 Simulation Example

The kinetic equation of dual-joint rigid manipulator is:

$$\begin{aligned} &\begin{pmatrix} H_{11}(q_2) & H_{12}(q_2) \\ H_{21}(q_2) & H_{22}(q_2) \end{pmatrix}\begin{pmatrix} \ddot{q}_1 \\ \ddot{q}_2 \end{pmatrix} + \begin{pmatrix} -C_{12}(q_2)\dot{q}_2 & -C_{12}(q_2)(\dot{q}_1 + \dot{q}_2) \\ C_{12}(q_2)\dot{q}_1 & 0 \end{pmatrix} \cdot \\ &\begin{pmatrix} g_1(q_1 + q_2)g \\ g_2(q_1 + q_2)g \end{pmatrix} + F(q,\dot{q},\ddot{q}) = \begin{pmatrix} \tau_1 \\ \tau_2 \end{pmatrix} \end{aligned}$$

where

$$\begin{aligned} H_{11}(q_2) &= (m_1 + m_2)r_1^2 + m_2 r_2^2 + 2m_2 r_1 r_2 \cos(q_2) \\ H_{12}(q_2) &= H_{21}(q_2) = m_2 r_2^2 + m_2 r_1 r_2 \cos(q_2) \\ H_{22}(q_2) &= m_2 r_2^2 \\ C_{12}(q_2) &= m_2 r_1 r_2 \sin(q_2) \end{aligned}$$

where m_1 and m_2 are the mass of link1 and link2, and r_1 and r_2 are the lengths of link1 and link2.

Let $y = [q_1 \ q_2]^T$, $\tau = [\tau_1 \ \tau_2]^T$, $x = [q_1 \ \dot{q}_1 \ q_2 \ \dot{q}_2]^T$. The parameters: $r_1 = 1\,\text{m}$, $r_2 = 0.8\,\text{m}$, $m_1 = 1\,\text{kg}$, $m_2 = 1.5\,\text{kg}$.

The control object is to make the outputs q_1, q_2 track the desired trajectories $y_{d1} = 0.3\sin t$ and $y_{d2} = 0.3\sin t$ respectively. The membership function is defined as:

$$\mu_{A_i^l}(x_i) = \exp\left(-\left(\frac{x_i - \bar{x}_i^l}{\pi/24}\right)^2\right)$$

where $\bar{x}_i^l$ are $-\pi/6$, $-\pi/12$, 0, $\pi/12$, and $\pi/6$, respectively, $i = 1, 2, \cdots, 5$, A_i^l is the fuzzy set including NB, NS, ZO, PS, PB belong to lth fuzzy rule.

The control based on friction compensation is used for the case with friction, and the controller parameters are: $\lambda_1 = 10$, $\lambda_2 = 10$, $\mathbf{K}_D = 20\mathbf{I}$, $\Gamma_1 = \Gamma_2 = 0.0001$. The initial states are: $q_1(0) = q_2(0) = \dot{q}_1(0) = \dot{q}_2(0) = 0$. The friction is $\mathbf{F}(\dot{q}) = \begin{bmatrix} 15\dot{q}_1 + 6\,\mathrm{sgn}(\dot{q}_1) \\ 15\dot{q}_2 + 6\,\mathrm{sgn}(\dot{q}_2) \end{bmatrix}$, $\mathbf{W} = \mathrm{diag}[2, 2]$. The fuzzy sliding mode controller is given in Eq. (9.35), and the adaptive rule is given in Eq. (9.36). The simulation results are shown in Fig. 9.21 – Fig. 9.23.

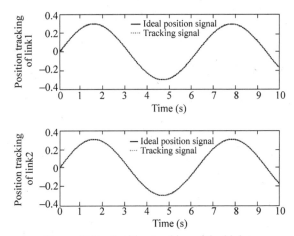

Figure 9.21 Position tracking of dual joints

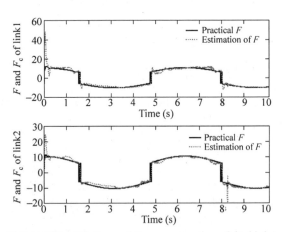

Figure 9.22 Friction and the compensation of dual joints

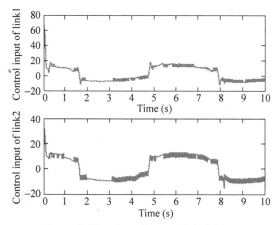

Figure 9.23 Control input of dual joints

Simulation program:
Control based on friction fuzzy compensation for manipulator

(1) Simulink main program: chap9_4sim.mdl

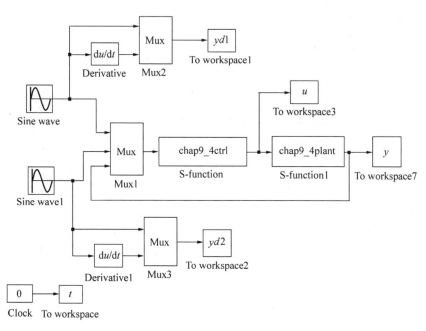

(2) S-function of controller: chap9_4ctrl.m

```
function [sys,x0,str,ts] = MIMO_Tong_s(t,x,u,flag)
switch flag,
case 0,
    [sys,x0,str,ts]=mdlInitializeSizes;
```

```
case 1,
    sys=mdlDerivatives(t,x,u);
case 3,
    sys=mdlOutputs(t,x,u);
case {2,4,9}
    sys=[];
otherwise
    error(['Unhandled flag = ',num2str(flag)]);
end
function [sys,x0,str,ts]=mdlInitializeSizes
global nmn1 nmn2 Fai
nmn1=10;nmn2=10;
Fai=[nmn1 0;0 nmn2];
sizes = simsizes;
sizes.NumContStates  = 10;
sizes.NumDiscStates  = 0;
sizes.NumOutputs     = 4;
sizes.NumInputs      = 8;
sizes.DirFeedthrough = 1;
sizes.NumSampleTimes = 0;
sys = simsizes(sizes);
x0  = [0.1*ones(10,1)];
str = [];
ts  = [];
function sys=mdlDerivatives(t,x,u)
global nmn1 nmn2 Fai
qd1=u(1);
qd2=u(2);
dqd1=0.3*cos(t);
dqd2=0.3*cos(t);
dqd=[dqd1 dqd2]';

ddqd1=-0.3*sin(t);
ddqd2=-0.3*sin(t);
ddqd=[ddqd1 ddqd2]';

q1=u(3);dq1=u(4);
q2=u(5);dq2=u(6);
%%%%%%%%%%%%%%%%%%%%%%%%%%%%%%%%%%%%%%%%%%%%%%
fsd1=0;
for l1=1:1:5
    gs1=-[(dq1+pi/6-(l1-1)*pi/12)/(pi/24)]^2;
    u1(l1)=exp(gs1);
end
fsd2=0;
for l2=1:1:5
    gs2=-[(dq2+pi/6-(l2-1)*pi/12)/(pi/24)]^2;
    u2(l2)=exp(gs2);
end
```

9 Fuzzy Sliding Mode Control

```
for l1=1:1:5
    fsu1(l1)=u1(l1);
    fsd1=fsd1+u1(l1);
end
for l2=1:1:5
    fsu2(l2)=u2(l2);
    fsd2=fsd2+u2(l2);
end
fs1=fsu1/(fsd1+0.001);
fs2=fsu2/(fsd2+0.001);
%%%%%%%%%%%%%%%%%%%%%%%%%%%%%%%%%%%%%%%%%%%%
e1=q1-qd1;
e2=q2-qd2;
e=[e1 e2]';
de1=dq1-dqd1;
de2=dq2-dqd2;
de=[de1 de2]';

s=de+Fai*e;
Gama1=0.0001;Gama2=0.0001;

S1=-1/Gama1*s(1)*fs1;
S2=-1/Gama2*s(2)*fs2;
for i=1:1:5
    sys(i)=S1(i);
end
for j=6:1:10
    sys(j)=S2(j-5);
end

function sys=mdlOutputs(t,x,u)
global nmn1 nmn2 Fai
q1=u(3);dq1=u(4);
q2=u(5);dq2=u(6);

r1=1;r2=0.8;
m1=1;m2=1.5;

H11=(m1+m2)*r1^2+m2*r2^2+2*m2*r1*r2*cos(q2);
H22=m2*r2^2;
H21=m2*r2^2+m2*r1*r2*cos(q2);
H12=H21;
H=[H11 H12;H21 H22];

C12=m2*r1*sin(q2);
C=[-C12*dq2 -C12*(dq1+dq2);C12*q1 0];

g1=(m1+m2)*r1*cos(q2)+m2*r2*cos(q1+q2);
g2=m2*r2*cos(q1+q2);
```

```
G=[g1;g2];

qd1=u(1);
qd2=u(2);
dqd1=0.3*cos(t);
dqd2=0.3*cos(t);
dqd=[dqd1 dqd2]';

ddqd1=-0.3*sin(t);
ddqd2=-0.3*sin(t);
ddqd=[ddqd1 ddqd2]';

e1=q1-qd1;
e2=q2-qd2;
e=[e1 e2]';
de1=dq1-dqd1;
de2=dq2-dqd2;
de=[de1 de2]';

s=de+Fai*e;

dqr=dqd-Fai*e;
ddqr=ddqd-Fai*de;

for i=1:1:5
    thta1(i,1)=x(i);
end
for i=1:1:5
    thta2(i,1)=x(i+5);
end

fsd1=0;
for l1=1:1:5
    gs1=-[(dq1+pi/6-(l1-1)*pi/12)/(pi/24)]^2;
    u1(l1)=exp(gs1);
end
fsd2=0;
for l2=1:1:5
    gs2=-[(dq2+pi/6-(l2-1)*pi/12)/(pi/24)]^2;
    u2(l2)=exp(gs2);
end

for l1=1:1:5
    fsu1(l1)=u1(l1);
    fsd1=fsd1+u1(l1);
end
for l2=1:1:5
    fsu2(l2)=u2(l2);
    fsd2=fsd2+u2(l2);
```

9 Fuzzy Sliding Mode Control

```
end
fs1=fsu1/(fsd1+0.001);
fs2=fsu2/(fsd2+0.001);

Fp(1)=thta1'*fs1';
Fp(2)=thta2'*fs2';

KD=20*eye(2);
W=[1.5 0;0 1.5];

tol=H*ddqr+C*dqr+G+1*Fp'-KD*s-W*sign(s);    %(4.134)

sys(1)=tol(1);
sys(2)=tol(2);
sys(3)=Fp(1);
sys(4)=Fp(2);
```

(3) Membership function program: chap9_4mf.m

```
clear all;
close all;

L1=-pi/6;
L2=pi/6;
L=L2-L1;

T=L*1/1000;

x=L1:T:L2;
figure(1);
for i=1:1:5
    gs=-[(x+pi/6-(i-1)*pi/12)/(pi/24)].^2;
    u=exp(gs);
    hold on;
    plot(x,u);
end
xlabel('x');ylabel('Membership function degree');
```

(4) S-function of the plant: chap9_4plant.m

```
function [sys,x0,str,ts]=MIMO_Tong_plant(t,x,u,flag)
switch flag,
case 0,
    [sys,x0,str,ts]=mdlInitializeSizes;
case 1,
    sys=mdlDerivatives(t,x,u);
case 3,
    sys=mdlOutputs(t,x,u);
case {2, 4, 9 }
    sys = [];
otherwise
```

```matlab
    error(['Unhandled flag = ',num2str(flag)]);
end
function [sys,x0,str,ts]=mdlInitializeSizes
sizes = simsizes;
sizes.NumContStates  = 4;
sizes.NumDiscStates  = 0;
sizes.NumOutputs     = 6;
sizes.NumInputs      = 4;
sizes.DirFeedthrough = 0;
sizes.NumSampleTimes = 0;
sys=simsizes(sizes);
x0=[0 0 0 0];
str=[];
ts=[];
function sys=mdlDerivatives(t,x,u)
r1=1;r2=0.8;
m1=1;m2=1.5;

H11=(m1+m2)*r1^2+m2*r2^2+2*m2*r1*r2*cos(x(3));
H22=m2*r2^2;
H21=m2*r2^2+m2*r1*r2*cos(x(3));
H12=H21;
H=[H11 H12;H21 H22];

C12=m2*r1*sin(x(3));
C=[-C12*x(4)  -C12*(x(2)+x(4));C12*x(1)  0];

g1=(m1+m2)*r1*cos(x(3))+m2*r2*cos(x(1)+x(3));
g2=m2*r2*cos(x(1)+x(3));
G=[g1;g2];

Fr=[15*x(2)+6*sign(x(2));15*x(4)+6*sign(x(4))];

tol=[u(1)  u(2)]';
S=inv(H)*(tol-C*[x(2);x(4)]-G-Fr);

sys(1)=x(2);
sys(2)=S(1);
sys(3)=x(4);
sys(4)=S(2);
function sys=mdlOutputs(t,x,u)
Fr=[15*x(2)+6*sign(x(2));15*x(4)+6*sign(x(4))];

sys(1)=x(1);
sys(2)=x(2);
sys(3)=x(3);
sys(4)=x(4);
sys(5)=Fr(1);
sys(6)=Fr(2);
```

(5) Plot program: chap9_4plot.m

```
close all;

figure(1);
subplot(211);
plot(t,yd1(:,1),'k',t,y(:,1),'r:','linewidth',2);
xlabel('time(s)');ylabel('Position tracking of link1');
legend('Ideal position signal','tracking signal');
subplot(212);
plot(t,yd2(:,1),'k',t,y(:,3),'r:','linewidth',2);
xlabel('time(s)');ylabel('Position tracking of link2');
legend('Ideal position signal','tracking signal');

figure(2);
subplot(211);
plot(t,y(:,5),'k',t,u(:,3),'r:','linewidth',2);
xlabel('time(s)');ylabel('F and Fc of link1');
legend('Practical F','Estimation of F');
subplot(212);
plot(t,y(:,6),'k',t,u(:,4),'r:','linewidth',2);
xlabel('time(s)');ylabel('F and Fc of link2');
legend('Practical F','Estimation of F');

figure(3);
subplot(211);
plot(t,u(:,1),'r','linewidth',2);
xlabel('time(s)');ylabel('Control input of Link1');
subplot(212);
plot(t,u(:,2),'r','linewidth',2);
xlabel('time(s)');ylabel('Control input of Link2');
```

9.5 Adaptive Sliding Mode Control Based on Switching Fuzzy

Using the adaptive fuzzy control method, the switching item in the sliding mode controller is approximated and the switching item is continued. Therefore, the chattering phenomenon can be reduced sufficiently[5].

9.5.1 Plant Description

Considering the following n-order SISO nonlinear system:

$$\begin{aligned}
\dot{x}_1 &= x_2 \\
\dot{x}_2 &= x_3 \\
&\vdots \\
\dot{x}_n &= f(\boldsymbol{x},t) + g(\boldsymbol{x},t)u(t) + d(t)
\end{aligned} \tag{9.37}$$

$$y = x_1$$

where f and g are the known nonlinear function, $x \in \mathbf{R}^n$, $u \in \mathbf{R}$, $y \in \mathbf{R}$, $d(t)$ is the unknown disturbance, $|d(t)| \leq D$, $g(x,t) > 0$.

9.5.2 Design of Adaptive Fuzzy Sliding Mode Controller

The switching function is defined as

$$s = -(k_1 e + k_2 \dot{e} + \cdots + k_{n-1} e^{(n-1)} + e^{(n-1)}) = -ke \tag{9.38}$$

where $e = x_d - x = [e \ \ \dot{e} \ \ \cdots \ \ e^{(n-1)}]^{\mathrm{T}}$, $k_1, k_2, \cdots, k_{n-1}$ is satisfied with Hurwitzian stability condition.

The sliding mode controller is designed as

$$u(t) = \frac{1}{g(x,t)} \left(-f(x,t) + \sum_{i=1}^{n-1} k_i e^{(i)} + x_d^{(n)} - u_{\mathrm{sw}} \right) \tag{9.39}$$

where $u_{\mathrm{sw}} = \eta \, \mathrm{sgn}(s)$, $\eta > D$.

From Eqs. (9.37) and (9.38), we get

$$\begin{aligned}
\dot{s} &= -\sum_{i=1}^{n-1} k_i e^{(i)} + x^{(n)} - x_d^{(n)} \\
&= -\sum_{i=1}^{n-1} k_i e^{(i)} + f(x,t) + g(x,t)u(t) + d(t) - x_d^{(n)}
\end{aligned} \tag{9.40}$$

And from Eq. (9.39), we have

$$\dot{s} = d(t) - \eta \, \mathrm{sgn}(s)$$

i.e.

$$s\dot{s} = d(t)s - \eta |s| \leq 0 \tag{9.41}$$

When d is relative large, the switching item η in controller (9.39) is large. This results in serious chattering phenomenon. Fuzzy system $\hat{h}$ is used to approximate $\eta \, \mathrm{sgn}(s)$. Therefore, the switching signal is weakened and the chattering phenomenon can be reduced.

Using product deduce, single-value fuzzy and center average fuzzy, the fuzzy output is $\hat{h}$. From Eq. (9.39), the controller is written as[5]

$$u(t) = \frac{1}{g(x,t)} \left(-f(x,t) + \sum_{i=1}^{n-1} k_i e^{(i)} + x_d^{(n)} - \hat{h}(s) \right) \tag{9.42}$$

$$\hat{h}(s \mid \boldsymbol{\theta}_{\mathrm{h}}) = \boldsymbol{\theta}_{\mathrm{h}}^{\mathrm{T}} \boldsymbol{\phi}(s) \tag{9.43}$$

where $\hat{h}(s \mid \boldsymbol{\theta}_{\mathrm{h}})$ is the fuzzy output of the universal approximation Eq. (9.18), $\boldsymbol{\phi}(s)$ is the fuzzy vector, vector $\boldsymbol{\theta}_{\mathrm{h}}^{\mathrm{T}}$ varies according to the adaptive rule. The ideal $\hat{h}(s \mid \boldsymbol{\theta}_{\mathrm{h}})$ is

$$\hat{h}(s \mid \boldsymbol{\theta}_{\mathrm{h}}^{*}) = \eta \operatorname{sgn}(s) \tag{9.44}$$

where $\eta > D$.

The adaptive rule is:

$$\dot{\boldsymbol{\theta}}_{\mathrm{h}} = \gamma s \boldsymbol{\phi}(s) \tag{9.45}$$

where $\gamma > 0$.

Proof:

The optimization parameter is defined as:

$$\boldsymbol{\theta}_{\mathrm{h}}^{*} = \arg \min_{\boldsymbol{\theta}_{\mathrm{h}} \in \Omega_{\mathrm{h}}}[\sup \mid \hat{h}(s \mid \boldsymbol{\theta}_{\mathrm{h}}) - \eta \operatorname{sgn}(s) \mid] \tag{9.46}$$

where Ω_{h} is the set of $\boldsymbol{\theta}_{\mathrm{h}}$.

Therefore, we have

$$\begin{aligned}
\dot{s} &= -\sum_{i=1}^{n-1} k_i e^{(i)} + x^{(n)} - x_{\mathrm{d}}^{(n)} \\
&= -\sum_{i=1}^{n-1} k_i e^{(i)} + f(x,t) + g(x,t)u(t) + d(t) - x_{\mathrm{d}}^{(n)} \\
&= -\hat{h}(s \mid \boldsymbol{\theta}_{\mathrm{h}}) + d(t) \\
&= -\hat{h}(s \mid \boldsymbol{\theta}_{\mathrm{h}}) + d(t) + \hat{h}(s \mid \boldsymbol{\theta}_{\mathrm{h}}^{*}) - \hat{h}(s \mid \boldsymbol{\theta}_{\mathrm{h}}^{*}) \\
&= \tilde{\boldsymbol{\theta}}_{\mathrm{h}}^{\mathrm{T}} \boldsymbol{\phi}(s) + d(t) - \hat{h}(s \mid \boldsymbol{\theta}_{\mathrm{h}}^{*})
\end{aligned} \tag{9.47}$$

where $\tilde{\boldsymbol{\theta}}_{\mathrm{h}} = \boldsymbol{\theta}_{\mathrm{h}}^{*} - \boldsymbol{\theta}_{\mathrm{h}}$.

The Lyapunov function is selected as

$$V = \frac{1}{2}\left(s^2 + \frac{1}{\gamma}\tilde{\boldsymbol{\theta}}_{\mathrm{h}}^{\mathrm{T}}\tilde{\boldsymbol{\theta}}_{\mathrm{h}}\right) \tag{9.48}$$

Therefore,

$$\begin{aligned}
\dot{V} &= s\dot{s} + \frac{1}{\gamma}\tilde{\boldsymbol{\theta}}_{\mathrm{h}}^{\mathrm{T}}\dot{\tilde{\boldsymbol{\theta}}}_{\mathrm{h}} \\
&= s(\tilde{\boldsymbol{\theta}}_{\mathrm{h}}^{\mathrm{T}}\boldsymbol{\phi}(s) + d(t) - \hat{h}(s \mid \boldsymbol{\theta}_{\mathrm{h}}^{*})) + \frac{1}{\gamma}\tilde{\boldsymbol{\theta}}_{\mathrm{h}}^{\mathrm{T}}\dot{\tilde{\boldsymbol{\theta}}}_{\mathrm{h}}
\end{aligned}$$

$$= s\tilde{\boldsymbol{\theta}}_h^T \boldsymbol{\phi}(s) + \frac{1}{\gamma}\tilde{\boldsymbol{\theta}}_h^T \dot{\tilde{\boldsymbol{\theta}}}_h + s(d(t) - \hat{h}(s \mid \boldsymbol{\theta}_h^*)) \tag{9.49}$$

Because

$$\hat{h}(s \mid \boldsymbol{\theta}_h^*) = \eta \operatorname{sgn}(s)$$

we have

$$\dot{V} = \frac{1}{\gamma}\tilde{\boldsymbol{\theta}}_h^T (\gamma s \boldsymbol{\phi}(s) - \dot{\boldsymbol{\theta}}_h) + sd(t) - \eta \mid s \mid \tag{9.50}$$

where $\dot{\tilde{\boldsymbol{\theta}}}_h = -\dot{\boldsymbol{\theta}}_h$.

From Eqs. (9.45) and (9.50), we get

$$\dot{V} = sd(t) - \eta \mid s \mid < 0$$

9.5.3　Simulation Example

The kinetic equation of the inverted pendulum is:

$$\begin{cases} \dot{x}_1 = x_2 \\ \dot{x}_2 = \dfrac{g\sin x_1 - mlx_2^2 \cos x_1 \sin x_1 /(m_c + m)}{l(4/3 - m\cos^2 x_1 /(m_c + m))} + \dfrac{\cos x_1 /(m_c + m)}{l(4/3 - m\cos^2 x_1 /(m_c + m))}u + d(t) \end{cases}$$

where x_1 and x_2 are the rolling angle and the rolling rate respectively. $g = 9.8 \text{ m/s}^2$, m_c is the mass of the vehicle, $m_c = 1 \text{ kg}$, m is the mass of the rolling pole, $m = 0.1 \text{ kg}$, l is one half of the rolling pole, $l = 0.5 \text{ m}$, u is the controller, and $d(t) = 10\sin t$.

The desired trajectory is $x_d(t) = 0.1\sin t$, the switching function is $s = -k_1 e - \dot{e}$, $k_1 = 30$. The membership function of the switching function is defined as $\mu_N(s) = \dfrac{1}{1 + \exp(5(s+3))}$, $\mu_Z(s) = \exp(-s^2)$, $\mu_P(s) = \dfrac{1}{1 + \exp(5(s-3))}$.

Let $\boldsymbol{\theta}_h^T$ is a 3×1 vector, and the initial value of each argument in the vector is 0.10. Controller (9.42) and adaptive rule (9.45) are adopted. The initial state of the inverted pendulum is $[-\pi/60 \ \ 0]$. The adaptive parameter is selected as $\gamma = 150$. In the program, fsd, fsu and fs denote the numerator, denominator and itself of $\phi(s)$ respectively. The simulation results are shown in Figs. 9.24 – 9.26.

274

9 Fuzzy Sliding Mode Control

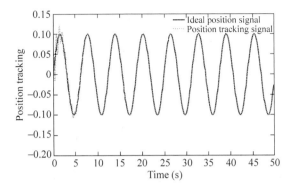

Figure 9.24 Tracking for sine position

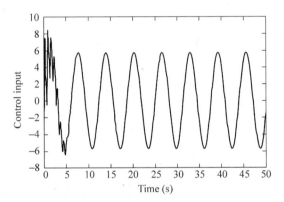

Figure 9.25 Control input

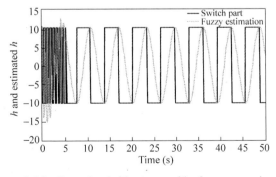

Figure 9.26 Control switching part and its fuzzy approximation

Advanced Sliding Mode Control for Mechanical Systems: Design, Analysis and MATLAB Simulation

Simulation programs:

(1) Simulink main program: chap9_5sim.mdl

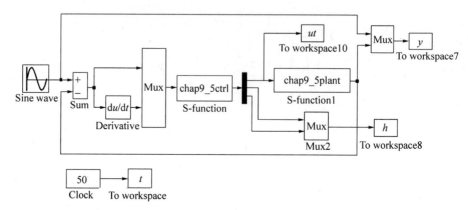

(2) S-function of controller: chap9_5ctrl.m

```
function [sys,x0,str,ts] = spacemodel(t,x,u,flag)
switch flag,
case 0,
    [sys,x0,str,ts]=mdlInitializeSizes;
case 1,
    sys=mdlDerivatives(t,x,u);
case 3,
    sys=mdlOutputs(t,x,u);
case {2,4,9}
    sys=[];
otherwise
    error(['Unhandled flag = ',num2str(flag)]);
end
function [sys,x0,str,ts]=mdlInitializeSizes
sizes = simsizes;
sizes.NumContStates  = 3;
sizes.NumDiscStates  = 0;
sizes.NumOutputs     = 3;
sizes.NumInputs      = 2;
sizes.DirFeedthrough = 1;
sizes.NumSampleTimes = 0;
sys = simsizes(sizes);
x0  = [0.1*ones(3,1)];
str = [];
ts  = [];
function sys=mdlDerivatives(t,x,u)
xd=0.1*sin(t);
dxd=0.1*cos(t);
ddxd=-0.1*sin(t);

e=u(1);
```

9 Fuzzy Sliding Mode Control

```
de=u(2);
x1=xd-e;
x2=de-dxd;

k1=30;
s=-(k1*e+de);

for i=1:1:3
    thtah(i,1)=x(i);
end
%%%%%%%%%%%%%%%%%%%%%%%%%%%%%%%%%%%%%
fsd=0;
gs=5*(s+3);
uh(1)=1/(1+exp(gs));

uh(2)=exp(-s^2);

gs=5*(s-3);
uh(3)=1/(1+exp(gs));
%%%%%%%%%%%%%%%%%%%%%%%%%%%%%%%%%%%%%

fsu=uh;
for i=1:1:3
    fsd=fsd+uh(i);
end
fs=fsu/(fsd+0.001);

gama=150;
S=gama*s*fs;
for j=1:1:3
    sys(j)=S(j);
end

function sys=mdlOutputs(t,x,u)
xd=0.1*sin(t);
dxd=0.1*cos(t);
ddxd=-0.1*sin(t);

e=u(1);
de=u(2);
x1=xd-e;
x2=de-dxd;

k1=30;
s=-(k1*e+de);

for i=1:1:3
    thtah(i,1)=x(i);
end
%%%%%%%%%%%%%%%%%%%%%%%%%%%%%%%%%%%%%
fsd=0;
```

277

Advanced Sliding Mode Control for Mechanical Systems: Design, Analysis and MATLAB Simulation

```
gs=5*(s+3);
uh(1)=1/(1+exp(gs));

uh(2)=exp(-s^2);

gs=5*(s-3);
uh(3)=1/(1+exp(gs));
%%%%%%%%%%%%%%%%%%%%%%%%%%%%%%%%%%%%%
fsu=uh;
for i=1:1:3
   fsd=fsd+uh(i);
end
fs=fsu/(fsd+0.001);
h=thtah'*fs';
%%%%%%%%%%%%%%%%%%%%%%%%%%%%%%%%%%%%%
g=9.8;mc=1.0;m=0.1;l=0.5;
S=l*(4/3-m*(cos(x1))^2/(mc+m));
fx=g*sin(x1)-m*l*x2^2*cos(x1)*sin(x1)/(mc+m);
fx=fx/S;
gx=cos(x1)/(mc+m);
gx=gx/S;
%%%%%%%%%%%%%%%%%%%%%%%%%%%%%%%%%%%%%
ut=1/gx*(-fx+ddxd-1*h+k1*de);

xite=10+0.01;
sys(1)=ut;
sys(2)=xite*sign(s);
sys(3)=h;
```

(3) S-function of the plant: chap9_5plant.m

```
function [sys,x0,str,ts]=s_function(t,x,u,flag)
switch flag,
case 0,
    [sys,x0,str,ts]=mdlInitializeSizes;
case 1,
    sys=mdlDerivatives(t,x,u);
case 3,
    sys=mdlOutputs(t,x,u);
case {2, 4, 9 }
    sys = [];
otherwise
    error(['Unhandled flag = ',num2str(flag)]);
end
function [sys,x0,str,ts]=mdlInitializeSizes
sizes = simsizes;
sizes.NumContStates  = 2;
sizes.NumDiscStates  = 0;
sizes.NumOutputs     = 1;
sizes.NumInputs      = 1;
sizes.DirFeedthrough = 0;
sizes.NumSampleTimes = 0;
```

9 Fuzzy Sliding Mode Control

```
sys=simsizes(sizes);
x0=[pi/60 0];
str=[];
ts=[];
function sys=mdlDerivatives(t,x,u)
g=9.8;mc=1.0;m=0.1;l=0.5;
S=l*(4/3-m*(cos(x(1)))^2/(mc+m));
fx=g*sin(x(1))-m*l*x(2)^2*cos(x(1))*sin(x(1))/(mc+m);
fx=fx/S;
gx=cos(x(1))/(mc+m);
gx=gx/S;

dt=10*sin(t);
sys(1)=x(2);
sys(2)=fx+gx*u-dt;
function sys=mdlOutputs(t,x,u)
sys(1)=x(1);
```

(4) Plot program: chap9_5plot.m

```
close all;

figure(1);
plot(t,y(:,1),'k',t,y(:,2),'r:','linewidth',2);
xlabel('time(s)');ylabel('Position tracking');
legend('ideal position signal','position tracking signal');

figure(2);
plot(t,ut(:,1),'k','linewidth',2);
xlabel('time(s)');ylabel('Control input');

figure(3);
plot(t,h(:,1),'k',t,h(:,2),'r:','linewidth',2);
xlabel('time(s)');ylabel('h and estiamted h');
legend('Switch part','fuzzy estination');
```

References

[1] Wang LX. A Course in Fuzzy System and Control, Prentice Hall, 1997
[2] Wang LX. Stable adaptive fuzzy control of nonlinear systems, IEEE Transactions on Fuzzy Systems, 1993, 1(2): 146 − 155
[3] Chen JY. Expert SMC-based fuzzy control with genetic algorithms, Journal of the Franklin Institute, 1999, 336: 589 − 610
[4] Yoo BK, Ham WC. Adaptive Control of Robot Manipulator Using Fuzzy Compensator. IEEE Transactions on Fuzzy Systems, 2000, 8(2): 186 − 199
[5] Wang J, Rad AB, Chan PT. Indirect adaptive fuzzy sliding mode control: Part I: fuzzy switching, Fuzzy Sets and systems, 2001, 122, 21 − 30

10 Neural Network Sliding Mode Control

Jinkun Liu

Beijing University of Aeronautics and Astronautics

P.R.China

E-mail: ljk@buaa.edu.cn

Xinhua Wang

National University of Singapore

Singapore

E-mail: wangxinhua04@gmail.com

Abstract This chapter introduces two kinds of neural network sliding mode controllers, including a sliding mode controller design based on RBF neural network approximation and an adaptive RBF network sliding mode control for manipulator.

Keywords sliding mode control, RBF neural network, manipulator

Past research of the universal approximation theorem[1, 2] show that any nonlinear function over a compact set with arbitrary accuracy can be approximated by the RBF neural network. There have been significant research efforts on the RBF neural control for nonlinear systems[3]. In section 10.1 an adaptive neural sliding mode control algorithm is proposed for a class of continuous time unknown nonlinear systems. This is in contrast to the existing sliding mode control design where the presence of hitting control may introduce problems to the controlled systems. These unknown nonlinearities are approximated by the RBF neural network whose weight value parameters are adjusted on-line according to some adaptive laws. The purpose of controlling the output of the nonlinear system is to track a given trajectory. Based on the RBF model, the Lyapunov synthesis approach is used to develop an adaptive control algorithm. The chattering action is attenuated and a robust performance can be ensured. The stability analysis for the proposed control algorithm is provided. In section 10.2 the RBF network is used to approximate the unknown part of the manipulator dynamic equation. This does not require modeling. Also, the approximation error and disturbance can be compensated by the sliding mode control.

10.1 Sliding Mode Control Based on RBF Neural Network Approximation

10.1.1 Problem Statement

Consider a second-order nonlinear system as follow:

$$\ddot{\theta} = f(\theta,\dot{\theta}) + g(\theta,\dot{\theta})u + d(t) \tag{10.1}$$

where $f(\cdot)$ and $g(\cdot)$ are all nonlinear functions, $u \in \mathbf{R}$ and $y \in \mathbf{R}$ are the input control and output respectively, $d(t)$ is the outer disturbance and $|d(t)| \leqslant D$.

Let the desired output be θ_{d} and denote

$$e = \theta_{\mathrm{d}} - \theta$$

Design sliding mode function as

$$s = \dot{e} + ce \tag{10.2}$$

where $c > 0$, then

$$\dot{s} = \ddot{e} + c\dot{e} = \ddot{\theta}_{\mathrm{d}} - \ddot{\theta} + c\dot{e} = \ddot{\theta}_{\mathrm{d}} - f - gu - d(t) + c\dot{e} \tag{10.3}$$

If f and g are known, we can design control law as

$$u = \frac{1}{g}(-f + \ddot{\theta}_{\mathrm{d}} + c\dot{e} + \eta\,\mathrm{sgn}(s)) \tag{10.4}$$

Then Eq. (10.3) becomes

$$\dot{s} = \ddot{e} + c\dot{e} = \ddot{\theta}_{\mathrm{d}} - \ddot{\theta} + c\dot{e} = \ddot{\theta}_{\mathrm{d}} - f - gu - d(t) + c\dot{e} = -\eta\,\mathrm{sgn}(s) - d(t)$$

Therefore, if $\eta \geqslant D$, we have

$$s\dot{s} = -\eta\,|s| - s \cdot d(t) \leqslant 0$$

If $f(x)$ is unknown, we should estimate $f(x)$ by some algorithms. In the following, we will simply recall RBF neural network approximate uncertain item $f(x)$.

10.1.2 Controller Design Based on a Radial Basis Function Neural Network

RBF networks are adaptively used to approximate the uncertain f. The algorithm of a radial basis function (RBF) networks is[2]:

$$h_j = g(\|\,\boldsymbol{x} - c_{ij}\,\|^2 / b_j^2)$$
$$f = \boldsymbol{W}^{\mathrm{T}}\boldsymbol{h}(\boldsymbol{x}) + \varepsilon$$

where $\boldsymbol{x}$ is the input state of the network, i is the input number of the network,

j is the number of hidden layer nodes in the network, $\boldsymbol{h} = [h_1 \quad h_2 \quad \cdots \quad h_n]^{\mathrm{T}}$ is the output of Gaussian function, $\boldsymbol{W}$ is the neural network weights, ε is approximation error of neural network, and $\varepsilon \leqslant \varepsilon_{\mathrm{N}}$.

RBF network approximation f is used. The network input is selected as $\boldsymbol{x} = [e \quad \dot{e}]^{\mathrm{T}}$, and the output of RBF neural network is

$$\hat{f}(\boldsymbol{x}) = \hat{\boldsymbol{W}}^{\mathrm{T}} \boldsymbol{h}(\boldsymbol{x}) \tag{10.5}$$

where $\boldsymbol{h}(\boldsymbol{x})$ is the Gaussian function of neural network.

We know that Gaussian function and the neural network weights are difficult to select.

The control input Eq. (10.4) is written as

$$u = \frac{1}{g}(-\hat{f}(\boldsymbol{x}) + \ddot{\theta}_{\mathrm{d}} + c\dot{e} + \eta \, \mathrm{sgn}(s)) \tag{10.6}$$

Submitting Eq. (10.6) to Eq. (10.3), we have

$$\dot{s} = \ddot{\theta}_{\mathrm{d}} - f(\boldsymbol{x}) - gu - d(t) + c\dot{e} = \ddot{\theta}_{\mathrm{d}} - f(\boldsymbol{x}) - (-\hat{f}(\boldsymbol{x}) + \ddot{\theta}_{\mathrm{d}} + c\dot{e} + \eta \, \mathrm{sgn}(t)) - d(t) + c\dot{e}$$
$$= -f(\boldsymbol{x}) + \hat{f}(\boldsymbol{x}) - \eta \, \mathrm{sgn}(s) - d(t) = -\tilde{f}(\boldsymbol{x}) - d(t) - \eta \, \mathrm{sgn}(s) \tag{10.7}$$

where

$$\tilde{f}(\boldsymbol{x}) = f(\boldsymbol{x}) - \hat{f}(\boldsymbol{x}) = \boldsymbol{W}^{\mathrm{T}} \boldsymbol{h}(\boldsymbol{x}) + \varepsilon - \hat{\boldsymbol{W}}^{\mathrm{T}} \boldsymbol{h}(\boldsymbol{x}) = \tilde{\boldsymbol{W}}^{\mathrm{T}} \boldsymbol{h}(\boldsymbol{x}) + \varepsilon \tag{10.8}$$

Define the Lyapunov function as

$$L = \frac{1}{2}s^2 + \frac{1}{2}\gamma \tilde{\boldsymbol{W}}^{\mathrm{T}} \tilde{\boldsymbol{W}}$$

where γ is a positive coefficient.

Derivative L, and from Eqs. (10.6) and (10.7), we have

$$\dot{L} = s\dot{s} + \gamma \tilde{\boldsymbol{W}}^{\mathrm{T}} \dot{\tilde{\boldsymbol{W}}} = s(-\tilde{f}(\boldsymbol{x}) - d(t) - \eta \, \mathrm{sgn}(s)) - \gamma \tilde{\boldsymbol{W}}^{\mathrm{T}} \dot{\hat{\boldsymbol{W}}}$$
$$= s(-\tilde{\boldsymbol{W}}^{\mathrm{T}} \boldsymbol{h}(\boldsymbol{x}) - \varepsilon - d(t) - \eta \, \mathrm{sgn}(s)) - \gamma \tilde{\boldsymbol{W}}^{\mathrm{T}} \dot{\hat{\boldsymbol{W}}}$$
$$= -\tilde{\boldsymbol{W}}^{\mathrm{T}} (s\boldsymbol{h}(\boldsymbol{x}) + \gamma \dot{\hat{\boldsymbol{W}}}) - s(\varepsilon + d(t) + \eta \, \mathrm{sgn}(s))$$

Let the adaptive rule be

$$\dot{\hat{\boldsymbol{W}}} = -\frac{1}{\gamma} s\boldsymbol{h}(\boldsymbol{x}) \tag{10.9}$$

Then

$$\dot{L} = -s(\varepsilon + d(t) + \eta \, \mathrm{sgn}(s)) = -s(\varepsilon + d(t)) - \eta \, |s|$$

We get $\dot{L} \leqslant 0$ approximately as the approximation error ε is sufficiently small in the design $\eta \geqslant \varepsilon_{\mathrm{N}} + D$.

10.1.3 Simulation Example

Consider the following inverted pendulum:

$$\begin{cases} \dot{x}_1 = x_2 \\ \dot{x}_2 = \dfrac{g\sin x_1 - mlx_2^2 \cos x_1 \sin x_1/(m_c+m)}{l(4/3 - m\cos^2 x_1/(m_c+m))} + \dfrac{\cos x_1/(m_c+m)}{l(4/3 - m\cos^2 x_1/(m_c+m))} u \end{cases}$$

where x_1 and x_2 are the swing angle and swing rate respectively. $g = 9.8$ m/s^2, $m_c = 1$ kg is the vehicle mass, m is the mass of the pendulum. l is one half of the pendulum length, and u is the control input.

Choosing $x_1 = \theta$, the desired trajectory is $\theta_d(t) = 0.1\sin t$. The initial state of the plant is $[\pi/60, 0]$. We adapt control law as Eq. (10.6) and adaptive law as Eq. (10.9), choose $c = 15$, $\eta = 0.1$ and adaptive parameter $\gamma = 0.05$.

The structure of RBF is chosen with two input-five hidden-one output, $c_{ij} = 0.20$, $b_j = 0.50$, the initial value of RBF weight value is set as 0.10. The curves of position tracking and uncertainty approximation are shown in Fig. 10.1 – Fig.10.3.

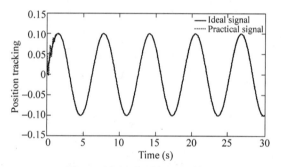

Figure 10.1 Position tracking

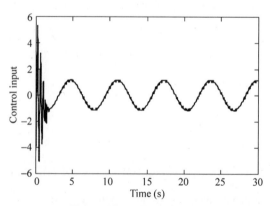

Figure 10.2 Control input

10 Neural Network Sliding Mode Control

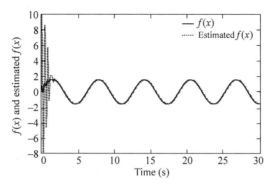

Figure 10.3 $f(x)$ and $\hat{f}(x)$

Simulation programs:

(1) Main Simulink program: chap10_1sim.mdl

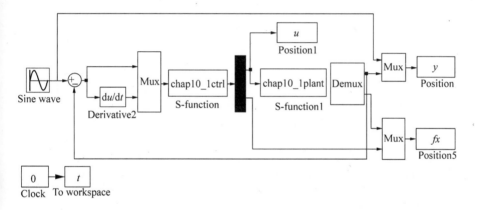

(2) Control law program: chap10_1ctrl.m

```
function [sys,x0,str,ts] = spacemodel(t,x,u,flag)
switch flag,
case 0,
    [sys,x0,str,ts]=mdlInitializeSizes;
case 1,
    sys=mdlDerivatives(t,x,u);
case 3,
    sys=mdlOutputs(t,x,u);
case {2,4,9}
    sys=[];
otherwise
    error(['Unhandled flag = ',num2str(flag)]);
end
function [sys,x0,str,ts]=mdlInitializeSizes
global c b n
sizes = simsizes;
```

285

```matlab
sizes.NumContStates  = 5;
sizes.NumDiscStates  = 0;
sizes.NumOutputs     = 2;
sizes.NumInputs      = 2;
sizes.DirFeedthrough = 1;
sizes.NumSampleTimes = 0;
sys = simsizes(sizes);
x0  = 0*ones(1,5);
str = [];
ts  = [];
c=0.10*ones(2,5);
b=0.50*ones(5,1);
n=15;
function sys=mdlDerivatives(t,x,u)
global c b n
e=u(1);
de=u(2);
s=n*e+de;

xi=[e;de];
h=zeros(5,1);
for j=1:1:5
    h(j)=exp(-norm(xi-c(:,j))^2/(2*b(j)*b(j)));
end
gama=0.015;
W=[x(1) x(2) x(3) x(4) x(5)]';
for i=1:1:5
    sys(i)=-1/gama*s*h(i);
end
function sys=mdlOutputs(t,x,u)
global c b n
e=u(1);
de=u(2);
thd=0.1*sin(t);
dthd=0.1*cos(t);
ddthd=-0.1*sin(t);
x1=thd-e;

s=n*e+de;
W=[x(1) x(2) x(3) x(4) x(5)]';
xi=[e;de];
h=zeros(5,1);
for j=1:1:5
    h(j)=exp(-norm(xi-c(:,j))^2/(2*b(j)*b(j)));
end
fn=W'*h;

g=9.8;mc=1.0;m=0.1;l=0.5;
S=l*(4/3-m*(cos(x1))^2/(mc+m));
gx=cos(x1)/(mc+m);
gx=gx/S;
```

10 Neural Network Sliding Mode Control

```
if t<=1.5
    xite=1.0;
else
    xite=0.10;
end
ut=1/gx*(-fn+ddthd+n*de+xite*sign(s));
sys(1)=ut;
sys(2)=fn;
```

(3) Plant program: chap10_1plant.m

```
function [sys,x0,str,ts]=s_function(t,x,u,flag)
switch flag,
case 0,
    [sys,x0,str,ts]=mdlInitializeSizes;
case 1,
    sys=mdlDerivatives(t,x,u);
case 3,
    sys=mdlOutputs(t,x,u);
case {2, 4, 9 }
    sys = [];
otherwise
    error(['Unhandled flag = ',num2str(flag)]);
end
function [sys,x0,str,ts]=mdlInitializeSizes
sizes = simsizes;
sizes.NumContStates  = 2;
sizes.NumDiscStates  = 0;
sizes.NumOutputs     = 2;
sizes.NumInputs      = 1;
sizes.DirFeedthrough = 0;
sizes.NumSampleTimes = 0;
sys=simsizes(sizes);
x0=[pi/60 0];
str=[];
ts=[];
function sys=mdlDerivatives(t,x,u)
g=9.8;mc=1.0;m=0.1;l=0.5;
S=l*(4/3-m*(cos(x(1)))^2/(mc+m));
fx=g*sin(x(1))-m*l*x(2)^2*cos(x(1))*sin(x(1))/(mc+m);
fx=fx/S;
gx=cos(x(1))/(mc+m);
gx=gx/S;
%%%%%%%%%
dt=0*10*sin(t);
%%%%%%%%%

sys(1)=x(2);
sys(2)=fx+gx*u+dt;
function sys=mdlOutputs(t,x,u)
g=9.8;
mc=1.0;
m=0.1;
```

287

Advanced Sliding Mode Control for Mechanical Systems: Design, Analysis and MATLAB Simulation

```
l=0.5;

S=l*(4/3-m*(cos(x(1)))^2/(mc+m));
fx=g*sin(x(1))-m*l*x(2)^2*cos(x(1))*sin(x(1))/(mc+m);
fx=fx/S;

sys(1)=x(1);
sys(2)=fx;
```

(4) Plot program: chap10_1plot.m

```
close all;

figure(1);
plot(t,y(:,1),'k',t,y(:,2),'r:','linewidth',2);
xlabel('time(s)');ylabel('Position tracking');
legend('ideal signal','practical signal');

figure(2);
plot(t,u(:,1),'k','linewidth',2);
xlabel('time(s)');ylabel('Control input');

figure(3);
plot(t,fx(:,1),'k',t,fx(:,2),'r:','linewidth',2);
xlabel('time(s)');ylabel('fx and estiamted fx');
legend('fx','estiamted fx');
```

10.2 RBF Network Adaptive Sliding Mode Control for Manipulator

10.2.1 Problem Statement

Consider the dynamic equation of an n-joint manipulator as follows:

$$H(q)\ddot{q} + C(q,\dot{q})\dot{q} + G(q) = \tau - F(\dot{q}) - \tau_d \qquad (10.10)$$

where $H(q)$ is an $n \times n$ positive definite inertial matrix, $C(q,\dot{q})$ is an $n \times n$ inertial matrix, $G(q)$ is an $n \times 1$ inertial vector, $F(\dot{q})$ is friction force, τ_d is the unknown disturbance, and τ is the control input.

Denote the tracking error as:

$$e(t) = q_d(t) - q(t)$$

Select the sliding variable as:

$$s = \dot{e} + \Lambda e \qquad (10.11)$$

where Λ is a symmetric positive definite constant matrix and $\Lambda = \Lambda^T > 0$, therefore,

288

we have

$$\dot{q} = -s + \dot{q}_d + \Lambda e$$

$$Hs = H(\ddot{q}_d - \ddot{q} + \Lambda\dot{e}) = H(\ddot{q}_d + \Lambda\dot{e}) - H\ddot{q}$$
$$= H(\ddot{q}_d + \Lambda\dot{e}) + C\dot{q} + G + F + \tau_d - \tau$$
$$= H(\ddot{q}_d + \Lambda\dot{e}) - Cs + C(\dot{q}_d + \Lambda e) + G + F + \tau_d - \tau$$
$$= -Cs - \tau + f + \tau_d \tag{10.12}$$

where $f(x) = H(\ddot{q}_d + \Lambda\dot{e}) + C(q_d + \Lambda e) + G + F$.

In engineering, $f(x)$ is unknown and, therefore, it is required to approximate $f(x)$. The RBF network is adopted to approximate $f(x)$. The network input is selected based on the expression of $f(x)$ [4]:

$$x = [e^T \quad \dot{e}^T \quad q_d^T \quad \dot{q}_d^T \quad \ddot{q}_d^T]$$

The controller is designed as:

$$\tau = \hat{f}(x) + K_v s \tag{10.13}$$

where K_v is a symmetric positive definite constant matrix, $\hat{f}(x)$ is the output of RBF network. $\hat{f}(x)$ approximates $f(x)$.

From Eqs. (10.13) and (10.12), we have

$$Hs = -Cs - \hat{f}(x) - K_v s + f(x) + \tau_d$$
$$= -(K_v + C)s + \tilde{f}(x) + \tau_d = -(K_v + C)s + \varsigma_0 \tag{10.14}$$

where $\tilde{f}(x) = f(x) - \hat{f}(x)$, $\varsigma_0 = \tilde{f}(x) + \tau_d$.

Select the Lyapunov function as:

$$L = \frac{1}{2}s^T Hs$$

Therefore,

$$\dot{L} = s^T H\dot{s} + \frac{1}{2}s^T \dot{H}s = -s^T K_v s + \frac{1}{2}s^T(\dot{H} - 2C)s + s^T\varsigma_0$$
$$\dot{L} = s^T\varsigma_0 - s^T K_v s$$

It indicates that, with K_v, the stability of control system depends on ς_0, i.e. the approximation precision and the magnitude of τ_d.

RBF network can be adopted to approximate $f(x)$. The desired algorithm of RBF network is:

$$\phi_i = g(\| x - c_i \|^2 / \sigma_i^2), \quad i = 1, 2, \cdots, n$$
$$y = W^{*T}\varphi(x), \quad f(x) = W^{*T}\varphi(x) + \varepsilon$$

where x is the input state of network, $\varphi(x) = [\phi_1 \quad \phi_2 \quad \cdots \quad \phi_n]^{\mathrm{T}}$, ε is the approximation error of neural network, W^* is the weight vector of desired RBF network.

10.2.2 Sliding Mode Control with Respect to the Approximation of $f(x)$

10.2.2.1 Design of Controller

RBF network is adopted to approximate $f(x)$, therefore, the output of RBF network is:

$$\hat{f}(x) = \hat{W}^{\mathrm{T}} \varphi(x) \tag{10.15}$$

Select

$$\tilde{W} = W^* - \hat{W}, \quad \|W^*\|_{\mathrm{F}} \leqslant W_{\max}$$

Therefore, we have

$$\varsigma_0 = \tilde{f}(x) + \tau_{\mathrm{d}} = \tilde{W}^{\mathrm{T}} \varphi(x) + \varepsilon + \tau_{\mathrm{d}}$$

Controller is designed as[4]:

$$\tau = \hat{f}(x) + K_v s - v \tag{10.16}$$

where v is the robust element required to overcome the network approximation error ε and the disturbance τ_{d}.

From Eqs. (10.16) and (10.12), we have

$$H\dot{s} = -(K_v + C)s + \tilde{W}^{\mathrm{T}} \varphi(x) + (\varepsilon + \tau_{\mathrm{d}}) + v = -(K_v + C)s + \varsigma_1 \tag{10.17}$$

where $\varsigma_1 = \tilde{W}^{\mathrm{T}} \varphi(x) + (\varepsilon + \tau_{\mathrm{d}}) + v$.

The robust element v is designed as:

$$v = -(\varepsilon_{\mathrm{N}} + b_{\mathrm{d}})\mathrm{sgn}(s) \tag{10.18}$$

where $\|\varepsilon\| \leqslant \varepsilon_{\mathrm{N}}$, $\|\tau_{\mathrm{d}}\| \leqslant b_{\mathrm{d}}$.

10.2.2.2 Stability Analysis

Select the Lyapunov function as

$$L = \frac{1}{2} s^{\mathrm{T}} H s + \frac{1}{2} \mathrm{tr}(\tilde{W}^{\mathrm{T}} F_{\mathrm{W}}^{-1} \tilde{W})$$

where H and F_{W} are positive matrices. Therefore, we have

10 Neural Network Sliding Mode Control

$$\dot{L} = s^{\mathrm{T}} H \dot{s} + \frac{1}{2} s^{\mathrm{T}} \dot{H} s + \mathrm{tr}(\tilde{W}^{\mathrm{T}} F_{\mathrm{W}}^{-1} \dot{\tilde{W}})$$

From Eq. (10.17), we have

$$\dot{L} = -s^{\mathrm{T}} K_{\mathrm{v}} s + \frac{1}{2} s^{\mathrm{T}} (\dot{H} - 2C) s + \mathrm{tr}\tilde{W}^{\mathrm{T}} (F_{\mathrm{W}}^{-1} \dot{\tilde{W}} + \varphi s^{\mathrm{T}}) + s^{\mathrm{T}} (\varepsilon + \tau_{\mathrm{d}} + \nu)$$

We know that the manipulator has the characteristic of $s^{\mathrm{T}} (\dot{H} - 2C) s = 0$. Select $\dot{\tilde{W}} = -F_{\mathrm{W}} \varphi s^{\mathrm{T}}$, i.e., the adaptive rule of the network is

$$\dot{\hat{W}} = F_{\mathrm{W}} \varphi s^{\mathrm{T}} \tag{10.19}$$

Therefore,

$$\dot{L} = -s^{\mathrm{T}} K_{\mathrm{v}} s + s^{\mathrm{T}} (\varepsilon + \tau_{\mathrm{d}} + \nu)$$

Because

$$s^{\mathrm{T}} (\varepsilon + \tau_{\mathrm{d}} + \nu) = s^{\mathrm{T}} (\varepsilon + \tau_{\mathrm{d}}) + s^{\mathrm{T}} \nu = s^{\mathrm{T}} (\varepsilon + \tau_{\mathrm{d}}) - \| s \| (\varepsilon_{\mathrm{N}} + b_{\mathrm{d}}) \leqslant 0$$

We have

$$\dot{L} \leqslant 0$$

10.2.3 Simulation Example

The kinetic equation of the two-joint manipulator is:

$$H(q)\ddot{q} + C(q,\dot{q})\dot{q} + G(q) = \tau - F(\dot{q}) - \tau_{\mathrm{d}}$$

where

$$H(q) = \begin{bmatrix} p_1 + p_2 + 2p_3 \cos q_2 & p_2 + p_3 \cos q_2 \\ p_2 + p_3 \cos q_2 & p_2 \end{bmatrix}$$

$$C(q,\dot{q}) = \begin{bmatrix} -p_3 \dot{q}_2 \sin q_2 & -p_3 (\dot{q}_1 + \dot{q}_2) \sin q_2 \\ p_3 \dot{q}_1 \sin q_2 & 0 \end{bmatrix}$$

$$G(q) = \begin{bmatrix} p_4 g \cos q_1 + p_5 g \cos(q_1 + q_2) \\ p_5 g \cos(q_1 + q_2) \end{bmatrix}$$

$$F(\dot{q}) = 0.02 \, \mathrm{sgn}(\dot{q}), \quad \tau_{\mathrm{d}} = [0.2 \sin t \quad 0.2 \sin t]^{\mathrm{T}}$$

Let $p = [p_1 \ p_2 \ p_3 \ p_4 \ p_5] = [2.9 \ 0.76 \ 0.87 \ 3.04 \ 0.87]$. The selection of the Gauss function of the RBF network is very important to the control of the

291

neural network. If the parameter is not suitable, then, the available mapping of the Gauss function cannot be obtained. Hence, the RBF network is unavailable. Therefore, c should be selected according to the scope of network input. We select $b = 0.20$. The initial weight matrix of the network is selected as 0 or 0.1, and the network input is selected as $z = [e \ \dot{e} \ q_d \ \dot{q}_d \ \ddot{q}_d]$.

The initial state vector of the system is $[0.09 \ 0 \ -0.09 \ 0]$. The desired position commands of the two joints are $q_{1d} = 0.1\sin t$ and $q_{2d} = 0.1\sin t$ respectively. The controller parameters are: $K_v = \text{diag}\{20, 20\}$, $F_W = \text{diag}\{15, 15\}$, $\Lambda = \text{diag}\{5, 5\}$. In the sliding robust element, select $\varepsilon_N = 0.20$ and $b_d = 0.10$. The controller is given in Eq. (10.16), and the adaptive rule is given in Eq. (10.19). Simulation results are shown in Fig.10.4 – Fig.10.7.

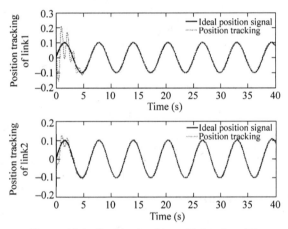

Figure 10.4 Position tracking of joints 1 and 2

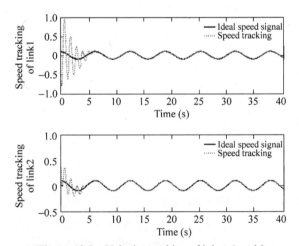

Figure 10.5 Velocity tracking of joints 1 and 2

10 Neural Network Sliding Mode Control

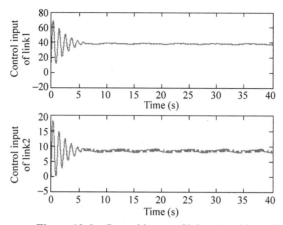

Figure 10.6 Control inputs of joints 1 and 2

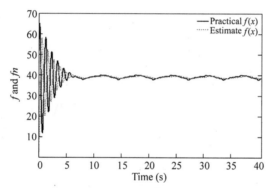

Figure 10.7 $\|f(x)\|$ and $\|\hat{f}(x)\|$ of joints 1 and 2

Simulation programs:

(1) Simulink main program: chap10_2sim.mdl

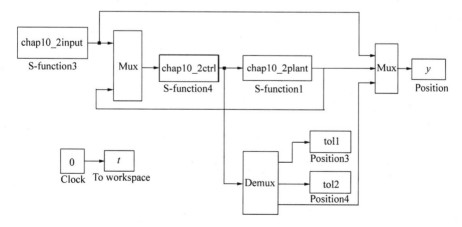

Advanced Sliding Mode Control for Mechanical Systems: Design, Analysis and MATLAB Simulation

(2) Program of position commands: chap10_2input.m

```matlab
function [sys,x0,str,ts] = spacemodel(t,x,u,flag)
switch flag,
case 0,
    [sys,x0,str,ts]=mdlInitializeSizes;
case 1,
    sys=mdlDerivatives(t,x,u);
case 3,
    sys=mdlOutputs(t,x,u);
case {2,4,9}
    sys=[];
otherwise
    error(['Unhandled flag = ',num2str(flag)]);
end
function [sys,x0,str,ts]=mdlInitializeSizes
sizes = simsizes;
sizes.NumContStates  = 0;
sizes.NumDiscStates  = 0;
sizes.NumOutputs     = 6;
sizes.NumInputs      = 0;
sizes.DirFeedthrough = 0;
sizes.NumSampleTimes = 1;
sys = simsizes(sizes);
x0  = [];
str = [];
ts  = [0 0];
function sys=mdlOutputs(t,x,u)
qd1=0.1*sin(t);
d_qd1=0.1*cos(t);
dd_qd1=-0.1*sin(t);
qd2=0.1*sin(t);
d_qd2=0.1*cos(t);
dd_qd2=-0.1*sin(t);

sys(1)=qd1;
sys(2)=d_qd1;
sys(3)=dd_qd1;
sys(4)=qd2;
sys(5)=d_qd2;
sys(6)=dd_qd2;
```

(3) Controller S function: chap10_2ctrl.m

```matlab
function [sys,x0,str,ts] = spacemodel(t,x,u,flag)
switch flag,
case 0,
    [sys,x0,str,ts]=mdlInitializeSizes;
case 1,
    sys=mdlDerivatives(t,x,u);
```

294

10 Neural Network Sliding Mode Control

```
case 3,
    sys=mdlOutputs(t,x,u);
case {2,4,9}
    sys=[];
otherwise
    error(['Unhandled flag = ',num2str(flag)]);
end
function [sys,x0,str,ts]=mdlInitializeSizes
global node c b Fai
node=7;
c=0.1*[-1.5 -1 -0.5 0 0.5 1 1.5;
       -1.5 -1 -0.5 0 0.5 1 1.5;
       -1.5 -1 -0.5 0 0.5 1 1.5;
       -1.5 -1 -0.5 0 0.5 1 1.5;
       -1.5 -1 -0.5 0 0.5 1 1.5];
b=10;
Fai=5*eye(2);

sizes = simsizes;
sizes.NumContStates  = 2*node;
sizes.NumDiscStates  = 0;
sizes.NumOutputs     = 3;
sizes.NumInputs      = 11;
sizes.DirFeedthrough = 1;
sizes.NumSampleTimes = 0;
sys = simsizes(sizes);
x0  = 0.1*ones(1,2*node);
str = [];
ts  = [];
function sys=mdlDerivatives(t,x,u)
global node c b Fai
qd1=u(1);
d_qd1=u(2);
dd_qd1=u(3);
qd2=u(4);
d_qd2=u(5);
dd_qd2=u(6);

q1=u(7);
d_q1=u(8);
q2=u(9);
d_q2=u(10);

q=[q1;q2];

e1=qd1-q1;
e2=qd2-q2;
de1=d_qd1-d_q1;
de2=d_qd2-d_q2;
```

295

```matlab
e=[e1;e2];
de=[de1;de2];
S=de+Fai*e;

qd=[qd1;qd2];
dqd=[d_qd1;d_qd2];
dqr=dqd+Fai*e;
ddqd=[dd_qd1;dd_qd2];
ddqr=ddqd+Fai*de;

z1=[e(1);de(1);qd(1);dqd(1);ddqd(1)];
z2=[e(2);de(2);qd(2);dqd(2);ddqd(2)];
for j=1:1:node
    h1(j)=exp(-norm(z1-c(:,j))^2/(b*b));
    h2(j)=exp(-norm(z2-c(:,j))^2/(b*b));
end

Fw=15*eye(node);
for i=1:1:node
    sys(i)=15*h1(i)*S(1);
    sys(i+node)=15*h2(i)*S(2);
end
function sys=mdlOutputs(t,x,u)
global node c b Fai
qd1=u(1);
d_qd1=u(2);
dd_qd1=u(3);
qd2=u(4);
d_qd2=u(5);
dd_qd2=u(6);

q1=u(7);
d_q1=u(8);
q2=u(9);
d_q2=u(10);

q=[q1;q2];

e1=qd1-q1;
e2=qd2-q2;
de1=d_qd1-d_q1;
de2=d_qd2-d_q2;
e=[e1;e2];
de=[de1;de2];
S=de+Fai*e;

qd=[qd1;qd2];
dqd=[d_qd1;d_qd2];
dqr=dqd+Fai*e;
```

10 Neural Network Sliding Mode Control

```
ddqd=[dd_qd1;dd_qd2];
ddqr=ddqd+Fai*de;

z=[e;de;qd;dqd;ddqd];
W_f1=[x(1:node)]';
W_f2=[x(node+1:node*2)]';

z1=[e(1);de(1);qd(1);dqd(1);ddqd(1)];
z2=[e(2);de(2);qd(2);dqd(2);ddqd(2)];
for j=1:1:node
    h1(j)=exp(-norm(z1-c(:,j))^2/(b*b));
    h2(j)=exp(-norm(z2-c(:,j))^2/(b*b));
end

fn=[W_f1*h1';
    W_f2*h2'];
Kv=20*eye(2);

epN=0.20;bd=0.1;
v=-(epN+bd)*sign(S);
tol=fn+Kv*S-v;

fn_norm=norm(fn);
sys(1)=tol(1);
sys(2)=tol(2);
sys(3)=fn_norm;
```

(4) Program of the plant: chap10_2plant.m

```
function [sys,x0,str,ts]=s_function(t,x,u,flag)

switch flag,
case 0,
    [sys,x0,str,ts]=mdlInitializeSizes;
case 1,
    sys=mdlDerivatives(t,x,u);
case 3,
    sys=mdlOutputs(t,x,u);
case {2, 4, 9 }
    sys = [];
otherwise
    error(['Unhandled flag = ',num2str(flag)]);
end
function [sys,x0,str,ts]=mdlInitializeSizes
global p g
sizes = simsizes;
sizes.NumContStates  = 4;
sizes.NumDiscStates  = 0;
sizes.NumOutputs     = 5;
sizes.NumInputs      =3;
```

```matlab
sizes.DirFeedthrough = 0;
sizes.NumSampleTimes = 0;
sys=simsizes(sizes);
x0=[0.09 0 -0.09 0];
str=[];
ts=[];

p=[2.9 0.76 0.87 3.04 0.87];
g=9.8;
function sys=mdlDerivatives(t,x,u)
global p g

H=[p(1)+p(2)+2*p(3)*cos(x(3)) p(2)+p(3)*cos(x(3));
    p(2)+p(3)*cos(x(3)) p(2)];
C=[-p(3)*x(4)*sin(x(3)) -p(3)*(x(2)+x(4))*sin(x(3));
    p(3)*x(2)*sin(x(3)) 0];
G=[p(4)*g*cos(x(1))+p(5)*g*cos(x(1)+x(3));
    p(5)*g*cos(x(1)+x(3))];
dq=[x(2);x(4)];
F=0.2*sign(dq);
told=[0.1*sin(t);0.1*sin(t)];

tol=u(1:2);

S=inv(H)*(tol-C*dq-G-F-told);

sys(1)=x(2);
sys(2)=S(1);
sys(3)=x(4);
sys(4)=S(2);
function sys=mdlOutputs(t,x,u)
global p g
H=[p(1)+p(2)+2*p(3)*cos(x(3)) p(2)+p(3)*cos(x(3));
    p(2)+p(3)*cos(x(3)) p(2)];
C=[-p(3)*x(4)*sin(x(3)) -p(3)*(x(2)+x(4))*sin(x(3));
    p(3)*x(2)*sin(x(3)) 0];
G=[p(4)*g*cos(x(1))+p(5)*g*cos(x(1)+x(3));
    p(5)*g*cos(x(1)+x(3))];
dq=[x(2);x(4)];
F=0.2*sign(dq);
told=[0.1*sin(t);0.1*sin(t)];

qd1=0.1*sin(t);
d_qd1=0.1*cos(t);
dd_qd1=-0.1*sin(t);
qd2=0.1*sin(t);
d_qd2=0.1*cos(t);
dd_qd2=-0.1*sin(t);
```

10 Neural Network Sliding Mode Control

```
q1=x(1);
d_q1=dq(1);
q2=x(3);
d_q2=dq(2);
q=[q1;q2];
e1=qd1-q1;
e2=qd2-q2;
de1=d_qd1-d_q1;
de2=d_qd2-d_q2;
e=[e1;e2];
de=[de1;de2];
Fai=5*eye(2);
dqd=[d_qd1;d_qd2];
dqr=dqd+Fai*e;
ddqd=[dd_qd1;dd_qd2];
ddqr=ddqd+Fai*de;
f=H*ddqr+C*dqr+G+F;
f_norm=norm(f);

sys(1)=x(1);
sys(2)=x(2);
sys(3)=x(3);
sys(4)=x(4);
sys(5)=f_norm;
```

(5) Plot program: chap10_2plot.m

```
close all;

figure(1);
subplot(211);
plot(t,y(:,1),'k',t,y(:,7),'r:','linewidth',2);
xlabel('time(s)');ylabel('Position tracking for link 1');
legend('Ideal position signal','Position tracking');
subplot(212);
plot(t,y(:,4),'k',t,y(:,9),'r:','linewidth',2);
xlabel('time(s)');ylabel('Position tracking for link 2');
legend('Ideal position signal','Position tracking');

figure(2);
subplot(211);
plot(t,y(:,2),'k',t,y(:,8),'r:','linewidth',2);
xlabel('time(s)');ylabel('Speed tracking for link 1');
legend('Ideal speed signal','Speed tracking');
subplot(212);
plot(t,y(:,5),'k',t,y(:,10),'r:','linewidth',2);
xlabel('time(s)');ylabel('Speed tracking for link 2');
legend('Ideal speed signal','Speed tracking');

figure(3);
```

```
subplot(211);
plot(t,tol1(:,1),'r','linewidth',2);
xlabel('time(s)');ylabel('control input of link 1');
subplot(212);
plot(t,tol2(:,1),'r','linewidth',2);
xlabel('time(s)');ylabel('control input of link 2');

figure(4);
plot(t,y(:,11),'k',t,y(:,12),'r:','linewidth',2);
xlabel('time(s)');ylabel('f and fn');
legend('Practical f(x)','Estimate f(x)');
```

References

[1] Hartman EJ, Keeler JD, Kowalski JM. Layered neural networks with Gaussian hidden units as universal approximations. Neural computation, 1990, 2(2): 210 – 215

[2] Park J, Sandberg IW. Universal approximation using radial-basis-function networks. Neural computation, 1991,3: 246 – 257

[3] Ge SS, Lee TH, Harris CJ. Adaptive Neural Network Control of Robotic Manipulators. World Scientific, London, 1998

[4] Lewis FL, Liu K, Yesildirek A. Neural Net Robot Controller with Guaranteed Tracking Performance. IEEE Transactions on Neural Networks, 1995, 6(3): 703 – 715

11　Sliding Mode Control for Robot

Jinkun Liu
Beijing University of Aeronautics and Astronautics
P.R.China
E-mail: ljk@buaa.edu.cn

Xinhua Wang
National University of Singapore
Singapore
E-mail: wangxinhua04@gmail.com

Abstract　This chapter introduces three kinds of sliding mode controllers design for robot, including sliding mode controller design based on input-output stability, sliding mode controller design based on computed torque method and adaptive sliding mode controller design for manipulator.

Keywords　sliding mode control, input-output stability, computed torque method, adaptive sliding mode control, manipulator

11.1　Model of Robotic Joints

11.1.1　Model Description

In engineering, robots not only can improve productivity but also can achieve high-strength and hazardous jobs. Manipulators are the usual plants in robotics.

Consider an n-joint manipulator as follows:

$$H(q)\ddot{q} + C(q,\dot{q})\dot{q} + G(q) + F(\dot{q}) + \tau_{\mathrm{d}} = \tau \tag{11.1}$$

where $q \in \mathbf{R}^n$ is the angle vector, $H(q) \in \mathbf{R}^{n \times n}$ is the inertia matrix, $C(q,\dot{q}) \in \mathbf{R}^n$ denotes the centrifugal and coriolis forces $G(q) \in \mathbf{R}^n$ is the gravity, $F(\dot{q}) \in \mathbf{R}^n$ I is the frictional force, $\tau \in \mathbf{R}^n$ is the control moment, and $\tau_{\mathrm{d}} \in \mathbf{R}^n$ is the disturbance moment.

The characteristics of the kinetic model of a manipulator[1]:

(1) Kinetic model contains more number of items. The number of items included in the equation increases with the increase in the number of robot joints.

(2) Highly nonlinearity: Each item of the equations contains non-linear factors such as sine and cosine, et al.

(3) High degree of coupling.

(4) Model uncertainty and time-variant: The load will vary when the robot moves the objects because the objects are not similar. Also, the Joint friction torque will also change over time.

The characteristics of the kinetic model of a manipulator:

(1) $H(q)$ is a positive-definite symmetrical and bounded matrix, i.e., there exist positive constants m_1 and m_2 such that $m_1 I \leqslant H(q) \leqslant m_2 I$;

(2) $C(q,\dot{q})$ is bounded, i.e., there exists known $c_b(q)$ such that $|C(q,\dot{q})| \leqslant c_b(q)\|\dot{q}\|$;

(3) Matrix $\dot{H} - 2C$ is a skew-symmetric matrix, i.e., $x^T(\dot{H} - 2C)x = 0$, where x is a vector;

(4) The known disturbance is satisfied with $\|\tau_d\| \leqslant \tau_M$, where τ_M is a known positive constant.

A classical dual-joint rigid manipulator is shown in Fig. 11.1.

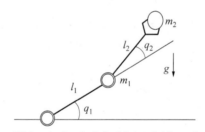

Figure 11.1 A classical dual-joint rigid manipulator

11.1.2 Model Description Example

Using the kinetic equation of a two-joint manipulator[3] as follows:

$$H(q)\ddot{q} + C(q,\dot{q})\dot{q} + G(q) = \tau \tag{11.2}$$

where $q = [q_1 \quad q_2]^T$, $\tau = [\tau_1 \quad \tau_2]^T$, and

$$H = \begin{bmatrix} \alpha + 2\varepsilon\cos(q_2) + 2\eta\sin(q_2) & \beta + \varepsilon\cos(q_2) + \eta\sin(q_2) \\ \beta + \varepsilon\cos(q_2) + \eta\sin(q_2) & \beta \end{bmatrix}$$

$$C = \begin{bmatrix} (-2\varepsilon\sin(q_2) + 2\eta\cos(q_2))\dot{q}_2 & (-\varepsilon\sin(q_2) + \eta\cos(q_2))\dot{q}_2 \\ (\varepsilon\sin(q_2) - \eta\cos(q_2))\dot{q}_1 & 0 \end{bmatrix}$$

11 Sliding Mode Control for Robot

$$G = \begin{bmatrix} \varepsilon e_2 \cos(q_1 + q_2) + \eta e_2 \sin(q_1 + q_2) + (\alpha - \beta + e_1)e_2 \cos(q_1) \\ \varepsilon e_2 \cos(q_1 + q_2) + \eta e_2 \sin(q_1 + q_2) \end{bmatrix}$$

where α, β, ε and η are constants, $\alpha = I_1 + m_1 l_{c1}^2 + I_e + m_e l_{ce}^2 + m_e l_1^2$, $\beta = I_e + m_e l_{ce}^2$, $\varepsilon = m_e l_1 l_{ce} \cos(\delta_e)$, $\eta = m_e l_1 l_{ce} \sin(\delta_e)$.

As an illustration, the practical parameters of a manipulator are shown in Table 11.1.[3]

Table 11.1   Parameters of a dual-joint manipulator

m_1	l_1	l_{c1}	I_1	m_e	l_{ce}	I_e	δ_e	e_1	e_2
1 kg	1 m	1/2 m	1/12 kg	3 kg	1 m	2/5 kg	0	$-7/12$	9.81

Let $a = [\alpha \ \ \beta \ \ \varepsilon \ \ \eta]^{\mathrm{T}}$, and $\hat{a}$ is the estimation of a, $\hat{a} = [\hat{\alpha} \ \ \hat{\beta} \ \ \hat{\varepsilon} \ \ \hat{\eta}]^{\mathrm{T}}$. We assume $\tilde{a} = \hat{a} - a$, since a is a constant vector, $\dot{\tilde{a}} = \dot{\hat{a}}$. The estimated matrices of the above three matrices can be written respectively as:

$$\hat{H} = \begin{bmatrix} \hat{\alpha} + 2\hat{\varepsilon}\cos(q_2) + 2\hat{\eta}\sin(q_2) & \hat{\beta} + \hat{\varepsilon}\cos(q_2) + \hat{\eta}\sin(q_2) \\ \hat{\beta} + \hat{\varepsilon}\cos(q_2) + \hat{\eta}\sin(q_2) & \hat{\beta} \end{bmatrix}$$

$$\hat{C} = \begin{bmatrix} (-2\hat{\varepsilon}\sin(q_2) + 2\hat{\eta}\cos(q_2))\dot{q}_2 & (-\hat{\varepsilon}\sin(q_2) + \hat{\eta}\cos(q_2))\dot{q}_2 \\ (\hat{\varepsilon}\sin(q_2) - \hat{\eta}\cos(q_2))\dot{q}_1 & 0 \end{bmatrix}$$

$$\hat{G} = \begin{bmatrix} \hat{\varepsilon} e_2 \cos(q_1 + q_2) + \hat{\eta} e_2 \sin(q_1 + q_2) + (\hat{\alpha} - \hat{\beta} + e_1)e_2 \cos(q_1) \\ \hat{\varepsilon} e_2 \cos(q_1 + q_2) + \hat{\eta} e_2 \sin(q_1 + q_2) \end{bmatrix}$$

11.2   Sliding Mode Control Based on Input-Output Stability

11.2.1   System Description

For the system (11.2), we assume α, β, ε and η are the unknown constant parameters.

Let $q_d(t)$ denote the desired trajectory. The tracking error is

$$e = q_d - q$$

Define

$$\dot{q}_r = \dot{q}_d + \Lambda(q_d - q)$$

303

where Λ is a positive diagonal matrix.

Let $p = [\alpha \quad \beta \quad \varepsilon \quad \eta]^{\mathrm{T}}$, $\hat{p}$ is the estimation of p. Therefore, the vector p is a constant vector. Let $\tilde{p} = \hat{p} - p$, therefore we can get $\dot{\tilde{p}} = \dot{\hat{p}}$.

According to the linear characteristic of robotics[1], we have

$$H(q)\ddot{q}_r + C(q,\dot{q})\dot{q}_r + G(q) = Y(q,\dot{q},\dot{q}_r,\ddot{q}_r)p \qquad (11.3\text{a})$$

$$\tilde{H}(q)\ddot{q}_r + \tilde{C}(q,\dot{q})\dot{q}_r + \tilde{G}(q) = Y(q,\dot{q},\dot{q}_r,\ddot{q}_r)\tilde{p} \qquad (11.3\text{b})$$

where $\tilde{H}(q) = H(q) - \hat{H}(q)$, $\tilde{C}(q,\dot{q}) = C(q,\dot{q}) - \hat{C}(q,\dot{q})$, $\tilde{G}(q) = G(q) - \hat{G}(q)$,

$$Y(q,\dot{q},q_r,\dot{q}_r) =$$

$$\begin{bmatrix} \ddot{q}_{r1} + & \ddot{q}_{r2} - & 2\cos(q_2)\ddot{q}_{r1} + \cos(q_2)\ddot{q}_{r2} & 2\sin(q_2)\ddot{q}_{r1} + \sin(q_2)\ddot{q}_{r2} \\ & & -2\sin(q_2)\dot{q}_2\dot{q}_{r1} & +2\cos(q_2)\dot{q}_2\dot{q}_{r1} \\ e_2\cos(q_1) & e_2\cos(q_1) & -\sin(q_2)\dot{q}_2\dot{q}_{r2} & +\cos(q_2)\dot{q}_2\dot{q}_{r2} \\ & & +e_2\cos(q_1+q_2) & +e_2\sin(q_1+q_2) \\ 0 & \ddot{q}_{r1} + \ddot{q}_{r2} & \cos(q_2)\ddot{q}_{r1} + \sin(q_2)\dot{q}_1\dot{q}_{r1} & \sin(q_2)\ddot{q}_{r1} - \cos(q_2)\dot{q}_1\dot{q}_{r1} \\ & & +e_2\cos(q_1+q_2) & +e_2\sin(q_1+q_2) \end{bmatrix}$$

The expression of $Y(q,\dot{q},q_r,\dot{q}_r)$ is called the dynamic regression matrix, which is deduced in Eq. (11.20).

11.2.2 Design of Controller

The sliding variable is selected as

$$s = \dot{e} + \Lambda e \qquad (11.4)$$

Select the Lyapunov function as

$$V(t) = \frac{1}{2}s^{\mathrm{T}}H(q)s$$

Therefore,

$$\dot{V}(t) = s^{\mathrm{T}}H(q)\dot{s} + \frac{1}{2}s^{\mathrm{T}}\dot{H}(q)s = s^{\mathrm{T}}H(q)\dot{s} + s^{\mathrm{T}}C(q,\dot{q})s$$

$$= s^{\mathrm{T}}[H(q)(\ddot{q}_r - \ddot{q}) + C(q,\dot{q})(\dot{q}_r - \dot{q})]$$

$$= s^{\mathrm{T}}[H(q)\ddot{q}_r + C(q,\dot{q})\dot{q}_r + G(q) - \tau] \qquad (11.5)$$

The following methods can be adopted to realize the sliding mode control.

Method 1: Sliding mode control based on the estimated model

The controller is designed as

$$\tau = \hat{H}(q)\ddot{q}_r + \hat{C}(q,\dot{q})\dot{q}_r + \hat{G}(q) + \tau_s \qquad (11.6)$$

where τ_s is the robustness element to be designed

From Eqs. (11.5) and (11.6), we have:

$$\dot{V}(t) = s^T[H(q)\ddot{q}_r + C(q,\dot{q})\dot{q}_r + G(q) - \hat{H}(q)\ddot{q}_r - \hat{C}(q,\dot{q})\dot{q}_r - \hat{G}(q) - \tau_s]$$
$$= s^T[\tilde{H}(q)\ddot{q}_r + \tilde{C}(q,\dot{q})\dot{q}_r + \tilde{G}(q) - \tau_s] = s^T[Y(q,\dot{q},\dot{q}_r,\ddot{q}_r)\tilde{p} - \tau_s]$$

where

$$\tilde{p} = [\tilde{p}_1 \quad \tilde{p}_2 \quad \tilde{p}_3 \quad \tilde{p}_4]^T, \quad |\tilde{p}_i| \leqslant \overline{\tilde{p}}_i, \quad i = 1,2,3,4$$
$$Y(q,\dot{q},\dot{q}_r,\ddot{q}_r) = [Y_{ij}], \quad |Y_{ij}| \leqslant \overline{Y}_{ij}, \quad i = 1,2; \quad j = 1,2,3,4$$

Therefore, we select

$$\tau_s = k\,\mathrm{sgn}(s) + s = \begin{bmatrix} k_1\,\mathrm{sgn}(s_1) + s_1 \\ k_2\,\mathrm{sgn}(s_2) + s_2 \end{bmatrix} \qquad (11.7)$$

where $k_i = \sum_{j=1}^{4} \overline{Y}_{ij}\overline{\tilde{p}}_j, \quad i = 1,2.$

Therefore, we have

$$\dot{V}(t) = \sum_{i=1}^{2}\sum_{j=1}^{4} s_i Y_{ij}\tilde{p}_j - \sum_{i=1}^{2} s_i k_i\,\mathrm{sgn}(s_i) - \sum_{i=1}^{2} s_i^2$$
$$= \sum_{i=1}^{2}\sum_{j=1}^{4} s_i Y_{ij}\tilde{p}_j - \sum_{i=1}^{2}\sum_{j=1}^{4} |s_i|\overline{Y}_{ij}\overline{\tilde{p}}_j - \sum_{i=1}^{2} s_i^2 \leqslant -\sum_{i=1}^{2} s_i^2 \leqslant 0$$

Method 2: Sliding mode control based on the bound of model
Equation (11.5) can be written as:

$$\dot{V}(t) = -s^T[\tau - (H(q)\ddot{q}_r + C(q,\dot{q})\dot{q}_r + G(q))]$$
$$= -s^T[\tau - Y(q,\dot{q},\dot{q}_r,\ddot{q}_r)p]$$

The controller can be designed as:

$$\tau = \overline{k}\,\mathrm{sgn}(s) + s = \begin{bmatrix} \overline{k}_1\,\mathrm{sgn}(s_1) + s_1 \\ \overline{k}_2\,\mathrm{sgn}(s_2) + s_2 \end{bmatrix} \qquad (11.8)$$

where $\overline{k}_i = \sum_{j=1}^{4} \overline{Y}_{ij}\overline{p}_j, \quad i = 1,2.$

Therefore, we have

$$\dot{V}(t) = -\left[\sum_{i=1}^{2} s_i \bar{k}_i \operatorname{sgn}(s_i) + \sum_{i=1}^{2} s_i^2 - \sum_{i=1}^{2}\sum_{j=1}^{4} s_i Y_{ij} p_j\right]$$

$$= -\left[\sum_{i=1}^{2}\sum_{j=1}^{4} |s_i| |\bar{Y}_{ij} \bar{p}_j| + \sum_{i=1}^{2} s_i^2 - \sum_{i=1}^{2}\sum_{j=1}^{4} s_i Y_{ij} p_j\right] \leq -\sum_{i=1}^{2} s_i^2 \leq 0$$

From the switching gain $\bar{k}_i$ in controller (11.8) and the switching gain k_i in Eq. (11.7), $\bar{k}_i$ is larger than k_i. Therefore, the chattering generated by controller (11.8) is larger than that generated by controller (11.6).

11.2.3 Simulation Example

We consider the plant as Eq. (11.2). The desired trajectories are $q_{d1} = \sin(2\pi t)$ and $q_{d2} = \sin(2\pi t)$. In sliding mode control, select $\Lambda = \begin{bmatrix} 5 & 0 \\ 0 & 5 \end{bmatrix}$. When $M=1$, the controller is given in Eq. (11.6) where $\bar{p}_i = |\tilde{p}_i| + 0.50$. The saturated function is used instead of the switch function where $\Delta = 0.05$. The simulation results are shown in Figs. 11.2 – 11.4. Simultaneously, when $M=2$, the controller is given in Eq. (11.8) where $\bar{p}_i = |p_i| + 0.50$. The same simulation results are obtained.

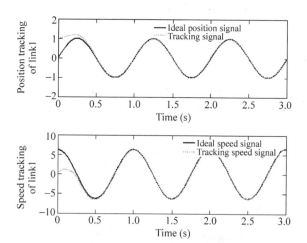

Figure 11.2 Tracking of position and velocity for the first joint

11 Sliding Mode Control for Robot

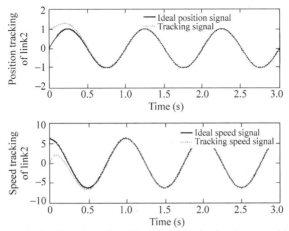

Figure 11.3 Tracking of position and velocity for the second joint

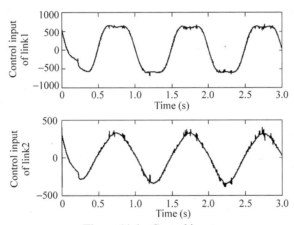

Figure 11.4 Control input

Simulation programs:

(1) Simulink main program: chap11_1sim.mdl

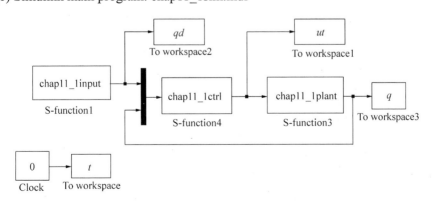

307

(2) Program of the controller: chap11_1ctrl.m

```matlab
function [sys,x0,str,ts] = control_strategy(t,x,u,flag)
switch flag,
case 0,
    [sys,x0,str,ts]=mdlInitializeSizes;
case 3,
    sys=mdlOutputs(t,x,u);
case {2,4,9}
    sys=[];
otherwise
    error(['Unhandled flag = ',num2str(flag)]);
end
function [sys,x0,str,ts]=mdlInitializeSizes
sizes = simsizes;
sizes.NumOutputs     = 2;
sizes.NumInputs      = 10;
sizes.DirFeedthrough = 1;
sizes.NumSampleTimes = 0;
sys = simsizes(sizes);
x0  = [];
str = [];
ts  = [];
function sys=mdlOutputs(t,x,u)
q1_d=u(1);dq1_d=u(2);ddq1_d=u(3);
q2_d=u(4);dq2_d=u(5);ddq2_d=u(6);
q1=u(7);dq1=u(8);
q2=u(9);dq2=u(10);
dq=[dq1;dq2];

p=[6.7 3.4 3.0 0]; %Practical p
ep=0.95*p;         %Estimated p

alfa_p=ep(1);
beta_p=ep(2);
epc_p=ep(3);
eta_p=ep(4);

m1=1;l1=1;
lc1=1/2;I1=1/12;
g=9.8;
e1=m1*l1*lc1-I1-m1*l1^2;
e2=g/l1;

dq_d=[dq1_d,dq2_d]';
ddq_d=[ddq1_d,ddq2_d]';

e=[q1_d-q1,q2_d-q2]';
de=[dq1_d-dq1,dq2_d-dq2]';

H_p=[alfa_p+2*epc_p*cos(q2)+2*eta_p*sin(q2),beta_p+epc_p*cos(q2)+eta_p*sin(q2);
    beta_p+epc_p*cos(q2)+eta_p*sin(q2),beta_p];
C_p=[(-2*epc_p*sin(q2)+2*eta_p*cos(q2))*dq2, (-epc_p*sin(q2)+eta_p*cos(q2))*dq2;
    (epc_p*sin(q2)-eta_p*cos(q2))*dq1,0];
```

11 Sliding Mode Control for Robot

```
G_p=[epc_p*e2*cos(q1+q2)+eta_p*e2*sin(q1+q2)+(alfa_p-beta_p+e1)*e2*cos(q1);
     epc_p*e2*cos(q1+q2)+eta_p*e2*sin(q1+q2)];

Fai=5*eye(2);
s=de+Fai*e;

delta=0.05;
kk=1/delta;
if abs(s)>delta
    sats=sign(s);
else
    sats=kk*s;
end

dqr=dq_d+Fai*e;
ddqr=ddq_d+Fai*de;

Y=[ddqr(1)+e2*cos(q1),ddqr(2)-e2*cos(q1),2*cos(q2)*ddqr(1)+cos(q2)*ddqr(2)
-2*sin(q2)*dq2*dqr(1)-sin(q2)*dq2*dqr(2)+e2*cos(q1+q2),2*sin(q2)*ddqr(1)+
sin(q2)*ddqr(2)+2*cos(q2)*dq2*dqr(1)+cos(q2)*dq2*dqr(2)+e2*sin(q1+q2);
0,ddqr(1)+ddqr(2),cos(q2)*ddqr(1)+sin(q2)*dq1*dqr(1)+e2*cos(q1+q2),sin(q2)
*ddqr(1)-cos(q2)*dq1*dqr(1)+e2*sin(q1+q2)];
Y_max=abs(Y)+0.10;

M=1;
if M==1
    ep_up=abs(p-ep)+0.50;        %Upper p-ep
    k=Y_max*ep_up';
%   tols=[sign(s(1)) 0;0 sign(s(2))]*k+s;
    tols=[sats(1) 0;0 sats(2)]*k+s;
    tol=H_p*ddqr+C_p*dqr+G_p+tols;
elseif M==2
    p_up=abs(p)+0.50;        %Upper p value
    k_up=Y_max*p_up';
%   tol=[sign(s(1)) 0;0 sign(s(2))]*k_up+s;
    tol=[sats(1) 0;0 sats(2)]*k_up+s;
end
sys(1)=tol(1);
sys(2)=tol(2);
```

(3) Program of the plant: chap11_1plant.m

```
function [sys,x0,str,ts]=s_function(t,x,u,flag)
switch flag,
case 0,
    [sys,x0,str,ts]=mdlInitializeSizes;
case 1,
    sys=mdlDerivatives(t,x,u);
case 3,
    sys=mdlOutputs(t,x,u);
case {2, 4, 9 }
    sys = [];
otherwise
    error(['Unhandled flag = ',num2str(flag)]);
end
```

Advanced Sliding Mode Control for Mechanical Systems: Design, Analysis and MATLAB Simulation

```matlab
function [sys,x0,str,ts]=mdlInitializeSizes
sizes = simsizes;
sizes.NumContStates  = 4;
sizes.NumDiscStates  = 0;
sizes.NumOutputs     = 4;
sizes.NumInputs      = 2;
sizes.DirFeedthrough = 0;
sizes.NumSampleTimes = 0;
sys=simsizes(sizes);
x0=[1.0,0,1.0,0];
str=[];
ts=[];
function sys=mdlDerivatives(t,x,u)
tol=[u(1);u(2)];
q1=x(1);
dq1=x(2);
q2=x(3);
dq2=x(4);

p=[6.7 3.4 3.0 0];

alfa=p(1);
beta=p(2);
epc=p(3);
eta=p(4);

m1=1;l1=1;
lc1=1/2;I1=1/12;
g=9.8;
e1=m1*l1*lc1-I1-m1*l1^2;
e2=g/l1;

H=[alfa+2*epc*cos(q2)+2*eta*sin(q2),beta+epc*cos(q2)+eta*sin(q2);
   beta+epc*cos(q2)+eta*sin(q2),beta];
C=[(-2*epc*sin(q2)+2*eta*cos(q2))*dq2,(-epc*sin(q2)+eta*cos(q2))*dq2;
   (epc*sin(q2)-eta*cos(q2))*dq1,0];
G=[epc*e2*cos(q1+q2)+eta*e2*sin(q1+q2)+(alfa-beta+e1)*e2*cos(q1);
   epc*e2*cos(q1+q2)+eta*e2*sin(q1+q2)];
%robot dynamic equation as
S=inv(H)*(tol-C*[dq1;dq2]-G);

sys(1)=x(2);
sys(2)=S(1);
sys(3)=x(4);
sys(4)=S(2);
function sys=mdlOutputs(t,x,u)
sys(1)=x(1);
sys(2)=x(2);
sys(3)=x(3);
sys(4)=x(4);
```

(4) Program of the input command: chap11_1input.m

```matlab
function [sys,x0,str,ts] = input(t,x,u,flag)
switch flag,
```

11 Sliding Mode Control for Robot

```
case 0,
    [sys,x0,str,ts]=mdlInitializeSizes;
case 3,
    sys=mdlOutputs(t,x,u);
case {2,4,9}
    sys=[];
otherwise
    error(['Unhandled flag = ',num2str(flag)]);
end
function [sys,x0,str,ts]=mdlInitializeSizes
sizes = simsizes;
sizes.NumOutputs =6;
sizes.NumInputs = 0;
sizes.DirFeedthrough = 0;
sizes.NumSampleTimes = 0;
sys = simsizes(sizes);
x0 = [];
str = [];
ts = [];
function sys=mdlOutputs(t,x,u)
q1_d=sin(2*pi*t);
q2_d=sin(2*pi*t);
dq1_d=2*pi*cos(2*pi*t);
dq2_d=2*pi*cos(2*pi*t);
ddq1_d=-(2*pi)^2*sin(2*pi*t);
ddq2_d=-(2*pi)^2*sin(2*pi*t);

sys(1)=q1_d;
sys(2)=dq1_d;
sys(3)=ddq1_d;
sys(4)=q2_d;
sys(5)=dq2_d;
sys(6)=ddq2_d;
```

(5) Plot program: chap11_1plot.m

```
close all;

figure(1);
subplot(211);
plot(t,qd(:,1),'k',t,q(:,1),'r:','linewidth',2);
xlabel('time(s)');ylabel('Position tracking of link 1');
legend('Ideal position signal','Tracking position signal');
subplot(212);
plot(t,qd(:,2),'k',t,q(:,2),'r:','linewidth',2);
xlabel('time(s)');ylabel('Speed tracking of link 1');
legend('Ideal speed signal','Tracking speed signal');

figure(2);
subplot(211);
plot(t,qd(:,4),'k',t,q(:,3),'r:','linewidth',2);
xlabel('time(s)');ylabel('Position tracking of link 2');
legend('Ideal position signal','Tracking position signal');
subplot(212);
```

Advanced Sliding Mode Control for Mechanical Systems: Design, Analysis and MATLAB Simulation

```
plot(t,qd(:,5),'k',t,q(:,4),'r:','linewidth',2);
xlabel('time(s)');ylabel('Speed tracking of link 2');
legend('Ideal speed signal','Tracking speed signal');

figure(3);
subplot(211);
plot(t,ut(:,1),'k','linewidth',2);
xlabel('time(s)');ylabel('Control input of link 1');
subplot(212);
plot(t,ut(:,2),'k','linewidth',2);
xlabel('time(s)');ylabel('Control input of link 2');
```

11.3 Sliding Mode Control Based on Computed Torque Method

11.3.1 Design of Controller

Using the computed torque method, the control law can be designed for system (11.2) as follows:

$$\tau = \hat{H}(q)v + \hat{C}(q,\dot{q})\dot{q} + \hat{G}(q) \tag{11.9}$$

where v is the auxiliary control input, $\hat{H}(q)$, $\hat{C}(q,\dot{q})$ and $\hat{G}(q)$ are the respective estimations of H, C and G by using inertial parameter $\hat{p}$ of manipulator.

Substituting Eq. (11.9) into Eq. (11.1), neglecting $F(\dot{q})$ and τ_{d}, considering Eq. (11.3b), we have

$$H(q)\ddot{q} + C(q,\dot{q})\dot{q} + G(q) = \hat{H}(q)v + \hat{C}(q,\dot{q})\dot{q} + \hat{G}(q) \tag{11.10}$$

i.e.

$$\hat{H}\ddot{q} = \hat{H}(q)v - [\tilde{H}(q)\ddot{q} + \tilde{C}(q,\dot{q})\dot{q} + \tilde{G}(q)] = \hat{H}(q)v - Y(q,\dot{q},\ddot{q})\tilde{p}$$

where $\tilde{H} = H - \hat{H}$, $\tilde{C} = C - \hat{C}$, $\tilde{G} = G - \hat{G}$, $\tilde{p} = p - \hat{p}$.

If the parameter estimation $\hat{p}$ makes $\hat{H}(q)$ invertible, then the above equation can be written as:

$$\ddot{q} = v - (\hat{H}(q))^{-1}Y(q,\dot{q},\ddot{q})\tilde{p} = v - \tilde{d}$$

where $\varphi(q,\dot{q},\ddot{q},\hat{p}) = (\hat{H}(q))^{-1}Y(q,\dot{q},\ddot{q})$, $\varphi(q,\dot{q},\ddot{q},\hat{p})\tilde{p} = \tilde{d}$.

The sliding variable can be selected as:

$$s = \dot{e} + \Lambda e \tag{11.11}$$

where $e = q_{\mathrm{d}} - q$, $\dot{e} = \dot{q}_{\mathrm{d}} - \dot{q}$, $s = [s_1 \ s_2 \ \cdots \ s_n]^{\mathrm{T}}$, Λ is a positive diagonal matrix.

312

Therefore,

$$\dot{s} = \ddot{e} + \Lambda\dot{e} = (\ddot{q}_d - \ddot{q}) + \Lambda\dot{e} = \ddot{q}_d - v + \tilde{d} + \Lambda\dot{e}$$

Select

$$v = \ddot{q}_d + \Lambda\dot{e} + d \qquad (11.12)$$

where $d = (\overline{d} + \eta)\operatorname{sgn}(s)$, $\|\tilde{d}\| \leqslant \overline{d}$, $\eta > 0$.
Therefore, we have

$$\dot{s} = \tilde{d} - d$$

The Lyapunov function is selected as $V = \dfrac{1}{2}s^T s$, therefore, we have

$$\dot{V} = s^T \dot{s} = s^T(\tilde{d} - d) = s^T \tilde{d} - \overline{d}s^T \operatorname{sgn}(s) - \eta s^T \operatorname{sgn}(s) \leqslant -\eta \|s\| \leqslant 0$$

From the controller, the more precise the estimation of $\hat{p}$ is, the smaller are $\|\tilde{p}\|$ and $\overline{d}$, and smaller is the chattering of the sliding mode.

11.3.2 Simulation Example

We consider the plant as Eq. (11.2). The initial state vector is $[0\ \ 0\ \ 0\ \ 0]^T$. The sliding mode controller is given in Eqs. (11.9) and (11.12). The desired trajectory is $q_{d1} = \sin t$, $q_{d2} = \sin t$. $\hat{H} = 0.6H$, $\hat{C} = 0.6C$, $\hat{G} = 0.6G$, $\overline{d} = 30$, $\eta = 0.10$, $\Lambda = \begin{bmatrix} 25 & 0 \\ 0 & 25 \end{bmatrix}$. The simulation results are shown in Fig. 11.5 and Fig. 11.6.

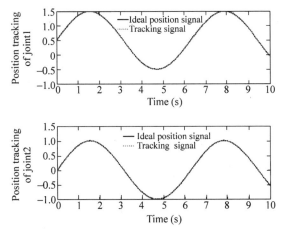

Figure 11.5 The position tracking of a dual-joint manipulator

Advanced Sliding Mode Control for Mechanical Systems: Design, Analysis and MATLAB Simulation

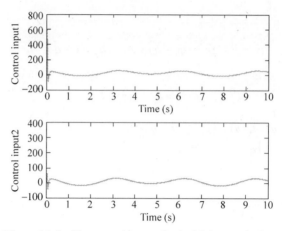

Figure 11.6 The control input of a dual-joint manipulator

Simulation program:

(1) Simulink main program: chap11_2sim.mdl

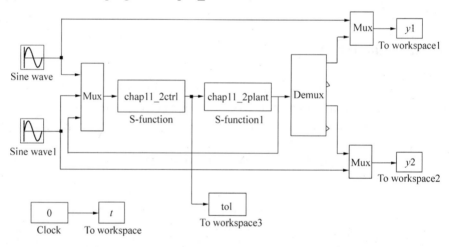

(2) Program of control law: chap11_2ctrl.m

```
function [sys,x0,str,ts] = spacemodel(t,x,u,flag)
switch flag,
case 0,
    [sys,x0,str,ts]=mdlInitializeSizes;
case 3,
    sys=mdlOutputs(t,x,u);
case {2,4,9}
    sys=[];
otherwise
    error(['Unhandled flag = ',num2str(flag)]);
end
function [sys,x0,str,ts]=mdlInitializeSizes
```

11 Sliding Mode Control for Robot

```
global nmn
nmn=25*eye(2);
sizes = simsizes;
sizes.NumContStates  = 0;
sizes.NumDiscStates  = 0;
sizes.NumOutputs     = 2;
sizes.NumInputs      = 6;
sizes.DirFeedthrough = 1;
sizes.NumSampleTimes = 1;
sys = simsizes(sizes);
x0  = [];
str = [];
ts  = [0 0];
function sys=mdlOutputs(t,x,u)
global nmn
qd1=u(1);
dqd1=cos(t);
ddqd1=-sin(t);
qd2=u(2);
dqd2=cos(t);
ddqd2=-sin(t);
ddqd=[ddqd1;ddqd2];

dqd=[dqd1;dqd2];
ddqd=[ddqd1;ddqd2];

q1=u(3);dq1=u(4);
q2=u(5);dq2=u(6);
dq=[dq1;dq2];

e1=qd1-q1;
e2=qd2-q2;
e=[e1;e2];
de1=dqd1-dq1;
de2=dqd2-dq2;
de=[de1;de2];

alfa=6.7;beta=3.4;
epc=3.0;eta=0;
m1=1;l1=1;
lc1=1/2;I1=1/12;
g=9.8;
e1=m1*l1*lc1-I1-m1*l1^2;
e2=g/l1;
H=[alfa+2*epc*cos(q2)+2*eta*sin(q2),beta+epc*cos(q2)+eta*sin(q2);
   beta+epc*cos(q2)+eta*sin(q2),beta];
C=[(-2*epc*sin(q2)+2*eta*cos(q2))*dq2,(-epc*sin(q2)+eta*cos(q2))*dq2;
   (epc*sin(q2)-eta*cos(q2))*dq1,0];
G=[epc*e2*cos(q1+q2)+eta*e2*sin(q1+q2)+(alfa-beta+e1)*e2*cos(q1);
   epc*e2*cos(q1+q2)+eta*e2*sin(q1+q2)];
H0=0.6*H;
C0=0.6*C;
G0=0.6*G;
```

Advanced Sliding Mode Control for Mechanical Systems: Design, Analysis and MATLAB Simulation

```
s=de+nmn*e;
d_up=30;
xite=0.10;

M=2;
if M==1
    d=(d_up+xite)*sign(s);
elseif M==2  %Saturated function
    delta=0.05;
    kk=1/delta;
    if abs(s)>delta
        sats=sign(s);
    else
        sats=kk*s;
    end
end
d=(d_up+xite)*sats;

v=ddqd+nmn*de+d;

tol=H0*v+C0*dq+G0;

sys(1)=tol(1);
sys(2)=tol(2);
```

(3) Program of the plant: chap11_2plant.m

```
function [sys,x0,str,ts]=s_function(t,x,u,flag)
switch flag,
case 0,
    [sys,x0,str,ts]=mdlInitializeSizes;
case 1,
    sys=mdlDerivatives(t,x,u);
case 3,
    sys=mdlOutputs(t,x,u);
case {2, 4, 9 }
    sys = [];
otherwise
    error(['Unhandled flag = ',num2str(flag)]);
end
function [sys,x0,str,ts]=mdlInitializeSizes
sizes = simsizes;
sizes.NumContStates  = 4;
sizes.NumDiscStates  = 0;
sizes.NumOutputs     = 4;
sizes.NumInputs      = 2;
sizes.DirFeedthrough = 0;
sizes.NumSampleTimes = 0;
sys=simsizes(sizes);
x0=[0;0;0;0];
str=[];
ts=[];
function sys=mdlDerivatives(t,x,u)
q1=x(1);dq1=x(2);
```

316

11 Sliding Mode Control for Robot

```
q2=x(3);dq2=x(4);
dq=[dq1;dq2];

% The model is given by Slotine and Weiping Li(MIT 1987)
alfa=6.7;beta=3.4;
epc=3.0;eta=0;
m1=1;l1=1;
lc1=1/2;I1=1/12;
g=9.8;
e1=m1*l1*lc1-I1-m1*l1^2;
e2=g/l1;

H=[alfa+2*epc*cos(q2)+2*eta*sin(q2),beta+epc*cos(q2)+eta*sin(q2);
   beta+epc*cos(q2)+eta*sin(q2),beta];
C=[(-2*epc*sin(q2)+2*eta*cos(q2))*dq2,(-epc*sin(q2)+eta*cos(q2))*dq2;
   (epc*sin(q2)-eta*cos(q2))*dq1,0];
G=[epc*e2*cos(q1+q2)+eta*e2*sin(q1+q2)+(alfa-beta+e1)*e2*cos(q1);
   epc*e2*cos(q1+q2)+eta*e2*sin(q1+q2)];

tol(1)=u(1);
tol(2)=u(2);

ddq=inv(H)*(tol'-C*dq-G);
sys(1)=x(2);
sys(2)=ddq(1);
sys(3)=x(4);
sys(4)=ddq(2);
function sys=mdlOutputs(t,x,u)
sys(1)=x(1);
sys(2)=x(2);
sys(3)=x(3);
sys(4)=x(4);
```

(4) Plot program: chap11_2plot.m

```
close all;

figure(1);
subplot(211);
plot(t,y1(:,1),'k',t,y1(:,2),'r:','linewidth',2);
xlabel('time(s)');ylabel('Position tracking of joint 1');
legend('Ideal position signal','tracking signal');
subplot(212);
plot(t,y2(:,1),'k',t,y2(:,2),'r:','linewidth',2);
xlabel('time(s)');ylabel('Position tracking of joint 2');
legend('Ideal position signal','tracking signal');

figure(2);
subplot(211);
plot(t,tol(:,1),'r','linewidth',2);
xlabel('time(s)');ylabel('Control input 1');
subplot(212);
plot(t,tol(:,2),'r','linewidth',2);
xlabel('time(s)');ylabel('Control input 2');
```

11.4 Adaptive Sliding Mode Control for Manipulator

We discussed an adaptive sliding mode controller design method for the manipulator. Refer to paper[2].

11.4.1 Adaptive Sliding Mode Controller

For the system (11.2), we assume α, β, ε and η are the unknown constant parameters.

Let $\tilde{q}(t) = q(t) - q_d(t)$ be the tracking error, and denote

$$\dot{q}_r = \dot{q}_d - \Lambda \tilde{q}, \quad \ddot{q}_r = \ddot{q}_d - \Lambda \dot{\tilde{q}} \tag{11.13}$$

where $\Lambda = \begin{bmatrix} \lambda_1 & 0 \\ 0 & \lambda_2 \end{bmatrix}$, $\lambda_i > 0$, $i = 1, 2$.

Define the sliding variable as:

$$s = \dot{\tilde{q}} + \Lambda \tilde{q} \tag{11.14}$$

Slotine et al. proposed the controller[2,3] as:

$$\tau = \hat{H}(q)\ddot{q}_r + \hat{C}(q, \dot{q})\dot{q}_r + \hat{G}(q) - K_D s \tag{11.15}$$

where $K_D = \begin{bmatrix} k_{d1} & 0 \\ 0 & k_{d2} \end{bmatrix}$, $k_{di} > 0$, $i = 1, 2$.

Because H is a positive-definite matrix, we select the Lyapunov function as

$$V(t) = \frac{1}{2}s^T H s + \frac{1}{2}\tilde{a}^T \Gamma \tilde{a} \tag{11.16}$$

where $\Gamma = \begin{bmatrix} \gamma_1 & 0 & 0 & 0 \\ 0 & \gamma_2 & 0 & 0 \\ 0 & 0 & \gamma_3 & 0 \\ 0 & 0 & 0 & \gamma_4 \end{bmatrix}$, $\gamma_i > 0$, $i = 1, 2, 3, 4$.

Therefore, we have

$$\dot{V}(t) = s^T H \dot{s} + \frac{1}{2}s^T \dot{H} s + \tilde{a}^T \Gamma \dot{\tilde{a}} = s^T (H\ddot{q} - H\ddot{q}_r) + \frac{1}{2}s^T \dot{H} s + \tilde{a}^T \Gamma \dot{\tilde{a}}$$

$$= s^T (\tau - C\dot{q} - G - H\ddot{q}_r) + \frac{1}{2}s^T \dot{H} s + \tilde{a}^T \Gamma \dot{\tilde{a}}$$

$$= s^T (\tau - C(s + \dot{q}_r) - G - H\ddot{q}_r) + \frac{1}{2}s^T \dot{H} s + \tilde{a}^T \Gamma \dot{\tilde{a}}$$

From Eq. (11.15), we can get

$$\dot{V}(t) = s^{\mathrm{T}}(\hat{H}\ddot{q}_{\mathrm{r}} + \hat{C}\dot{q}_{\mathrm{r}} + \hat{G} - K_{\mathrm{D}}s - C(s + \dot{q}_{\mathrm{r}}) - G - H\ddot{q}_{\mathrm{r}}) + \frac{1}{2}s^{\mathrm{T}}\dot{H}s + \tilde{a}^{\mathrm{T}}\Gamma\dot{\tilde{a}}$$

$$= s^{\mathrm{T}}(\tilde{H}\ddot{q}_{\mathrm{r}} + \tilde{C}\dot{q}_{\mathrm{r}} + \tilde{G} - K_{\mathrm{D}}s - Cs) + \frac{1}{2}s^{\mathrm{T}}\dot{H}s + \tilde{a}^{\mathrm{T}}\Gamma\dot{\tilde{a}}$$

From the linear characteristic of the kinetic equation of the manipulator[3], just like Eq. (11.3b), it follows:

$$\tilde{H}\ddot{q}_{\mathrm{r}} + \tilde{C}\dot{q}_{\mathrm{r}} + \tilde{G} = Y(q, \dot{q}, \dot{q}_{\mathrm{r}}, \ddot{q}_{\mathrm{r}})\tilde{a} \tag{11.17}$$

Therefore,

$$\dot{V}(t) = s^{\mathrm{T}}(Y\tilde{a} - K_{\mathrm{D}}s - Cs) + \frac{1}{2}s^{\mathrm{T}}\dot{H}s + \tilde{a}^{\mathrm{T}}\Gamma\dot{\tilde{a}}$$

$$= s^{\mathrm{T}}(Y\tilde{a} - K_{\mathrm{D}}s) + \frac{1}{2}s^{\mathrm{T}}(\dot{H} - 2C)s + \tilde{a}^{\mathrm{T}}\Gamma\dot{\tilde{a}}$$

$$= s^{\mathrm{T}}(Y\tilde{a} - K_{\mathrm{D}}s) + \tilde{a}^{\mathrm{T}}\Gamma\dot{\tilde{a}} = \tilde{a}^{\mathrm{T}}Y^{\mathrm{T}}s - s^{\mathrm{T}}K_{\mathrm{D}}s + \tilde{a}^{\mathrm{T}}\Gamma\dot{\tilde{a}}$$

$$= \tilde{a}^{\mathrm{T}}(Y^{\mathrm{T}}s + \Gamma\dot{\tilde{a}}) - s^{\mathrm{T}}K_{\mathrm{D}}s$$

Adaptive rule[2, 3] was designed by slotine et al. as follows:

$$\dot{\hat{a}} = -\Gamma^{-1}Y^{\mathrm{T}}s \tag{11.18}$$

Therefore,

$$\dot{V}(t) = -s^{\mathrm{T}}K_{\mathrm{D}}s \leqslant 0$$

Then $\tilde{q} \to 0$ as $t \to \infty$.

11.4.2 Simulation Example

We consider the plant as Eq. (11.2). The desired trajectories of the two arms are $q_{\mathrm{d1}} = \sin(2\pi t)$ and $q_{\mathrm{d2}} = \sin(2\pi t)$ respectively. The controller and the adaptive rule are shown in Eqs. (11.15) and (11.18) respectively. $Y(q, \dot{q}, q_{\mathrm{r}}, \dot{q}_{\mathrm{r}})$ is given in

Eq. (11.20). Select $\Lambda = \begin{bmatrix} 5 & 0 \\ 0 & 5 \end{bmatrix}$, $K_{\mathrm{D}} = \begin{bmatrix} 100 & 0 \\ 0 & 100 \end{bmatrix}$, $\Gamma = \begin{bmatrix} 1 & 0 & 0 & 0 \\ 0 & 1 & 0 & 0 \\ 0 & 0 & 1 & 0 \\ 0 & 0 & 0 & 1 \end{bmatrix}$ (See the

appendix). The simulation results are shown in Fig. 11.7 – Fig. 11.10. We can see from Fig. 11.9 and Fig. 11.10 that the effects of identification to α, β, ε, and η are not satisfied. The convergence of trajectories tracking can be guaranteed by the adaptive rule. However, the estimations cannot converge to the desired values, the reason is explained in Section 6.1. The information of desired trajectories must be abundant[2] to improve the estimation precision.

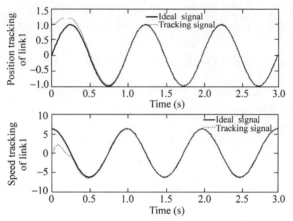

Figure 11.7 Position and velocity tracking of the first joint

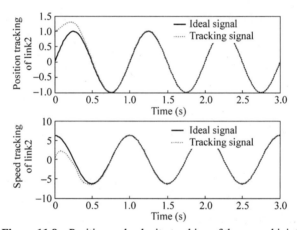

Figure 11.8 Position and velocity tracking of the second joint

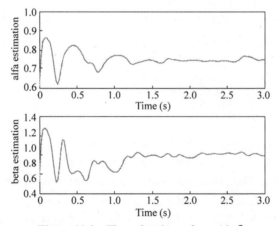

Figure 11.9 The estimations of α and β

11 Sliding Mode Control for Robot

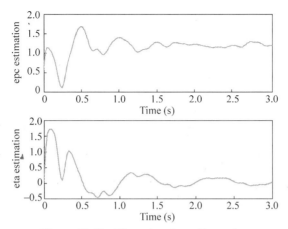

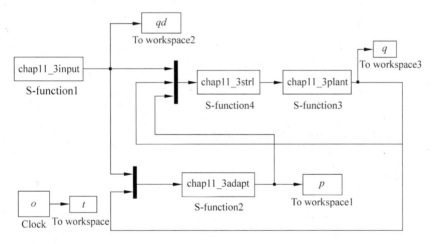

Figure 11.10 The estimations of ε and η

Simulation programs:

(1) Simulink main program: chap11_3sim.mdl

(2) Program of input command: chap11_3input.m

```
function [sys,x0,str,ts] = input(t,x,u,flag)
switch flag,
case 0,
    [sys,x0,str,ts]=mdlInitializeSizes;
case 3,
    sys=mdlOutputs(t,x,u);
case {2,4,9}
    sys=[];
otherwise
    error(['Unhandled flag = ',num2str(flag)]);
end
```

```
function [sys,x0,str,ts]=mdlInitializeSizes
sizes = simsizes;
sizes.NumOutputs =6;
sizes.NumInputs = 0;
sizes.DirFeedthrough = 0;
sizes.NumSampleTimes = 0;
sys = simsizes(sizes);
x0  = [];
str = [];
ts  = [];
function sys=mdlOutputs(t,x,u)
q1_d=sin(2*pi*t);
q2_d=sin(2*pi*t);
dq1_d=2*pi*cos(2*pi*t);
dq2_d=2*pi*cos(2*pi*t);
ddq1_d=-(2*pi)^2*sin(2*pi*t);
ddq2_d=-(2*pi)^2*sin(2*pi*t);

sys(1)=q1_d;
sys(2)=dq1_d;
sys(3)=ddq1_d;
sys(4)=q2_d;
sys(5)=dq2_d;
sys(6)=ddq2_d;
```

(3) Program of controller: chap11_3ctrl.m

```
function [sys,x0,str,ts] = control_strategy(t,x,u,flag)
switch flag,
case 0,
    [sys,x0,str,ts]=mdlInitializeSizes;
case 3,
    sys=mdlOutputs(t,x,u);
case {2,4,9}
    sys=[];
otherwise
    error(['Unhandled flag = ',num2str(flag)]);
end

function [sys,x0,str,ts]=mdlInitializeSizes
sizes = simsizes;
sizes.NumOutputs    = 2;
sizes.NumInputs     = 14;
sizes.DirFeedthrough = 1;
sizes.NumSampleTimes = 0;
sys = simsizes(sizes);
x0  = [];
str = [];
ts  = [];
function sys=mdlOutputs(t,x,u)
q1_d=u(1);dq1_d=u(2);ddq1_d=u(3);
```

11 Sliding Mode Control for Robot

```
q2_d=u(4);dq2_d=u(5);ddq2_d=u(6);
q1=u(7);dq1=u(8);
q2=u(9);dq2=u(10);

alfa_p=u(11);
beta_p=u(12);
epc_p=u(13);
eta_p=u(14);

m1=1;l1=1;
lc1=1/2;I1=1/12;
g=9.8;
e1=m1*l1*lc1-I1-m1*l1^2;
e2=g/l1;

dq_d=[dq1_d,dq2_d]';
ddq_d=[ddq1_d,ddq2_d]';

q_error=[q1-q1_d,q2-q2_d]';
dq_error=[dq1-dq1_d,dq2-dq2_d]';

H_p=[alfa_p+2*epc_p*cos(q2)+2*eta_p*sin(q2),beta_p+epc_p*cos(q2)+eta_p*sin(q2);
    beta_p+epc_p*cos(q2)+eta_p*sin(q2),beta_p];
C_p=[(-2*epc_p*sin(q2)+2*eta_p*cos(q2))*dq2,(-epc_p*sin(q2)+eta_p*cos(q2))*dq2;
    (epc_p*sin(q2)-eta_p*cos(q2))*dq1,0];
G_p=[epc_p*e2*cos(q1+q2)+eta_p*e2*sin(q1+q2)+(alfa_p-beta_p+e1)*e2*cos(q1);
    epc_p*e2*cos(q1+q2)+eta_p*e2*sin(q1+q2)];

Fai=5*eye(2);
dqr=dq_d-Fai*q_error;
ddqr=ddq_d-Fai*dq_error;
s=Fai*q_error+dq_error;
Kd=100*eye(2);
tol=H_p*ddqr+C_p*dqr+G_p-Kd*s;

sys(1)=tol(1);
sys(2)=tol(2);
```

(4) Program of adaptive rule: chap11_3adapt.m

```
function [sys,x0,str,ts]=para_estimate(t,x,u,flag)
switch flag,
case 0,
    [sys,x0,str,ts]=mdlInitializeSizes;
case 1,
    sys=mdlDerivatives(t,x,u);
case 3,
    sys=mdlOutputs(t,x,u);
case {2, 4, 9 }
    sys = [];
```

323

```
otherwise
    error(['Unhandled flag = ',num2str(flag)]);
end
function [sys,x0,str,ts]=mdlInitializeSizes
sizes = simsizes;
sizes.NumContStates  = 4;
sizes.NumDiscStates  = 0;
sizes.NumOutputs     = 4;
sizes.NumInputs      = 10;
sizes.DirFeedthrough = 1;
sizes.NumSampleTimes = 0;
sys=simsizes(sizes);
x0=[4.1,1.9,1.7,0];
str=[];
ts=[];
function sys=mdlDerivatives(t,x,u)
g=9.8;l1=1;
e2=g/l1;

gama=eye(4);

q1_d=u(1);dq1_d=u(2);ddq1_d=u(3);
q2_d=u(4);dq2_d=u(5);ddq2_d=u(6);

q1=u(7);dq1=u(8);
q2=u(9);dq2=u(10);

q_error=[q1-q1_d,q2-q2_d]';
dq_error=[dq1-dq1_d,dq2-dq2_d]';

    Fai=5*eye(2);
    s=Fai*q_error+dq_error;
    ddq_d=[ddq1_d,ddq2_d]';
    dq_d=[dq1_d,dq2_d]';

    dqr=dq_d-Fai*q_error;
    ddqr=ddq_d-Fai*dq_error;

Y=[ddqr(1)+e2*cos(q1),ddqr(2)-e2*cos(q1),2*cos(q2)*ddqr(1)+cos(q2)*ddqr(2)
    -2*sin(q2)*dq2*dqr(1)-sin(q2)*dq2*dqr(2)+e2*cos(q1+q2),2*sin(q2)*ddqr(1)
    +sin(q2)*ddqr(2)+2*cos(q2)*dq2*dqr(1)+cos(q2)*dq2*dqr(2)+e2*sin(q1+q2);

    0,ddqr(1)+ddqr(2),cos(q2)*ddqr(1)+sin(q2)*dq1*dqr(1)+e2*cos(q1+q2),
    sin(q2)*ddqr(1)-cos(q2)*dq1*dqr(1)+e2*sin(q1+q2)];
    A_law=-inv(gama)*Y'*s;    %Adaptive law
% The parameter update law is proposed by Slotine and Weiping Li(MIT 1987)
for i=1:1:4
    sys(i)=A_law(i);
end
function sys=mdlOutputs(t,x,u)
```

```matlab
sys(1)=x(1);
sys(2)=x(2);
sys(3)=x(3);
sys(4)=x(4);
```

(5) Program of the plant: chap11_3plant.m

```matlab
function [sys,x0,str,ts]=s_function(t,x,u,flag)
switch flag,
case 0,
    [sys,x0,str,ts]=mdlInitializeSizes;
case 1,
    sys=mdlDerivatives(t,x,u);
case 3,
    sys=mdlOutputs(t,x,u);
case {2, 4, 9 }
    sys = [];
otherwise
    error(['Unhandled flag = ',num2str(flag)]);
end

function [sys,x0,str,ts]=mdlInitializeSizes
sizes = simsizes;
sizes.NumContStates  = 4;
sizes.NumDiscStates  = 0;
sizes.NumOutputs     = 4;
sizes.NumInputs      = 2;
sizes.DirFeedthrough = 0;
sizes.NumSampleTimes = 0;
sys=simsizes(sizes);
x0=[1.0,0,1.0,0];
str=[];
ts=[];
function sys=mdlDerivatives(t,x,u)
tol=[u(1);u(2)];
q1=x(1);
dq1=x(2);
q2=x(3);
dq2=x(4);

alfa=6.7;
beta=3.4;
epc=3.0;
eta=0;

m1=1;l1=1;
lc1=1/2;I1=1/12;
g=9.8;
e1=m1*l1*lc1-I1-m1*l1^2;
e2=g/l1;
```

Advanced Sliding Mode Control for Mechanical Systems: Design, Analysis and MATLAB Simulation

```
H=[alfa+2*epc*cos(q2)+2*eta*sin(q2),beta+epc*cos(q2)+eta*sin(q2);
   beta+epc*cos(q2)+eta*sin(q2),beta];
C=[(-2*epc*sin(q2)+2*eta*cos(q2))*dq2,(-epc*sin(q2)+eta*cos(q2))*dq2;
   (epc*sin(q2)-eta*cos(q2))*dq1,0];
G=[epc*e2*cos(q1+q2)+eta*e2*sin(q1+q2)+(alfa-beta+e1)*e2*cos(q1);
   epc*e2*cos(q1+q2)+eta*e2*sin(q1+q2)];
S=inv(H)*(tol-C*[dq1;dq2]-G);

sys(1)=x(2);
sys(2)=S(1);
sys(3)=x(4);
sys(4)=S(2);
function sys=mdlOutputs(t,x,u)
sys(1)=x(1);
sys(2)=x(2);
sys(3)=x(3);
sys(4)=x(4);
```

(6) Plot program: chap11_3plot.m

```
close all;

figure(1);
subplot(211);
plot(t,qd(:,1),'k',t,q(:,1),'r:','linewidth',2);
xlabel('time(s)');ylabel('position tracking of link 1');
legend('ideal signal','tracking signal');
subplot(212);
plot(t,qd(:,2),'k',t,q(:,2),'r:','linewidth',2);
xlabel('time(s)');ylabel('speed tracking of link 1');
legend('ideal signal','tracking signal');

figure(2);
subplot(211);
plot(t,qd(:,4),'k',t,q(:,3),'r:','linewidth',2);
xlabel('time(s)');ylabel('position tracking of link 2');
legend('ideal signal','tracking signal');
subplot(212);
plot(t,qd(:,5),'k',t,q(:,4),'r:','linewidth',2);
xlabel('time(s)');ylabel('speed tracking of link 2');
legend('ideal signal','tracking signal');

figure(3);
subplot(211);
plot(t,p(:,1)/6.7,'r','linewidth',2);
xlabel('time(s)');ylabel('alfa estimation');
subplot(212);
plot(t,p(:,2)/3.4,'r','linewidth',2);
xlabel('time(s)');ylabel('beta estimation');
```

```
figure(4);
subplot(211);
plot(t,p(:,3)/3.0,'r','linewidth',2);
xlabel('time(s)');ylabel('epc estimation');
subplot(212);
plot(t,p(:,4)/3,'r','linewidth',2);
xlabel('time(s)');ylabel('eta estimation');
```

Appendix: The Expression of Matrix Y

For the system (11.2), the estimations of the joints are:

$$\tilde{H} = \hat{H} - H = \begin{bmatrix} \tilde{\alpha} + 2\tilde{\varepsilon}\cos(q_2) + 2\tilde{\eta}\sin(q_2) & \tilde{\beta} + \tilde{\varepsilon}\cos(q_2) + \tilde{\eta}\sin(q_2) \\ \tilde{\beta} + \tilde{\varepsilon}\cos(q_2) + \tilde{\eta}\sin(q_2) & \tilde{\beta} \end{bmatrix}$$

$$\tilde{C} = \hat{C} - C = \begin{bmatrix} (-2\tilde{\varepsilon}\sin(q_2) + 2\tilde{\eta}\cos(q_2))\dot{q}_2 & (-\tilde{\varepsilon}\sin(q_2) + \tilde{\eta}\cos(q_2))\dot{q}_2 \\ (\tilde{\varepsilon}\sin(q_2) - \tilde{\eta}\cos(q_2))\dot{q}_1 & 0 \end{bmatrix}$$

$$\tilde{G} = \hat{G} - G = \begin{bmatrix} \tilde{\varepsilon}e_2\cos(q_1 + q_2) + \tilde{\eta}e_2\sin(q_1 + q_2) + (\tilde{\alpha} - \tilde{\beta})e_2\cos(q_1) \\ \tilde{\varepsilon}e_2\cos(q_1 + q_2) + \tilde{\eta}e_2\sin(q_1 + q_2) \end{bmatrix}$$

Therefore, we have

$$\tilde{H}\ddot{q}_\mathrm{d} + \tilde{C}\dot{q}_\mathrm{d} + \tilde{G} = \begin{bmatrix} (\tilde{\alpha} + 2\tilde{\varepsilon}\cos(q_2) + 2\tilde{\eta}\sin(q_2))\ddot{q}_{\mathrm{d1}} + (\tilde{\beta} + \tilde{\varepsilon}\cos(q_2) + \tilde{\eta}\sin(q_2))\ddot{q}_{\mathrm{d2}} \\ (\tilde{\beta} + \tilde{\varepsilon}\cos(q_2) + \tilde{\eta}\sin(q_2))\ddot{q}_{\mathrm{d1}} + \tilde{\beta}\ddot{q}_{\mathrm{d2}} \end{bmatrix}$$

$$+ \begin{bmatrix} (-2\tilde{\varepsilon}\sin(q_2) + 2\tilde{\eta}\cos(q_2))\dot{q}_2\dot{q}_{\mathrm{d1}} + (-\tilde{\varepsilon}\sin(q_2) + \tilde{\eta}\cos(q_2))\dot{q}_2\dot{q}_{\mathrm{d2}} \\ (\tilde{\varepsilon}\sin(q_2) - \tilde{\eta}\cos(q_2))\dot{q}_1\dot{q}_{\mathrm{d1}} \end{bmatrix} + \tilde{G}$$

$$= \begin{bmatrix} (\ddot{q}_{\mathrm{d1}} + e_2\cos(q_1))\tilde{\alpha} + (\ddot{q}_{\mathrm{d2}} - e_2\cos(q_1))\tilde{\beta} \\ \quad + (2\cos(q_2)\ddot{q}_{\mathrm{d1}} + \cos(q_2)\ddot{q}_{\mathrm{d2}} - 2\sin(q_2)\dot{q}_2\dot{q}_{\mathrm{d1}} - \sin(q_2)\dot{q}_2\dot{q}_{\mathrm{d2}} \\ \quad + e_2\cos(q_1 + q_2))\tilde{\varepsilon} + (2\sin(q_2)\ddot{q}_{\mathrm{d1}} + \sin(q_2)\ddot{q}_{\mathrm{d2}} + 2\cos(q_2)\dot{q}_2\dot{q}_{\mathrm{d1}} \\ \quad + \cos(q_2)\dot{q}_2\dot{q}_{\mathrm{d2}} + e_2\sin(q_1 + q_2))\tilde{\eta} \\ 0 \cdot \tilde{\alpha} + (\ddot{q}_{\mathrm{d1}} + \ddot{q}_{\mathrm{d2}})\tilde{\beta} + (\cos(q_2)\ddot{q}_{\mathrm{d1}} + \sin(q_2)\dot{q}_1\dot{q}_{\mathrm{d1}} + e_2\cos(q_1 + q_2))\tilde{\varepsilon} \\ \quad + (\sin(q_2)\ddot{q}_{\mathrm{d1}} - \cos(q_2)\dot{q}_1\dot{q}_{\mathrm{d1}} + e_2\sin(q_1 + q_2))\tilde{\eta} \end{bmatrix}$$

$$= Y(q, \dot{q}, q_\mathrm{d}, \dot{q}_\mathrm{d}) \cdot \begin{bmatrix} \tilde{\alpha} \\ \tilde{\beta} \\ \tilde{\varepsilon} \\ \tilde{\eta} \end{bmatrix}$$

Therefore, form Eq. (11.3b), we can get $Y(q, \dot{q}, q_\mathrm{d}, \dot{q}_\mathrm{d})$ and $\tilde{a}$ as Eqs. (11.19). At the same time, in Eq. (11.19), substituting $\dot{q}_\mathrm{d}, \ddot{q}_\mathrm{d}$ for $\dot{q}_\mathrm{r}, \ddot{q}_\mathrm{r}$, we can get $Y(q, \dot{q}, q_\mathrm{r}, \dot{q}_\mathrm{r})$ as Eq. (11.20).

$$Y(q,\dot{q},\dot{q}_\mathrm{d},\ddot{q}_\mathrm{d}) = \begin{bmatrix} \ddot{q}_\mathrm{d1} + e_2\cos(q_1) & \ddot{q}_\mathrm{d2} - e_2\cos(q_1) & \begin{matrix} 2\cos(q_2)\ddot{q}_\mathrm{d1} + \cos(q_2)\ddot{q}_\mathrm{d2} - 2\sin(q_2)\dot{q}_2\dot{q}_\mathrm{d1} \\ -\sin(q_2)\dot{q}_2\dot{q}_\mathrm{d2} + e_2\cos(q_1+q_2) \end{matrix} & \begin{matrix} 2\sin(q_2)\ddot{q}_\mathrm{d1} + \sin(q_2)\ddot{q}_\mathrm{d2} + 2\cos(q_2)\dot{q}_2\dot{q}_\mathrm{d1} \\ +\cos(q_2)\dot{q}_2\dot{q}_\mathrm{d2} + e_2\sin(q_1+q_2) \end{matrix} \\ 0 & \ddot{q}_\mathrm{d1} + \ddot{q}_\mathrm{d2} & \cos(q_2)\ddot{q}_\mathrm{d1} + \sin(q_2)\dot{q}_1\dot{q}_\mathrm{d1} + e_2\cos(q_1+q_2) & \sin(q_2)\ddot{q}_\mathrm{d1} - \cos(q_2)\dot{q}_1\dot{q}_\mathrm{d1} + e_2\sin(q_1+q_2) \end{bmatrix} \tag{11.19}$$

$$\tilde{a} = \begin{bmatrix} \tilde{\alpha} & \tilde{\beta} & \tilde{\varepsilon} & \tilde{\eta} \end{bmatrix}^\mathrm{T}$$

$$Y(q,\dot{q},\dot{q}_\mathrm{r},\ddot{q}_\mathrm{r}) = \begin{bmatrix} \ddot{q}_\mathrm{r1} + e_2\cos(q_1) & \ddot{q}_\mathrm{r2} - e_2\cos(q_1) & \begin{matrix} 2\cos(q_2)\ddot{q}_\mathrm{r1} + \cos(q_2)\ddot{q}_\mathrm{r2} - 2\sin(q_2)\dot{q}_2\dot{q}_\mathrm{r1} \\ -\sin(q_2)\dot{q}_2\dot{q}_\mathrm{r2} + e_2\cos(q_1+q_2) \end{matrix} & \begin{matrix} 2\sin(q_2)\ddot{q}_\mathrm{r1} + \sin(q_2)\ddot{q}_\mathrm{r2} + 2\cos(q_2)\dot{q}_2\dot{q}_\mathrm{r1} \\ +\cos(q_2)\dot{q}_2\dot{q}_\mathrm{r2} + e_2\sin(q_1+q_2) \end{matrix} \\ 0 & \ddot{q}_\mathrm{r1} + \ddot{q}_\mathrm{r2} & \cos(q_2)\ddot{q}_\mathrm{r1} + \sin(q_2)\dot{q}_1\dot{q}_\mathrm{r1} + e_2\cos(q_1+q_2) & \sin(q_2)\ddot{q}_\mathrm{r1} - \cos(q_2)\dot{q}_1\dot{q}_\mathrm{r1} + e_2\sin(q_1+q_2) \end{bmatrix} \tag{11.20}$$

References

[1] Sadao kawamura, Mikhail Svinin. eds., Advances in Robot Control: From Everyday physics to Human-like Movements. Springer, 2006

[2] Slotine JE, Li WP. On the adaptive control of robot manipulators. The Interational Journal of Robotics Research, 1987, 6(3): 49 – 59

[3] Slotine JE, Li WP. Applied Non Linear Control. Prentice Hall, 1991

12 Sliding Mode Control for Aircraft

Jinkun Liu
Beijing University of Aeronautics and Astronautics
P.R.China
E-mail: ljk@buaa.edu.cn

Xinhua Wang
National University of Singapore
Singapore
E-mail: wangxinhua04@gmail.com

Abstract This chapter introduces two kinds of sliding mode controllers for aircrafts. They are a sliding mode controller for helicopter and a sliding mode controller for an uncertain VTOL aircraft. Stability analysis and simulation examples are given.

Keywords sliding mode control, helicopter, VTOL aircraft

12.1 Sliding Mode Control for a Helicopter

12.1.1 Mathematical Model of a Helicopter

The control system of a helicopter is a multiple input multiple output (MIMO) system. The nonlinear motion characteristics of helicopter are obvious. Moreover, the stability, operation, and maneuverability are relatively worse. The height of a helicopter varies according to the pitch angle. Ignoring the ground effect, the kinetic equation of a helicopter is described as follows:

$$\left.\begin{array}{c} \dot{x} = f(x) + g_1(x)u_1 + g_2(x)u_2 \\ y = [y_1 \ \ y_2]^{\mathrm{T}} = [x_1 \ \ x_4]^{\mathrm{T}} \end{array}\right\} \tag{12.1}$$

where $g_1(x) = [0 \ 0 \ 1 \ 0 \ 0]^{\mathrm{T}}$, $g_2(x) = [0 \ 0 \ 0 \ 0 \ 1]^{\mathrm{T}}$, $f(x) = [f_1 \ f_2 \ f_3 \ f_4 \ f_5]^{\mathrm{T}}$,

$$f(x) = [f_1 \ f_2 \ f_3 \ f_4 \ f_5]^{\mathrm{T}} = \begin{bmatrix} x_2 \\ a_0 + a_1 x_2 + a_2 x_2^2 + (a_3 + a_4 x_4 - \sqrt{a_5 + a_6 x_4})x_3^2 \\ a_7 + a_8 x_3 + (a_9 \sin x_4 + a_{10})x_3^2 \\ x_5 \\ a_{11} + a_{12}x_4 + a_{13}x_3^2 \sin x_4 + a_{14}x_5 \end{bmatrix},$$

Advanced Sliding Mode Control for Mechanical Systems: Design, Analysis and MATLAB Simulation

$x = [x_1 \ x_2 \ x_3 \ x_4 \ x_5]^T = [h \ \dot{h} \ \omega \ \theta \ \dot{\theta}]^T$, h is the height, ω is the rotating speed of the rotor blade, θ is the collective pitch angle of the rotor blade, u_1 is the gas control input, and u_2 is the collective control input.

Equation (12.1) can be written as:

$$
\left.
\begin{aligned}
\dot{x}_1 &= x_2 \\
\dot{x}_2 &= f_2 = a_0 + a_1 x_2 + a_2 x_2^2 + (a_3 + a_4 x_4 - \sqrt{a_5 + a_6 x_4}) x_3^2 \\
\dot{x}_3 &= f_3 + u_1 = a_7 + a_8 x_3 + (a_9 \sin x_4 + a_{10}) x_3^2 + u_1 \\
\dot{x}_4 &= f_4 = x_5 \\
\dot{x}_5 &= f_5 + u_2 = a_{11} + a_{12} x_4 + a_{13} x_3^2 \sin x_4 + a_{14} x_5 + u_2
\end{aligned}
\right\}
\tag{12.2}
$$

From Eq. (12.2) we find that two kinds of couplings exist. The first one is caused by the system states and is called the dynamic coupling. The second one is caused by the control input and is called the operating coupling. Linearization of the couplings achieves two objectives. Firstly, it makes u_1 operate directly on the height h or its derivatives. Secondly, it makes u_2 operate directly on the pitch angle θ or its derivatives. Accordingly, the direct relation of the control input and control output can be exhibited.

12.1.2 Dynamic Inversion Uncoupling Linearization

From Eq. (12.2), we have

$$
\left.
\begin{aligned}
\dot{x}_1 &= x_2 \\
\ddot{x}_1 &= \dot{x}_2 = f_2 = a_0 + a_1 x_2 + a_2 x_2^2 + (a_3 + a_4 x_4 - \sqrt{a_5 + a_6 x_4}) x_3^2 \\
\dddot{x}_1 &= \dot{f}_2 = (a_1 + 2a_2 x_2)\dot{x}_2 + 2 x_3 \dot{x}_3 (a_3 + a_4 x_4 - \sqrt{a_5 + a_6 x_4}) \\
&\quad + \left(a_4 \dot{x}_4 - \frac{a_6 \dot{x}_4}{2\sqrt{a_5 + a_6 x_4}} \right) x_3^2 \\
&= (a_1 + 2a_2 x_2) f_2 + \left(a_4 x_5 - \frac{a_6 x_5}{2\sqrt{a_5 + a_6 x_4}} \right) x_3^2 \\
&\quad + 2 x_3 (a_3 + a_4 x_4 - \sqrt{a_5 + a_6 x_4})(f_3 + u_1) \\
\dot{x}_4 &= f_4 = x_5 \\
\ddot{x}_4 &= f_5 + u_2 = a_{11} + a_{12} x_4 + a_{13} x_3^2 \sin x_4 + a_{14} x_5 + u_2
\end{aligned}
\right\}
\tag{12.3}
$$

We can obtain that the relative degree of model Eq. (12.3) is (3 2). Based on feedback linearization, we can get

332

12 Sliding Mode Control for Aircraft

$$(\xi_{11},\xi_{12},\xi_{13},\xi_{21},\xi_{22}) = (y_1,L_f y_1,L_f^2 y_1,y_2,L_f y_2)$$
$$= (x_1,\dot{x}_1,\ddot{x}_1,x_4,\dot{x}_4) = (h,\dot{h},\ddot{h},\theta,\dot{\theta}) \tag{12.4}$$

Considering uncertainties and disturbances d_1, d_2, the linearization model of the helicopter is given as:

$$\left. \begin{aligned} \dot{\xi}_{11} &= \xi_{12} \\ \dot{\xi}_{12} &= \xi_{13} \\ \dot{\xi}_{13} &= F + v_1 + d_1 \\ \dot{\xi}_{21} &= \xi_{22} \\ \dot{\xi}_{22} &= f_5 + v_2 + d_2 \end{aligned} \right\} \tag{12.5}$$

where $F = (a_1 + 2a_2 x_2)f_2 + 2x_3 f_3 r + k$, $v_1 = 2x_3 r u_1$, $v_2 = u_2$, $r = a_3 + a_4 x_4 -$
$\sqrt{a_5 + a_6 x_4}$, $k = \left[a_4 x_5 - \dfrac{1}{2} a_6 x_5 (a_5 + a_6 x_4)^{-\frac{1}{2}} \right] x_3^2$, $|d_1| \leqslant D_1$, $|d_2| \leqslant D_2$.

The actual control law is designed as:

$$\left. \begin{aligned} u_1 &= v_1 /(2x_3 r) \\ u_2 &= v_2 \end{aligned} \right\} \tag{12.6}$$

The normal affine linear system can be obtained by uncoupling linearization of the helicopter. Accordingly, some linear control methods can be used to design the control law of the helicopter. The traditional control method is adopted to design the control laws v_1 and v_2 for model Eq. (12.5). Then, the actual control law can be obtained by Eq. (12.6). Thus, the control of the helicopter is realized.

12.1.3 Sliding Mode Controller Design

Corresponding actual physical quantity of model Eq. (12.5):

$$(\xi_{11},\xi_{12},\xi_{13},\xi_{21},\xi_{22}) = (x_1,\dot{x}_1,f_2,x_4,\dot{x}_4) = (h,\dot{h},\ddot{h},\theta,\dot{\theta}) \tag{12.7}$$

To control the height of the helicopter, let us suppose that the input command is r_1 and the tracking error is $e_1 = r_1 - \xi_1$. The sliding variable is designed as:

$$s_1 = c_{11} e_1 + c_{12} \dot{e}_1 + \ddot{e}_1$$

where $c_{11} > 0$, $c_{12} > 0$.

Therefore,

333

Advanced Sliding Mode Control for Mechanical Systems: Design, Analysis and MATLAB Simulation

$$s_1 = c_{11}(r_1 - \xi_{11}) - c_{12}\dot{\xi}_{11} - \ddot{\xi}_{11} = c_{11}(r_1 - \xi_{11}) - c_{12}\xi_{12} - \xi_{13}$$

$$\dot{s}_1 = -c_{11}\dot{\xi}_{11} - c_{12}\ddot{\xi}_{11} - \dddot{\xi}_{11} = -c_{11}\xi_{12} - c_{12}\xi_{13} - (F + v_1 + d_1)$$

The auxiliary controller is designed as:

$$v_1 = -F - c_{11}\xi_{12} - c_{12}\xi_{13} + D_1 \operatorname{sgn}(s_1) \tag{12.8}$$

Substituting Eq. (12.8) into $\dot{s}_1$, we have

$$\dot{s}_1 = -D_1 \operatorname{sgn}(s_1) - d_1$$

Therefore,

$$s_1\dot{s}_1 = -|s|_1 D_1 - s_1 d_1 \leqslant 0$$

To derive the collective pitch angle control of the helicopter let us suppose that the input command is a constant r_2 and the tracking error is $e_2 = r_2 - \xi_{21}$. The sliding variable is designed as:

$$s_2 = c_{21}e_2 + \dot{e}_2$$

where $c_{21} > 0$.

Therefore,

$$s_2 = c_{21}(r_2 - \xi_{21}) - \dot{\xi}_{21}$$

$$\dot{s}_2 = -c_{21}\dot{\xi}_{21} - \ddot{\xi}_{21} = -c_{21}\xi_{22} - \dot{\xi}_{22} = -c_{21}\xi_{22} - (f_5 + v_2 + d_2)$$

The auxiliary control law is designed as:

$$v_2 = -f_5 + D_2 \operatorname{sgn}(s_2) - c_{21}\xi_{22} \tag{12.9}$$

Substituting Eq. (12.9)into $\dot{s}_2$, we have

$$\dot{s}_2 = -D_2 \operatorname{sgn}(s_2) - d_2$$

Therefore, we have

$$s_2\dot{s}_2 = -|s|_2 D_2 - s_2 d_2 \leqslant 0$$

12.1.4 Simulation Example

The simulation for the problem of the height and the collective pitch angle. The mode of the helicopter is given in Eq. (12.1), the initial states: $h = 1.5$, $\theta = 0.15$,

$\omega = 200$, $\dot{h} = \dot{\theta} = 0$. The parameters of the model are: $a_0 = -17.67$, $a_1 = a_2 = -0.1$, $a_3 = 5.31 \times 10^{-4}$, $a_4 = 1.5364 \times 10^{-2}$, $a_5 = 2.82 \times 10^{-7}$, $a_6 = 1.632 \times 10^{-5}$, $a_7 = -13.92$, $a_8 = -0.7$, $a_9 = a_{10} = -0.0028$, $a_{11} = 434.88$, $a_{12} = -800$, $a_{13} = -0.1$, $a_{14} = -65$.

Let $c_{11} = 120$, $c_{12} = 20$, $c_{21} = 25$ in a switch function. The supper bounds of the uncertainties and disturbances are $D_1 = 5.0$ and $D_2 = 1.0$ respectively. The control laws are selected as Eqs. (12.6), (12.8) and (12.9). The tracking results of the height and the collective pitch angle are shown in Fig. 12.1 and Fig. 12.2. In the simulation, the saturated function is adopted instead of switch function to reduce the chattering phenomenon where the boundary layer is $\Delta = 0.05$.

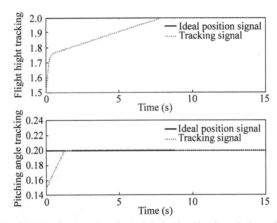

Figure 12.1 Tracking for height and collective pitch angle

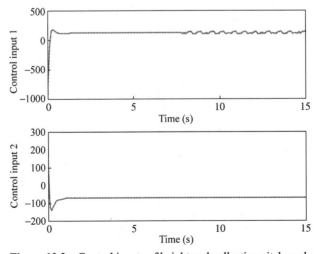

Figure 12.2 Control inputs of height and collective pitch angle

Advanced Sliding Mode Control for Mechanical Systems: Design, Analysis and MATLAB Simulation

Simulation programs:

(1) Simulink main program: chap12_1sim.mdl

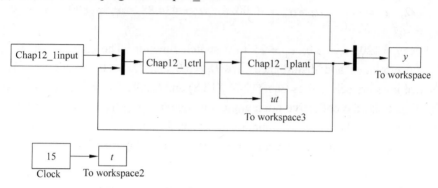

(2) S-function of control law: chap12_1ctrl.m

```
function [sys,x0,str,ts]=s_function(t,x,u,flag)
switch flag,
    case 0,
        [sys,x0,str,ts]=mdlInitializeSizes;
    case 3,
        sys=mdlOutputs(t,x,u);
    case {1,2,4,9},
        sys=[];
    otherwise
        error(['unhandled flag=',num2str(flag)]);
end
function [sys,x0,str,ts]=mdlInitializeSizes
sizes=simsizes;
sizes.NumContStates=0;
sizes.NumDiscStates=0;
sizes.NumOutputs=2;
sizes.NumInputs=7;
sizes.DirFeedthrough=1;
sizes.NumSampleTimes=0;
sys=simsizes(sizes);
x0=[];
str=[];
ts=[];
function sys=mdlOutputs(t,x,u)
x1d=u(1);x4d=u(2);
x1=u(3);x2=u(4);x3=u(5);x4=u(6);x5=u(7);

a0=-17.66;a1=-0.1;a2=-0.1;a3=5.31e-4;
a4=1.534e-2;a5=2.82e-7;a6=1.632e-5;
a7=-13.92;a8=-0.7;a9=-0.0028;a10=-0.0028;
a11=434.88;a12=-800;a13=-0.1;a14=-65;

f1=x2;
f2=a0+a1*x2+a2*x2^2+(a3+a4*x4-sqrt(a5+a6*x4))*x3^2;
f3=a7+a8*x3+(a9*sin(x4)+a10)*x3^2;
```

12 Sliding Mode Control for Aircraft

```
f4=x5;
f5=a11+a12*x4+a13*x3^2*sin(x4)+a14*x5;

r=a3+a4*x4-sqrt(a5+a6*x4);
k=x3^2*(a4*x5-1/2*a6*x5*(a5+a6*x4)^(-0.5));

c11=120;c12=20;c21=25;

z11=x1;
z12=x2;
z13=f2;
s1=c11*(x1d-z11)-c12*z12-z13;

z21=x4;
dz21=x5;
s2=c21*(x4d-z21)-dz21;

D1=5;D2=1.0;
F=(a1+2*a2*x2)*f2+2*x3*f3*r+k;

delta1=0.05;
if abs(s1)>delta1
    sat1=sign(s1);
else
    sat1=1/delta1*s1;
end
%v1=-F-c11*z12-c12*z13+D1*sign(s1);
v1=-F-c11*z12-c12*z13+D1*sat1;

z22=x5;

delta2=0.05;
if abs(s2)>delta1
    sat2=sign(s2);
else
    sat2=1/delta2*s2;
end
%v2=-f5+D2*sign(s2)-c21*z22;
v2=-f5+D2*sat2-c21*z22;

u1=v1/(2*x3*r+0.01);
u2=v2;

sys(1)=u1;
sys(2)=u2;
```

(3) S-function of the plant: chap12_1plant.m

```
function [sys,x0,str,ts]=s_function(t,x,u,flag)
switch flag,
    case 0,
        [sys,x0,str,ts]=mdlInitializeSizes;
    case 1,
        sys=mdlDerivatives(t,x,u);
```

```
    case 3,
        sys=mdlOutputs(t,x,u);
    case {2,4,9},
        sys=[];
    otherwise
        error(['unhandled flag=',num2str(flag)]);
end
function [sys,x0,str,ts]=mdlInitializeSizes
sizes=simsizes;
sizes.NumContStates=5;
sizes.NumDiscStates=0;
sizes.NumOutputs=5;
sizes.NumInputs=2;
sizes.DirFeedthrough=1;
sizes.NumSampleTimes=0;
sys=simsizes(sizes);
x0=[1.5,0,200,0.15,0];
str=[];
ts=[];
function sys=mdlDerivatives(t,x,u)
a0=-17.66;a1=-0.1;a2=-0.1;a3=5.31e-4;
a4=1.534e-2;a5=2.82e-7;a6=1.632e-5;
a7=-13.92;a8=-0.7;a9=-0.0028;a10=-0.0028;
a11=434.88;a12=-800;a13=-0.1;a14=-65;

f1=x(2);
f2=a0+a1*x(2)+a2*x(2)^2+(a3+a4*x(4)-sqrt(a5+a6*x(4)))*x(3)^2;
f3=a7+a8*x(3)+(a9*sin(x(4))+a10)*x(3)^2;
f4=x(5);
f5=a11+a12*x(4)+a13*x(3)^2*sin(x(4))+a14*x(5);

g1=[0,0,1,0,0]';
g2=[0,0,0,0,1]';
u1=u(1);
u2=u(2);
dt=[0,0,0,0,0]';
f=[f1,f2,f3,f4,f5]';
sys=f+g1*u1+g2*u2+dt;
function sys=mdlOutputs(t,x,u)
sys(1)=x(1);
sys(2)=x(2);
sys(3)=x(3);
sys(4)=x(4);
sys(5)=x(5);
```

(4) S-function of input command: chap12_1input.m

```
function [sys,x0,str,ts]=s_function(t,x,u,flag)
switch flag,
    case 0,
        [sys,x0,str,ts]=mdlInitializeSizes;
    case 3,
        sys=mdlOutputs(t,x,u);
    case {1,2,4,9},
```

```matlab
        sys=[];
    otherwise
        error(['unhandled flag=',num2str(flag)]);
end
function [sys,x0,str,ts]=mdlInitializeSizes
sizes=simsizes;
sizes.NumContStates=0;
sizes.NumDiscStates=0;
sizes.NumOutputs=2;
sizes.NumInputs=0;
sizes.DirFeedthrough=0;
sizes.NumSampleTimes=0;
sys=simsizes(sizes);
x0=[];
str=[];
ts=[];
function sys=mdlOutputs(t,x,u)
sys(1)=2;
sys(2)=0.2;
```

(5) Plot program: chap12_1plot.m

```matlab
close all;
figure(1);
subplot(211);
plot(t,y(:,1),'k',t,y(:,3),'r:','linewidth',2);
xlabel('time(sec)');ylabel('Flight hight tracking');
legend('Ideal position signal','tracking signal');
subplot(212);
plot(t,y(:,2),'k',t,y(:,6),'r:','linewidth',2);
xlabel('time(sec)');ylabel('Pitching angle tracking');
legend('Ideal position signal','tracking signal');

figure(2);
subplot(211);
plot(t,ut(:,1),'r','linewidth',2);
xlabel('time(sec)');ylabel('Control input 1');
subplot(212);
plot(t,ut(:,2),'r','linewidth',2);
xlabel('time(sec)');ylabel('Control input 2');
```

12.2 Sliding Mode Control for an Uncertain Vertical Take-Off and Landing Aircraft

12.2.1 System Description

In a vertical take-off and landing (VTOL) aircraft, the roll moment reaction jets in the wingtip create a force that is not perpendicular to the y-body axis. Thus, the production of a positive rolling moment will also produce slight acceleration of aircraft to the right. As will be demonstrated, this phenomenon makes the aircraft non-minimum phase. From Fig. 12.3 and by using Newton's law, the dynamic model of the VTOL aircraft can be obtained as

$$\begin{aligned}-m\ddot{X} &= -(T+\delta_1(t))\sin\theta + \varepsilon_0(l+\delta_2(t))\cos\theta \\ -m\ddot{Y} &= (T+\delta_1(t))\cos\theta + \varepsilon_0(l+\delta_2(t))\sin\theta - mg \\ I_z\ddot{\theta} &= l+\delta_2(t)\end{aligned} \qquad (12.10)$$

where ε_0 is a small coefficient that characterizes the coupling between the rolling moment and the lateral force, $\varepsilon_0 l$, on the aircraft.

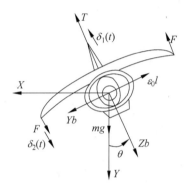

Figure 12.3 Planar vertical take-off and landing aircraft

Define $x=-X/g$, $y=-Y/g$, $u_1=T/(mg)$, $u_2=l/I_z$, $\varepsilon=\varepsilon_0 I_z/(mg)$, $\xi_1(t)=\delta_1(t)/(mg)$, $\xi_1(t)=\delta_2(t)/I_z$, then the rescaled dynamics becomes

$$\begin{aligned}\ddot{x} &= -(u_1+\xi_1(t))\sin\theta + \varepsilon(u_2+\xi_2(t))\cos\theta \\ \ddot{y} &= (u_1+\xi_1(t))\cos\theta + \varepsilon(u_2+\xi_2(t))\sin\theta - g \\ \ddot{\theta} &= u_2+\xi_2(t)\end{aligned} \qquad (12.11)$$

We let

$$x_1=x, \quad x_2=\dot{x}, \quad y_1=y, \quad y_2=\dot{y} \qquad (12.12)$$

Therefore, the scaled mathematical model of a VTOL aircraft can be described as

$$\begin{aligned}\dot{x}_1 &= x_2 \\ \dot{x}_2 &= -(u_1+\xi_1(t))\sin\theta + \varepsilon(u_2+\xi_2(t))\cos\theta \\ \dot{y}_1 &= y_2 \\ \dot{y}_2 &= (u_1+\xi_1(t))\cos\theta + \varepsilon(u_2+\xi_2(t))\sin\theta - g \\ \dot{\theta} &= \omega \\ \dot{\omega} &= u_2+\xi_2(t)\end{aligned} \qquad (12.13)$$

where $x_1(t)$, $y_1(t)$, $\theta(t)$ denote position of the aircraft center of mass and roll angle at time t; $x_2(t)$, $y_2(t)$, $\omega(t)$ denote linear and roll angular velocities of the aircraft, respectively; u_1 and u_2 are the vertical control force and rotational moment, $g > 0$ is the gravitational acceleration and ε is the constant coupling between the roll moment and the lateral force. δ_1, δ_2 and δ_3 are the uncertainties. It is seen that the aircraft model Eq. (12.10) is underactuated and that the VTOL aircraft is non-minimum phase for $\varepsilon \neq 0$ with respect to the nominal output $y(t) = [x_1(t),\, y_1(t),\, \theta(t)]^{\mathrm{T}}$.

Let

$$d_1(t) = -\xi_1(t)\sin\theta + \varepsilon\xi_2(t)\cos\theta$$
$$d_2(t) = \xi_1(t)\cos\theta + \varepsilon\xi_2(t)\sin\theta$$

Let the desired trajectory is (x_d, y_d), and the tracking error system is

$$\left.\begin{aligned}
\dot{e}_1 &= e_2 \\
\dot{e}_2 &= -(u_1 + \xi_1(t))\sin\theta + \varepsilon(u_2 + \xi_2(t))\cos\theta - \ddot{x}_d \\
\dot{e}_3 &= e_4 \\
\dot{e}_4 &= (u_1 + \xi_1(t))\cos\theta + \varepsilon(u_2 + \xi_2(t))\sin\theta - g - \ddot{y}_d \\
\dot{\theta} &= \omega \\
\dot{\omega} &= u_2 + \xi_2(t)
\end{aligned}\right\} \tag{12.14}$$

12.2.2 Transform of Model

From Eq. (12.14), we have

$$\begin{bmatrix} \dot{e}_2 \\ \dot{e}_4 \end{bmatrix} = \begin{bmatrix} -\sin\theta & \varepsilon\cos\theta \\ \cos\theta & \varepsilon\sin\theta \end{bmatrix} \begin{bmatrix} u_1 \\ u_2 \end{bmatrix} + \begin{bmatrix} -\xi_1(t)\sin\theta + \varepsilon\xi_2(t)\cos\theta \\ \xi_1(t)\cos\theta + \varepsilon\xi_2(t)\sin\theta \end{bmatrix} + \begin{bmatrix} -\ddot{x}_d \\ -g - \ddot{y}_d \end{bmatrix}$$

For Eq. (12.14), the vector relative degree corresponding to the output is $[2\ \ 2]$ and input state linearization can be used by choosing the control law proposed in[1,2].

$$\begin{bmatrix} u_1 \\ u_2 \end{bmatrix} = \begin{bmatrix} -\sin\theta & \varepsilon\cos\theta \\ \cos\theta & \varepsilon\sin\theta \end{bmatrix}^{-1} \begin{bmatrix} v_1 + \ddot{x}_d \\ v_2 + \ddot{y}_d + g \end{bmatrix} \tag{12.15}$$

where v_1 and v_2 will be designed as follows:

$$\begin{bmatrix} -\sin\theta & \varepsilon\cos\theta \\ \cos\theta & \varepsilon\sin\theta \end{bmatrix}^{-1} = \begin{bmatrix} -\sin\theta & \cos\theta \\ \dfrac{1}{\varepsilon}\cos\theta & \dfrac{1}{\varepsilon}\sin\theta \end{bmatrix} \tag{12.16}$$

Therefore, Eq. (12.14) becomes

$$
\left.\begin{aligned}
\dot{e}_1 &= e_2 \\
\dot{e}_2 &= v_1 + d_1(t) \\
\dot{e}_3 &= e_4 \\
\dot{e}_4 &= v_2 + d_2(t) \\
\dot{\theta} &= \omega \\
\dot{\omega} &= u_2 + \xi_2(t)
\end{aligned}\right\} \tag{12.17}
$$

From Eqs. (12.15) and (12.16), we can get

$$
u_2 = \frac{1}{\varepsilon} v_1 \cos\theta + \frac{1}{\varepsilon} v_2 \sin\theta + \frac{g}{\varepsilon}\sin\theta + \frac{1}{\varepsilon}\ddot{x}_d \cos\theta + \frac{1}{\varepsilon}\ddot{y}_d \sin\theta \tag{12.18}
$$

Therefore, we have

$$
\left.\begin{aligned}
\dot{e}_1 &= e_2 \\
\dot{e}_2 &= v_1 + d_1(t) \\
\dot{e}_3 &= e_4 \\
\dot{e}_4 &= v_2 + d_2(t) \\
\dot{\theta} &= \omega \\
\dot{\omega} &= \frac{1}{\varepsilon} v_1 \cos\theta + \frac{1}{\varepsilon} v_2 \sin\theta + \frac{g}{\varepsilon}\sin\theta + \frac{1}{\varepsilon}\ddot{x}_d \cos\theta + \frac{1}{\varepsilon}\ddot{y}_d \sin\theta + \xi_2(t)
\end{aligned}\right\} \tag{12.19}
$$

To eliminate v_1 and v_2 in $\dot{\omega}$, we design a new variable η instead of ω [1, 2],

$$
\eta = \varepsilon\omega - e_2 \cos\theta - e_4 \sin\theta \tag{12.20}
$$

Remark1: from Eq. (12.20), we can see if $e_2 \to 0$, $e_4 \to 0$, then $\eta \to \varepsilon\omega$, and if $\eta \to 0$, then $\omega \to 0$, so we can use η instead of ω;

Remark2: from Eq. (12.20), we can see $\dot{\omega}$ includes v_1 and v_2, $\dot{e}_2$ includes v_1, $\dot{e}_4$ includes v_2, therefore η can be designed by the combination of ω, e_2 and e_4. So we can get $\dot{\eta}$ equation with $\dot{\omega}$, $\dot{e}_2$ and $\dot{e}_4$, then v_1, v_2 can be eliminated.

Form Eq. (12.20), we get

$$
\omega = \frac{1}{\varepsilon}(\eta + e_2 \cos\theta + e_4 \sin\theta) \tag{12.21}
$$

We get

$$
\dot{\theta} = \frac{1}{\varepsilon}(\eta + e_2 \cos\theta + e_4 \sin\theta)
$$

$$\dot{\eta} = \varepsilon\dot{\omega} - \dot{e}_2\cos\theta + e_2\dot{\theta}\sin\theta - \dot{e}_4\sin\theta - e_4\dot{\theta}\cos\theta$$

$$= \varepsilon\left(\frac{1}{\varepsilon}v_1\cos\theta + \frac{1}{\varepsilon}v_2\sin\theta + \frac{g}{\varepsilon}\sin\theta + \frac{1}{\varepsilon}\ddot{x}_d\cos\theta + \frac{1}{\varepsilon}\ddot{y}_d\sin\theta + \xi_2(t)\right)$$

$$- (v_1 - \xi_1(t)\sin\theta + \varepsilon\xi_2(t)\cos\theta)\cos\theta - (v_2 + \xi_1(t)\cos\theta \qquad (12.22)$$

$$+ \varepsilon\xi_2(t)\sin\theta)\sin\theta + \frac{1}{\varepsilon}(e_2\sin\theta - e_4\cos\theta)(\eta + e_2\cos\theta + e_4\sin\theta)$$

$$= \frac{1}{\varepsilon}(e_2\sin\theta - e_4\cos\theta)(\eta + e_2\cos\theta + e_4\sin\theta)$$

$$+ g\sin\theta + \ddot{x}_d\cos\theta + \ddot{y}_d\sin\theta$$

From Eq. (12.22), the driven dynamics of non-minimum phase part can be written as

$$\dot{\bar{\eta}} = q(e_1,e_2,e_3,e_4,\theta,\eta,Y_d) \qquad (12.23)$$

where $\bar{\eta} = [\theta \quad \eta]^{\mathrm{T}}$, $Y_d = [\ddot{x}_d \quad \ddot{y}_d]^{\mathrm{T}}$, and

$$q(e_1,e_2,e_3,e_4,\theta,\eta,Y_d)$$

$$= \begin{bmatrix} \dfrac{1}{\varepsilon}(\eta + e_2\cos\theta + e_4\sin\theta) \\[2mm] \dfrac{1}{\varepsilon}(e_2\sin\theta - e_4\cos\theta)(\eta + e_2\cos\theta + e_4\sin\theta) + g\sin\theta + \ddot{x}_d\cos\theta + \ddot{y}_d\sin\theta \end{bmatrix}$$

We infer from the above equation that at zero state $q(\cdot)$ is related with $[e_1 \quad e_2]$ and is not related with $[e_3 \quad e_4]$. Then, we get

$$\left.\frac{\partial q(e_1,e_2,e_3,e_4,\theta,\eta,Y_d)}{\partial(e_3 \quad e_4)}\right|_O = O_{2\times2} \qquad (12.24)$$

$$\left.\frac{\partial q(e_1,e_2,e_3,e_4,\theta,\eta,Y_d)}{\partial(e_1 \quad e_2)}\right|_O \neq O_{2\times2} \qquad (12.25)$$

For example,

$$\left.\frac{\partial q(e_1,e_2,e_3,e_4,\theta,\eta,Y_d)}{\partial e_4}\right|_O$$

$$= \left.\begin{bmatrix} \dfrac{1}{\varepsilon}\sin\theta \\[2mm] -\dfrac{1}{\varepsilon}\cos\theta(\eta + e_2\cos\theta + e_4\sin\theta) + \dfrac{1}{\varepsilon}(e_2\sin\theta - e_4\cos\theta)\sin\theta \end{bmatrix}\right|_O = O_{2\times1}$$

According to Eqs. (12.24) and (12.25), the model Eq. (12.19) can be obviously decomposed into a minimum phase part for control of vertical flight dynamics

$$\left.\begin{aligned} \dot{e}_3 &= e_4(t) \\ \dot{e}_4 &= v_2 + d_2(t) \end{aligned}\right\} \tag{12.26}$$

and a non-minimum phase part for control of the coupled horizontal and roll flight dynamics

$$\left.\begin{aligned} \dot{e}_1 &= e_2 \\ \dot{e}_2 &= v_1 + d_1(t) \\ \dot{\theta} &= \frac{1}{\varepsilon}[\eta + e_2 \cos\theta + e_4 \sin\theta] \\ \dot{\eta} &= \frac{1}{\varepsilon}[\eta + e_2 \cos\theta + e_4 \sin\theta][e_2 \sin\theta - e_4 \cos\theta] \\ &\quad + \ddot{x}_d \cos\theta + (\ddot{y}_d + g)\sin\theta \end{aligned}\right\} \tag{12.27}$$

12.2.3 Controller Design

Based on the above decomposition technique, feedback inversion can be used to solve the output tracking problem for the minimum phase dynamics Eq. (12.26).

We define the sliding mode function and choose a conventional sliding mode controller as

$$\sigma_1 = ce_3 + \dot{e}_3, \quad e_3(t) = y_1 - y_d, \quad e_4(t) = y_2 - \dot{y}_d \tag{12.28}$$

where $c > 0$.

We select a controller

$$v_2 = -ce_4 - \bar{h}_2 \text{sign}(\sigma_1) \tag{12.29}$$

where $\bar{h}_1 \geq |d_2(t)|$.

Define the Lyapunov function as $V_1 = \frac{1}{2}\sigma_1^2$, and then we have

$$\begin{aligned} \dot{V}_1 &= \sigma_1 \dot{\sigma}_1 = \sigma_1(c\dot{e}_3 + \dot{e}_4) \\ &= \sigma_1(ce_4 + (v_2 + d_2)) \\ &= \sigma_1(ce_4 + (-ce_4 - \bar{h}_2 \text{sign}(\sigma_1) + d_2)) \\ &= \sigma_1(-\bar{h}_1 \text{sign}(\sigma_1) + d_2) \\ &= c(-\bar{h}_1|\sigma_1| + d_2\sigma_1) \leq 0 \end{aligned}$$

344

12 Sliding Mode Control for Aircraft

Hence, for any differentiable output command y_d, $y_1(t) \to y_d$ and $y_2(t) \to \dot{y}_d$ as $t \to \infty$.

Note that the minimum phase dynamics is completely decoupled from the non-minimum phase dynamics. This means that the vertical dynamics will not be affected by the aircraft horizontal and roll dynamics. Our approach is to design a sliding mode controller for the system Eq. (12.25) such that the origin of Eq. (12.25) is an asymptotical stable equilibrium.

For the Eq. (12.25), we denote

$$\mu_1 = e_2, \quad \mu_2 = [e_1 \quad \theta \quad \eta]^{\mathrm{T}} \tag{12.30}$$

$$e_1 = x_1 - x_d, \quad e_2 = x_2 - \dot{x}_d$$

We rewrite system Eq. (12.25) as

$$\left. \begin{aligned} \dot{\mu}_1 &= v_1 + d_1(t) \\ \dot{\mu}_2 &= p(e_1, e_2, e_3, e_4, \theta, \eta, Y_d) \end{aligned} \right\} \tag{12.31}$$

where $p(e_1, e_2, e_3, e_4, \theta, \eta, Y_d)$ is defined as

$$p(e_1, e_2, e_3, e_4, \theta, \eta, Y_d)$$

$$= \begin{bmatrix} e_2 \\ \dfrac{1}{\varepsilon}(\eta + e_2 \cos\theta + e_4 \sin\theta) \\ \dfrac{1}{\varepsilon}(\eta + e_2 \cos\theta + e_4 \sin\theta)(e_2 \sin\theta - e_4 \cos\theta) + \ddot{x}_d \cos\theta + (\ddot{y}_d + g)\sin\theta \end{bmatrix}$$

Using Taylor expansion, we write Eq. (12.31) as

$$\dot{\mu}_2 = \left. \frac{\partial p}{\partial e_2} \right|_0 e_2 + \left. \frac{\partial p}{\partial [e_1 \quad \theta \quad \eta_2]} \right|_0 [e_1 \quad \theta \quad \eta_2]^{\mathrm{T}} + o(e_1, e_2, e_3, e_4, \theta, \eta, Y_d) \tag{12.32}$$

$$= \tilde{A}_{21}\mu_1 + \tilde{A}_{22}\mu_2 + o(e_1, e_2, e_3, e_4, \theta, \eta, Y_d)$$

where

$$\tilde{A}_{21} = \left. \frac{\partial p(e_1, e_2, e_3, e_4, \theta, \eta, Y_d)}{\partial e_2} \right|_0 = [1 \quad \varepsilon^{-1} \quad 0]^{\mathrm{T}},$$

$$\tilde{A}_{22} = \left. \frac{\partial p(e_1, e_2, e_3, e_4, \theta, \eta, Y_d)}{\partial (e_1 \quad \theta \quad \eta_2)} \right|_0 = \begin{bmatrix} 0 & 0 & 0 \\ 0 & 0 & \varepsilon^{-1} \\ 0 & g & 0 \end{bmatrix},$$

$$o(e_1,e_2,e_3,e_4,\theta,\eta,Y_d) = p(e_1,e_2,e_3,e_4,\theta,\eta,Y_d) - \tilde{A}_{22}\mu_2 - \tilde{A}_{21}\mu_1 \qquad (12.33)$$

We have that $(\tilde{A}_{22}, \tilde{A}_{21})$ is completely controllable.

For Eq. (12.31), we define a sliding variable as:

$$\sigma_2 = \mu_1 - M\mu_2 \qquad (12.34)$$

where

$$M = [m_1 \quad m_2 \quad m_3]$$

where M can be chosen such that $\tilde{A}_{22} + \tilde{A}_{21}M$ is Hurwitz.

From Eq. (12.34), if the sliding mode exists, there exists time t_s, for $t \geqslant t_s$, such that $\sigma_2 = \mu_1 - M\mu_2 = 0$, then $\mu_1 = M\mu_2$. From Eq. (12.32), we have

$$\begin{aligned}
\dot{\mu}_2 &= \tilde{A}_{21}M\mu_2 + \tilde{A}_{22}\mu_2 + o(e_1,e_2,e_3,e_4,\theta,\eta,Y_d) \\
&= (\tilde{A}_{21}M + \tilde{A}_{22})\mu_2 + o(e_1,e_2,e_3,e_4,\theta,\eta,Y_d)
\end{aligned} \qquad (12.35)$$

Because $o(e_1,e_2,e_3,e_4,\theta,\eta,Y_d)$ is high-order item, and if M is selected such that $\tilde{A}_{22} + \tilde{A}_{21}M$ is Hurwitz, the closed loop non-minimum phase part is exponentially stable and hence, $\mu_2 \to 0$, and $\mu_1 = M\mu_2 \to 0$. From Eqs. (12.20) and (12.30), we have $e_1(t) \to 0$, $e_2(t) \to 0$, $\theta(t) \to 0$ and $\omega(t) \to 0$ as $t \to \infty$.

We select a controller

$$v_1 = Mp(e_1,e_2,e_3,e_4,\theta,\eta,Y_d) - \bar{h}_2 \text{sgn}(\sigma_2) \qquad (12.36)$$

where $\bar{h}_2 \geqslant |d_1(t)|$.

We select the Lyapunov function as

$$V = \frac{1}{2}\sigma_2^2$$

Therefore, we have

$$\begin{aligned}
\dot{V} &= \sigma_2(\dot{\mu}_1 - M\dot{\mu}_2) \\
&= \sigma_2(v_1 + d_1(t) - M\dot{\mu}_2) \\
&= \sigma_2\{Mp(e_1,e_2,e_3,e_4,\theta,\eta,Y_d) - \bar{h}_2\text{sgn}(\sigma_2) + d_1(t) \\
&\quad - Mp(e_1,e_2,e_3,e_4,\theta,\eta,Y_d)\} \\
&= \sigma_2\{d_1(t) - \bar{h}_2\text{sgn}(\sigma_2)\} = \sigma_2 d_1(t) - \bar{h}_2|\sigma_2| \leqslant 0
\end{aligned}$$

12 Sliding Mode Control for Aircraft

In the following, we will carry out the value of the vector M and make $\tilde{A}_{22} + \tilde{A}_{21}M$ Hurwitz. Since $M = [m_1 \quad m_2 \quad m_3]$, we have

$$\tilde{A}_{22} + \tilde{A}_{21}M = \begin{bmatrix} 0 & 0 & 0 \\ 0 & 0 & \varepsilon^{-1} \\ 0 & g & 0 \end{bmatrix} + \begin{bmatrix} 1 \\ \varepsilon^{-1} \\ 0 \end{bmatrix}(m_1 \quad m_2 \quad m_3)$$

$$= \begin{bmatrix} 0 & 0 & 0 \\ 0 & 0 & \varepsilon^{-1} \\ 0 & g & 0 \end{bmatrix} + \begin{bmatrix} m_1 & m_2 & m_3 \\ \varepsilon^{-1}m_1 & \varepsilon^{-1}m_2 & \varepsilon^{-1}m_3 \\ 0 & 0 & 0 \end{bmatrix}$$

$$= \begin{bmatrix} m_1 & m_2 & m_3 \\ \varepsilon^{-1}m_1 & \varepsilon^{-1}m_2 & \varepsilon^{-1}+\varepsilon^{-1}m_3 \\ 0 & g & 0 \end{bmatrix} \tag{12.37}$$

Therefore we have

$$| sI - (\tilde{A}_{22} + \tilde{A}_{21}M) | = s^3 - (m_1 + \varepsilon^{-1}m_2)s^2 - g(\varepsilon^{-1} + \varepsilon^{-1}m_3)s + g\varepsilon^{-1}m_1 \tag{12.38}$$

From the rule of Routh, we get the relations as follows:

$$m_1 > 0, \quad m_2 < -\varepsilon m_1, \quad m_3 < -\frac{\varepsilon^{-1}m_2}{m_1 + \varepsilon^{-1}m_2} \tag{12.39}$$

We can select only three parameters presented by Eq. (12.39) to make the system exponentially stable.

12.2.4 Simulation Example

In this section, we perform a numerical simulation to illustrate the effectiveness of the proposed controller with $\varepsilon = 0.5$, gravity acceleration $g = 9.8$.

For the system Eq. (12.13), using the controller Eqs. (12.15), (12.36) and (12.29), and the control gains are chosen as: $m_1 = 2$, $m_2 = -8$, $m_3 = -4$, $\bar{h}_1 = 2$, $\bar{h}_2 = 5$, $c = 50$. The ideal signal is $x_d = 0$, $\dot{x}_d = 0$, $\ddot{x}_d = 0$, $y_d = 0.1\sin t$, $\dot{y}_d = 0.1\cos t$, $\ddot{y}_d = -0.1\sin t$, $\xi_1(t) = 0.5\sin t$, $\xi_2(t) = 0.5\cos t$.

The initial conditions of the plant are $x_1(0) = 0.05$, $x_2(0) = 0.01$, $y_1(0) = 0.05$, $y_2(0) = 0.01$, $\theta(0) = 0.05$, $\omega(0) = 0.01$. The simulation results are shown in Fig. 12.4 – Fig. 12.7. It is seen that the tracking errors asymptotically converge to zero and the controller $u(t)$ is bounded.

347

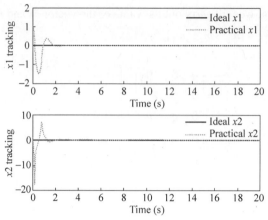

Figure 12.4 The tracking of $x_1(t)$

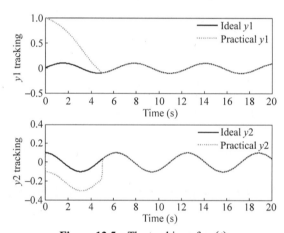

Figure 12.5 The tracking of $y_1(t)$

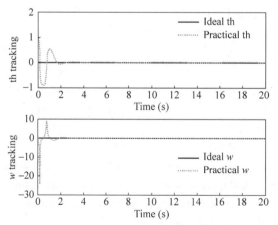

Figure 12.6 The tracking of $\theta(t)$

12 Sliding Mode Control for Aircraft

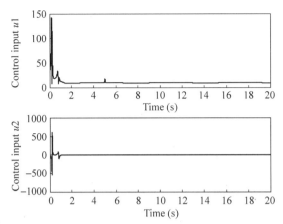

Figure 12.7 Control input $u_1(t)$ and $u_2(t)$

Simulation programs:

(1) Simulink main program: chap12_2sim.mdl

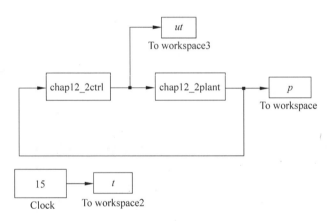

(2) S-function of control law: chap12_2ctrl.m

```
function [sys,x0,str,ts]=s_function(t,x,u,flag)
switch flag,
case 0,
    [sys,x0,str,ts]=mdlInitializeSizes;
case 3,
    sys=mdlOutputs(t,x,u);
case {1, 2, 4, 9 }
    sys = [];
otherwise
    error(['Unhandled flag = ',num2str(flag)]);
end
function [sys,x0,str,ts]=mdlInitializeSizes
sizes = simsizes;
```

349

```matlab
sizes.NumDiscStates  = 0;
sizes.NumOutputs     = 2;
sizes.NumInputs      = 6;
sizes.DirFeedthrough = 1;
sizes.NumSampleTimes = 1;
sys=simsizes(sizes);
x0=[ ];
str=[];
ts=[0 0];
function sys=mdlOutputs(t,x,u)
xd=0;dxd=0;ddxd=0; %ideal xd signal
yd=0.1*sin(t);dyd=0.1*cos(t);ddyd=-0.1*sin(t); %ideal yd signal
epc=0.50;

x1=u(1);x2=u(2);
y1=u(3);y2=u(4);
th=u(5);    %angle
omega=u(6); %angle rate

e1=x1-xd;e2=x2-dxd;
e3=y1-yd;e4=y2-dyd;

eta=epc*omega-e2*cos(th)-e4*sin(th);%coordinate transformation of estimation

%%%%%%%%%%%%%%%%%%%%%%%%M=[2 -8 -4];
g=9.8;
%Lauce stability criterion for M design
m1=5;    % m1>0
m2=-epc*m1-5; % m2<-epc*m1=-0.8*2=-1.6
epc1=1/epc;
m3=-epc1*m2/(m1+epc1*m2)-2; % m3<-epc1*m2/(m1+epc1*m2)=-2*(-8)/(2+2*(-8))=-16/14
M=[m1 m2 m3];
AM=[m1 m2 m3;(1/epc)*m1 (1/epc)*m2 (1/epc)+(1/epc)*m3;0 g 0];
%Stability Judgement
eig(AM);
%%%%%%%%%%%%%%%%%%%%%%%%%%
M=[m1 m2 m3];
mu1=e2;
mu2=[e1 th eta]';

s=mu1-M*mu2;

p1=e2;
p2=(1/epc)*(eta+e2*cos(th)+e4*sin(th));
p3=(1/epc)*(eta+e2*cos(th)+e4*sin(th))*(e2*sin(th)-e4*cos(th))+ddxd
    *cos(th)+(ddyd+g)*sin(th);
p=[p1;p2;p3];

fai=0.05;
if abs(s)<=fai
   sat=s/fai;
```

12 Sliding Mode Control for Aircraft

```
else
   sat=sign(s);
end
hb=5;
%v1=M*p-hb*sign(s);
v1=M*p-hb*sat;

%%%%%%%%%%%%%%%%%%%%%%%%%%%%%%%%%%%%%%%%
c=50;
rou1=c*e3+e4;
fai=0.05;
if abs(rou1)<=fai
   sat1=rou1/fai;
else
   sat1=sign(rou1);
end

hb2=10;
%v2=-c*e4-hb2*sign(rou1);
v2=-c*e4-hb2*sat1;

%%%%%%%%%%%%%%%%%%%%%%%%%%%%%%%%%%%%%%%%
M=[-sin(th) epc*cos(th);cos(th) epc*sin(th)];
ut=inv(M)*[v1+ddxd;v2+ddyd+g];

sys(1)=ut(1);
sys(2)=ut(2);
```

(3) S-function of the plant: chap12_2plant.m

```
function [sys,x0,str,ts]=s_function(t,x,u,flag)
switch flag,
case 0,
   [sys,x0,str,ts]=mdlInitializeSizes;
case 1,
   sys=mdlDerivatives(t,x,u);
case 3,
   sys=mdlOutputs(t,x,u);
case {2, 4, 9 }
   sys = [];
otherwise
   error(['Unhandled flag = ',num2str(flag)]);
end
function [sys,x0,str,ts]=mdlInitializeSizes
sizes = simsizes;
sizes.NumContStates  = 6;
sizes.NumDiscStates  = 0;
sizes.NumOutputs     = 6;
sizes.NumInputs      =2;
sizes.DirFeedthrough = 0;
```

351

```
sizes.NumSampleTimes = 1;
sys=simsizes(sizes);
x0=[1 1 1 0 1 1];
%x0=[0.05 0.01 0.05 0.01 0.05 0.01];
str=[];
ts=[-1 0];
function sys=mdlDerivatives(t,x,u)
x1=x(1);x2=x(2);
y1=x(3);y2=x(4);
th=x(5);w=x(6);

epc=0.50;
g=9.8;

delta1=-0.5*sin(t)*sin(th)+epc*0.5*sin(t)*cos(th);
delta2=0.5*sin(t)*cos(th)+epc*0.5*sin(t)*sin(th);
delta3=0.5*sin(t);

sys(1)=x(2);
sys(2)=-u(1)*sin(th)+epc*u(2)*cos(th)+delta1;

sys(3)=x(4);
sys(4)=u(1)*cos(th)+epc*u(2)*sin(th)-g+delta2;

sys(5)=x(6);
sys(6)=u(2)+delta3;

function sys=mdlOutputs(t,x,u)
epc=0.50;

x1=x(1);x2=x(2);
y1=x(3);y2=x(4);
th=x(5);w=x(6);

delta1=-0.5*sin(t)*sin(th)+epc*0.5*sin(t)*cos(th);
delta2=0.5*sin(t)*cos(th)+epc*0.5*sin(t)*sin(th);
delta3=0.5*sin(t);

sys(1)=x1;
sys(2)=x2;
sys(3)=y1;
sys(4)=y2;
sys(5)=th;
sys(6)=w;
```

(4) Plot program: chap12_2plot.m

```
close all;

figure(1);
```

12 Sliding Mode Control for Aircraft

```
subplot(211);
plot(t,0*t,'k',t,p(:,1),'r:','linewidth',2);
xlabel('time(s)');ylabel('x1 tracking');
legend('ideal x1','practical x1');
subplot(212);
plot(t,0*t,'k',t,p(:,2),'r:','linewidth',2);
xlabel('time(s)');ylabel('x2 tracking');
legend('ideal x2','practical x2');

figure(2);
subplot(211);
plot(t,0.1*sin(t),'k',t,p(:,3),'r:','linewidth',2);
xlabel('time(s)');ylabel('y1 tracking');
legend('ideal y1','practical y1');
subplot(212);
plot(t,0.1*cos(t),'k',t,p(:,4),'r:','linewidth',2);
xlabel('time(s)');ylabel('y2 tracking');
legend('ideal y2','practical y2');

figure(3);
subplot(211);
plot(t,0*t,'k',t,p(:,5),'r:','linewidth',2);
xlabel('time(s)');ylabel('th tracking');
legend('ideal th','practical th');
subplot(212);
plot(t,0*t,'k',t,p(:,6),'r:','linewidth',2);
xlabel('time(s)');ylabel('w tracking');
legend('ideal w','practical w');

figure(4);
subplot(211);
plot(t,ut(:,1),'k','linewidth',2);
xlabel('time(s)');ylabel('control input u1');
subplot(212);
plot(t,ut(:,2),'k','linewidth',2);
xlabel('time(s)');ylabel('control input u2');
```

References

[1] Wang XH, Liu JK, Cai KY. Tracking control for a velocity-sensorless VTOL aircraft with delayed outputs, Automatica, 2009, 45: 2876 − 2882

[2] Wang XH, Liu JK, Cai KY. Tracking control for VTOL aircraft with disabled IMUs. International Journal of Systems Science, 2010, 41(10): 1231 − 1239

Index

A

adaptive neural sliding mode control, 281

B

backstepping design, 91
boundary layer, 20, 25

C

chattering phenomenon can, 271

D

disturbance observer, 103
disturbance observer, 211
dynamic sliding mode control, 111
dynamic switching function, 112

E

equivalent control, 31
extended state observer, 175

F

Fast Terminal sliding mode control, 155
fast terminal sliding surface, 155
feedback linearization, 332
four reaching laws, 9
fuzzification method, 235
fuzzy control, 235
fuzzy system, 252
fuzzy systems, 251
fuzzy vector, 253

G

Gaussian function, 283
global fast sliding mode controller, 157
global fast terminal sliding surface, 156

Global sliding mode control, 50

H

helicopter, 331
high-gain observer, 163
Hurwitz condition, 2

I

inequality, 83
input-output feedback linearization, 70
integral-chain differentiator, 192

L

linearization feedback, 61
low pass filter, 75

M

manipulator, 301
membership functions, 244

N

nominal model, 41
non-minimum phase, 343
nonsingular sliding mode controller, 148
nonsingular sliding variable, 148

P

peaking phenomenon, 177

Q

quasi-sliding mode, 25

R

RBF neural network, 281
reaching phase, 8

Relay function, 25

S

Saturation function, 25
sgn function, 25
simulation, 37
sliding mode control, 1
sliding mode function, 2
sliding phase, 8
slow time-varying disturbance, 206
switching control, 31
symmetric positive-definite matrix, 83

T

Taylor expansion, 345
Terminal sliding mode control, 137
terminal sliding surface, 137

U

uncertain mechanical system, 117
universal approximation theorem, 251
upper bound, 26

V

variable structure control, 1